FERRIES

British Isles and Northern Europe Edition

ISBN 978 1 911268079

Ferry Publications, PO Box 33,
Ramsey, Isle of Man IM99 4LP

Email: ferrypubs@manx.net Website: www.ferrypubs.co.uk

Europe's **Leading** Guide To The Ferry Industry

Contents...

CONTENTS

Introduction . . . 3
Foreword . . . 4
A Guide to using this book . . . 8
Silja Line – 60 Years of Service . . . 12
Tallinn-Helsinki: Fit for the future . . . 22
To Iceland in Wind and Storm . . . 36
Round Britain and Ireland Review 2016/17 . . . 49
Section 1 - GB and Ireland - Major Passenger operators . . . 60
Section 2 - GB and Ireland - Minor Passenger operators . . . 112
Section 3 - GB & Ireland - Ro-Ro Freight-ferries . . . 126
Section 4 - Ro-Ro Operators Conveying Private Traffic . . . 142
Section 5 - GB & Ireland - Chain, Cable etc Ferries . . . 145
Section 6 - GB & Ireland - Major Passenger-only Ferries . . . 147
Scandinavian and Northern Europe review 2016/17 . . . 156
Section 7 - Northern Europe . . . 162
Section 8 - Other Vessels . . . 212
Section 9 - Sisters . . . 212
Section 10 - Changes since 'Ferries 2017 - British Isles & Northern Europe' . . . 217
Ferries Illustrated . . . 218
Late News . . . 219
Index . . . 220

Britannia Seaways *(DFDS)*

Europe's **Leading** Guide To The Ferry Industry

Introduction...

This is the thirtieth edition of this book, which first appeared in 1983 as the 24-page 'home published' *'Car Ferries from Great Britain and Ireland'*. The book aims to list every passenger/vehicle ferry in Great Britain and Ireland, ro-ro freight vessels which operate regular services between Great Britain and Ireland and to nearby Continental destinations and major passenger/vehicle ferries in other parts of Northern Europe. The coverage of Northern Europe is not fully comprehensive (to make it so would probably triple the size of the book) and does not include freight-only operations and vessels - although freight-only vessels have been included where the operators also run passenger services. Where operators use a mixture of ro-ro and container ships, I have only included the ro-ro ships. Exceptionally I have included the *Arx* of CLdN/Cobelfret Ferries and the *Elisabeth* of P&O Ferries, as they both operate to provide additional container capacity on ro-ro routes.

Each operator is listed alphabetically within sections - major operators, minor operators, freight-only operators, non-public freight operators, chain, cable and float ferries, passenger-only ferries, other North European passenger operators and vehicle/passenger vessels owned by companies not currently engaged in operating services. After details relating to each company's management, address, telephone numbers, email, website and services, there is a fleet list with technical data and then a potted history of each vessel with previous names and dates.

2016 will be known as 'the year of Brexit' or at least the year of the referendum which narrowly voted for the UK to leave the European Union. The implications of this on the ferry business are still unknown and in the short term business seems to be booming, especially on the freight side. For example, on the Humber - Maas axis several operators have chartered extra tonnage and ordered new, larger ships. When we actually leave it may of course be a different story. If we leave the customs union it may be possible to resume selling duty free goods to passengers. But as any observer at Dover, Britain's busiest port, will note these days freight is king and the implications on the freight market will be of much greater significance.

Nick Widdows

Whitstable, Kent

August 2017

Foreword...

Brexit, Trump, emissions regulations, fluctuating oil prices, changeable exchange rates, an emboldened Russia - the list of things which could affect north European ferry operators but are outside their control is limitless. It would be understandable were many companies to throw aside their historic inclination to gradually order new generations of ships in favour of a form of cautious inertia, a willingness to tread water in the short or medium term and prudently defer new orders in the hope of more certain times down the line. Fortunately, whilst there must be plenty of doubts in many ferry boardrooms, the past year has seen an easing of what had become a dearth of newbuilding contracts with the likes of Stena Line, Brittany Ferries, Irish Ferries, Color Line, Polferries and Viking Line all now having new ships on order.

Despite this, the north European ferry fleet is gradually ageing as ferries built in the 1990s or even the 1980s provide sufficient capacity for present demand and prove challenging to replace. Stena's *Stena Europe* and *Stena Danica*, for example, look set to serve their owner well into their fourth decades, unprecedented lengths of service which would have seemed inconceivable even 20 years ago. Even at Dover, with no new vessels presently on order, the gap between the most recent new-build, the *Spirit of France* of 2013, and whatever vessel is next built to operate from the port will be the longest since the Second World War.

A RADICAL TRADITION

One of the most intriguing aspects of the ferry industry is its ever-changing nature: the rise and fall of operators, the delivery of new ships and recycling of older ones. Historically, risk takers have often been successful, a pattern most marked in the early years of what we can consider the modern car ferry era in western Europe, between the 1950s and 1970s. In that period, car ferries replaced legacy packet operations and new companies, often led by a single enterprising businessman, could find a small vessel, a pair of willing ports and swiftly enter service. These endeavours led to what remain some of the key players in the modern industry - the likes of Viking Line, TT Line and the predecessors of the modern P&O Ferries and Color Line flowered in this entrepreneurial age.

The era was best demonstrated by the first decade of Stena Line - in the ten years after Sten Olsson founded his ferry company in 1962, as many as 20 new routes were established; 16 of them closed within the same time frame and only two, Gothenburg-Frederikshavn and Gothenburg-Kiel, remain today. Had social media existed at the time, Olsson's whimsical entry into the ferry market, its ever-changing focus and the constant chopping and changing of vessels and routes, would probably have been roundly criticised, much like LD Lines' efforts in recent times. The line between innovative businessman and unreliable opportunist is a thin one indeed but today Olsson is rightly remembered as one of the industry's great founding fathers.

THE MODERN INDUSTRY - A MATURE MARKET

The passage of time, the increasing maturity of the market and the ever-growing capital costs of today's, much larger, ships and shoreside infrastructure mean that these sort of opportunistic endeavours are now rarely practical and the cyclical rise and fall of operators and ships has slowed. Not many markets are under-served (although many are monopolies or oligopolies dependent on access to the best slots at the best ports) whilst the myriad rival routes of earlier decades have largely been whittled down to the optimal crossings or most developed ports.

New operators can still find a market and enjoy strong growth, however, and Tallink and their new *Megastar*, profiled elsewhere in this volume, demonstrate what can be achieved with steady leadership and investment. The company's rise to prominence after Estonia gained its independence from the USSR in 1991 is as impressive as that of Stena in the 1960s - although effectively developed from the old Soviet ESCO, Tallink grasped the opportunities that the established companies couldn't or wouldn't and, within 20 years, became the pre-eminent Baltic ferry operator.

Pont-Aven *(Andrew Cooke)*

Superspeed 2 *(John Bryant)*

Stena Superfast VIII *(George Holland)*

Aurora af Helsingborg *(Scandlines)*

In concept, technology and in her passenger spaces the LNG-fuelled *Megastar* reflects the latest thinking in a market which has largely dispensed with the smaller fast ferries that just 20 years ago many thought might come to dominate. Fast conventional ships with large freight capacity and comfortable, modern passenger spaces are now the appropriate solution for many of the most heavily-trafficked ferry crossings in the world.

BRITISH UPHEAVAL

On the short crossings of the English Channel, the past two decades have seen operators focus on the rapid movement of vast volumes of freight at a time when the passenger market has been in comparative decline following the end of Duty Free sales. P&O's *Spirit of Britain* and *Spirit of France* represent the culmination of this evolution with huge freight capacity and a transport-oriented passenger environment featuring relatively small shopping areas compared to the supermarkets of years past with their rows of check out counters and clinking bottles of alcohol.

A British exit from the European single market and Customs Union and the re-introduction of import controls would present a tremendous logistical challenge to the fast-moving ports of Dover and Calais which have little space for detailed inspection of large numbers of lorries. Conversely, were Duty Free to re-appear the ferry industry may see renewed demand for the 'booze cruises' of old. Passengers would, however, probably need greater incentives to return to the ferries than a mere revival of the short-sea day trip experience which, by the 1990s, was a slightly numbing, often rowdy one. In this respect the *Megastar*, operating on a route on which shopping remains a vital component, is an important reference, building on the success of the earlier *Star*. Both vessels, as well as the comprehensive rebuilding of Fjord Line's *Oslofjord* (ex-*Bergen*) for the Sandefjord-Stromstad route, present spacious and modern interiors alongside their vast shopping arcades.

THE CHALLENGE OF OLDER VESSELS

For some routes, particularly marginal or peripheral ones, the mature nature of the business means that traffic has reached a steady state which is unlikely to increase significantly even with the expensive addition of a new ship - the aforementioned *Stena Europe* at Fishguard being a good example.

Older vessels are generally less efficient to operate than their more modern brethren but, when well maintained by reputable operators, these greater operational expenses are not always sufficient to offset the huge capital cost of a brand new ship. At some stage, however, maintaining elderly ships becomes prohibitively expensive and some difficult decisions will have to be made about the next step with a limited pool of second hand vessels to turn to.

Complicating all these calculations are modern emissions standards whose areas are gradually being extended and mean that elderly vessels will either have to be modified with 'scrubbers' or revert to burning more expensive low sulphur fuel - directly affecting the economic decisions made by operators, forcing them to invest either in elderly ships, new ships or expensive fuel.

OTHER OPPORTUNITIES

Innovation need not stop at new tonnage however and there remain lots of smaller ways in which the business of ferrying can be improved: dingy decor, dismal food, queues of passengers waiting to disembark in dark companionways, a lack of seating and space, remote and unpleasant pet kennels. Much can be done to address some of these longstanding issues, common to many operators, at relatively little cost.

We could not realistically hope for a return to the industry's swashbuckling and adventurous early days, especially in such uncertain times. Whether existing operators choose to invest in new ships or upgrade existing ones they should always remember that, for most travellers apart from regular truck drivers, the ferry crossing is out of the ordinary, it is uncommon. The passenger experience and the passenger environment should strive to reflect this by rising above the everyday - and there is no reason to wait for new ships to achieve that. Despite the global challenges facing operators, such ambitions are within their control, need not cost substantial amounts to address but can have a large effect on people's perceptions of both that ferry operator and of ferry travel more widely.

Matthew Murtlland

A **Guide** To Using This Book

A GUIDE TO USING THIS BOOK

Sections Listing is in seven sections. ***Section 1*** - Services from Great Britain and Ireland to the Continent and between Great Britain and Ireland (including services to/from the Isle of Man and Channel Islands), ***Section 2*** - Domestic services within Great Britain and Ireland, ***Section 3*** - Freight-only services from Great Britain and Ireland and domestic routes, ***Section 4*** - Minor vehicle ferries in Great Britain and Ireland (chain and cable ferries etc), ***Section 5*** - Major passenger-only operators, ***Section 6*** - Major car ferry operators in Northern Europe, ***Section 7*** - Companies not operating regular services possessing vehicle ferries which may be chartered or sold to other operators.

Order The company order within each section is alphabetical. Note that the definite article and words meaning 'company' or 'shipping company' (eg. 'AG', 'Reederei') do not count. However, where this is part of a ship's name it does count. Sorting is by normal English convention eg. 'Å' is treated the same as 'A' and comes at the start, not as a separate character which comes at the end of the alphabet as is the Scandinavian convention. Where ships are numbered, order is by number whether the number is expressed in Arabic or Latin digits.

Listing of Ships When a ship owned by a company listed in this book is on charter to another company listed, then she is shown under the company which operates her. When a ship owned by a company listed in this book is on charter to another company not listed, then she is shown under the company which owns her.

IMO Number All ships of 100t or greater (except vessels solely engaged in fishing, ships without mechanical means of propulsion (eg. chain ferries), pleasure yachts, ships engaged on special service (eg. lightships), hopper barges, hydrofoils, air cushion vehicles, floating docks and structures classified in a similar manner, warships and troopships, wooden ships) are required to be registered by the International Maritime Organisation (IMO), an agency of the United Nations. The number is retained by the ship throughout her life, however much the vessel is rebuilt. This number is now required to be displayed on the ship externally and on top so that it can be read from the air. The scheme is administered by Lloyd's Register-Fairplay, who maintain a database of all ships in excess of 100t (with some exceptions), not just those classified through them.

Company Information This section gives general information regarding the status of the company. That is, nationality, whether it is public or private sector and whether it is part of a larger group.

Management The Managing Director and Marketing Director or Manager of each company are listed. Where these posts do not exist, other equivalent people are listed. Where only initials are given, that person is, as far as is known, male.

Address This is the address of the company's administrative headquarters. In the case of some international companies, British and overseas addresses are given.

Telephone and Fax Numbers are expressed as follows: + [*number*] (this is the international dialling code which is dialled in combination with the number dialled for international calls (00 in the UK, Ireland and most other European countries); it is not used for calling within the country), ([*number*]) (this is the number which precedes area codes when making long-distance domestic calls - it is not dialled when calling from another country or making local calls (not all countries have this)), [*number*] (this is the rest of the number including, where appropriate, the area dialling code). UK '08' numbers are sometimes not available from overseas and the full number must be dialled in all circumstances.

Internet Email addresses and **Website** URLs are given where these are available; the language(s) used is shown. The language listed first is that which appears on the home page when accessed from a UK based computer; the others follow in alphabetical order. In a few cases Email facility is only available through the Website. To avoid confusion, there is no other punctuation on the Internet line.

Routes operated After each route there are, in brackets, details of **1** normal journey time, **2** regular vessel(s) used on the route (number as in list of vessels) and **3** frequencies (where a number per day is given, this relates to return sailings). In the case of freight-only sailings which operate to a regular schedule, departure times are given where they have been supplied. Please note that times are subject to quite frequent change and cancellation.

Winter and Summer In this book, Winter generally means the period between October and Easter while Summer means Easter to October. The peak Summer period is generally June, July and August. In Scandinavia, the Summer peak ends in mid-August whilst in the UK it starts rather later and generally stretches into the first or second week of September. Dates vary according to operator.

Spelling The convention is used in respect of town and country names is that English names are used for towns and areas of countries where such names exist (eg. Gothenburg rather than Göteborg) and English names for countries (eg. Germany rather than Deutschland). Otherwise local names are used, accented as appropriate. In a few cases, English names have slipped out of common usage and the local name is more commonly used in Britain, ie Dunkerque not Dunkirk, Helsingør not Elsinore and Vlissingen not Flushing. Many towns in Finland have both Finnish and Swedish names; we have used the Finnish name except in the case of Åland which is a Swedish-speaking area. In the case of Danish towns, the alternative use of 'å' or 'aa' follows local convention. The following towns, islands and territories are expressed using their English names - the local name is shown following: Antwerp - Antwerpen/Anvers, Fyn - Funen, Genoa - Génova, Ghent - Gent, Gothenburg - Göteborg, Hook of Holland - Hoek van Holland, Jutland - Jylland, Copenhagen - København, Ostend - Oostende, Oporto - Porto, Seville - Sevilla, Sealand - Sjælland and Venice - Venezia.

Terms The following words mean ***'shipping company'*** in various languages: Redereja (Latvian), Rederi (Danish, Norwegian, Swedish), Rederij (Dutch), Reederei (German) and Zegluga (Polish). The following words mean ***'limited company'***: AB - Aktiebolaget (Swedish) (Finnish companies who use both the Finnish and Swedish terms sometimes express it as Ab), AG - Aktiengesellschaft (German), AS - Aksjeselskap (Norwegian), A/S - Aktie Selskabet (Danish), BV - Besloten Vennootschap (Dutch), GmbH - Gesellschaft mit beschränkter Haftung (German), NV - Naamloze Vennootschap (Dutch), Oy - (Finnish), Oyj - (Finnish (plc)) and SA - Société Anonyme (French).

Types of Ferry

These distinctions are necessarily general and many ships will have features of more than one category.

Car Ferry Until about 1970, most vehicle ferries were primarily designed for the conveyance of cars and their passengers and foot passengers. Little regard was paid to the conveyance of lorries and trailers, since this sort of traffic had not begun to develop. Few vessels of this type are still in service.

Multi-purpose Ferry From about 1970 onwards vehicle ferries began to make more provision for freight traffic, sharing the same ship with passengers and cars. Features usually include higher vehicle decks, often with retractable mezzanine decks, enabling two levels of cars or one level of freight and coaches, and separate facilities (including cabins on quite short crossings) for freight drivers.

Cruise Ferry In the 1980s the idea of travelling on a ferry, not just to get from A to B but for the pleasure of the travel experience, became more and more popular and ferries were built with increasingly luxurious and varied passenger accommodation. Such vessels also convey cars and freight but the emphasis is on passenger accommodation with a high level of berths (sometimes providing berths for all passengers).

Ro-pax Ferry A vessel designed primarily for the carriage of freight traffic but which also carries a limited number of ordinary passengers. Features generally include a moderate passenger capacity - up to about 500 passengers - and a partly open upper vehicle deck. Modern ro-pax vessels are becoming increasingly luxurious with facilities approaching those of a cruise ferry.

Ro-ro Ferry A vessel designed for the conveyance of road freight, unaccompanied trailers and containers on low trailers (known as 'Mafis' although often made by other manufacturers). Some such vessels have no passenger accommodation but the majority can accommodate up to 12 passengers - the maximum allowed without a passenger certificate. On routes where there is a low level of driver-accompanied traffic (mainly the longer ones), ordinary passengers, with or without cars, can sometimes be conveyed. On routes with a high level of driver-accompanied traffic, passenger capacity will sometimes be higher but facilities tend to be geared to the needs of freight drivers eg. lounge with video, high level of cabins on routes of three hours or more. Technically such vessels are passenger ferries (having a passenger certificate).

Con-ro Many ro-ro vessels are capable of having ISO (International Standards Organisation) containers crane-loaded on the upper 'weather' deck. In this book the term con-ro applies only to vessels whose upper deck can only take containers and has no vehicle access.

Fast Ferry Streamlined vessel of catamaran or monohull construction, speed in excess of 30 knots, water jet propulsion, generally aluminium-built but some have steel hulls, little or no freight capacity and no cabins.

Timescale Although the book goes to press in June 2017, I have sought to reflect the situation as it will exist in early Summer 2017 with regard to the introduction of new ships or other known changes. Vessels due to enter service after July 2017 are shown as '**Under Construction**'. This term does not necessarily mean that physical work has started but an order has been placed with a shipyard. The book is updated at all stages of the production process where this is feasible, although major changes once the text has been paginated are not possible; there is also a 'Late News' section on page xxx for changes which cannot be incorporated into the text.

List of vessels

NO (A)		GROSS TONNAGE (B)		SERVICE SPEED (KNOTS)		NUMBER OF PASSENGERS			VEHICLE ACCESS DECK (D)		IMO NUMBER
1	**NAME**	**‡26433t**	**87**	**22.0k**	**150m**	**290P**	**650C**	**100L**	**BA2**	**UK**	**1234567**
	NAME		YEAR BUILT		LENGTH OVERALL		VEHICLE (C) DECK CAPACITY	VEHICLE (C) DECK CAPACITY		FLAG (E)	

(A) » = fast ferry, • = vessel laid up, F = freight-only vessel (max 12 passengers), F‡ = freight-only vessel (with passenger certificate), p = passenger-only vessel

(B) C = Cars, L = Lorries (**15m**), T = Trailers (**13.5m**), r = can also take rail wagons, - = No figure quoted.

(C) B = Bow, A = Aft, S = Side, Q = Quarterdeck, R = Slewing ramp, 2 = Two decks can be loaded at the same time, C = Vehicles must be crane-loaded aboard, t = turntable ferry.

(D) The following abbreviations are used:

AG	= Antigua and Barbuda	DK	= Denmark	IR	= Republic of Ireland	PT	= Portugal
		EE	= Estonia			PL	= Poland
AL	= Åland Islands	ES	= Spain	LU	= Luxembourg	RU	= Russia
BB	= Barbados	FO	= Faroes	LT	= Lithuania	SG	= Singapore
BE	= Belgium	FI	= Finland	LV	= Latvia	SE	= Sweden
BM	= Bermuda	FR	= France	MT	= Malta	TR	= Turkey
BS	= Bahamas	GI	= Gibraltar	NL	= Netherlands	UK	= United Kingdom
CY	= Cyprus	IM	= Isle of Man	NO	= Norway		
DE	= Germany	IT	= Italy	PA	= Panama		

In the notes ships are in CAPITAL LETTERS, shipping lines and other institutions are in *italics*.

Capacity In this book, capacities shown are the maxima. Sometimes vessels operate at less than their maximum passenger capacity due to reduced crewing or to operating on a route on which they are not permitted to operate above a certain level. Car and lorry/trailer capacities are the maximum for either type. The two figures are not directly comparable. Some parts of a vessel may allow cars on two levels to occupy the space that a trailer or lorry occupies on one level, some may not; some parts of a vessel with low headroom may only be accessible to cars. All figures have to be approximate.

Ownership The ownership of many vessels is very complicated. Some are actually owned by finance companies and banks, some by subsidiary companies of the shipping lines, some by subsidiary companies of a holding company of which the shipping company is also a subsidiary and some by companies which are jointly owned by the shipping company and other interests like a bank, set up specifically to own one ship or a group of ships. In all these cases the vessel is technically chartered to the shipping company. However, in this book, only those vessels chartered from one shipping company to another or from a ship-owning company unconnected with the shipping line are recorded as being on charter. Vessels are listed under the current operator rather than the owner. Charter is 'bareboat' (without crew) unless otherwise stated. If chartered with crew, vessels are 'time-chartered'.

Gross Tonnage This is a measure of enclosed capacity rather than weight, based on a formula of one gross ton = 100 cubic feet. Even small alterations can alter the gross tonnage. Under old measurement systems, the capacity of enclosed car decks was not included but, under the 1969 Convention, all vessels laid down after 1982 have been measured by a new system which includes enclosed vehicle decks as enclosed space, thereby considerably increasing the tonnage of vehicle ferries. Under this Convention, from 1st January 1995 all vessels were due to be re-measured under this system. Tonnages quoted here are, where possible, those given by the shipping companies themselves.

The following people are gratefully thanked for their assistance with this publication, many of them in ferry companies in the UK and abroad: Matthew Murtland, Matthew Punter, Kai Ortel, Kalle Id, Gary Andrews, John Bryant, Andrew Cooke, Matthew Davies, Ian Hall, Peter Therkildsen, Ian Smith (Camrose Media), and Gomer Press Ltd.

Whilst every effort has been made to ensure that the facts contained here are correct, neither the publishers nor the writer can accept any responsibility for errors contained herein. We would, however, appreciate comments from readers, which we will endeavour to reflect in the next edition which we plan to publish in summer 2018.

SILJA LINE - 60 YEARS OF SERVICE

In the 1950s, ferry services between Finland and Sweden were a monopoly of Finska Ångfartygs Aktiebolaget (FÅA), Ångfartygs Aktiebolaget Bore and Rederi AB Svea, collectively known as De Samseglande Rederierna (roughly 'the joint service shipping companies') which operated passenger steamers on routes linking Helsinki and Turku in Finland to Stockholm in Sweden. To answer the demands for a car ferry service, in 1957 De Samseglande established a joint subsidiary, Siljarederiet. The new company purchased an old Svea steamer which, after a refit, started service on the Turku - Stockholm line as the *Silja*. She could transport 600 passengers and 47 cars – but these had to be lifted on and off the ship.

THE FIRST RORO FERRIES

De Samseglande's conservative approach ultimately cost them their monopoly position, as during 1958 and 1959 several competing ro-ro ferries were introduced on the Finland-Sweden routes. This finally spurred Siljarederiet's owners into action; the company got permission to commission a purpose-built car-passenger ferry from the Wärtsilä shipyard in Helsinki (which offered a low price as they were keen to enter the ferry building market), delivered in 1961 as the *Skandia* and placed on a service linking Turku to Norrtälje (at the time, it was thought best for car ferries to sail from remote ports that passengers could drive to). The 1,200-passenger and 175-car ferry ushered in a new era; not only did she introduce loading via gates at both bow and stern, she also did away with class-divided accommodation. The success of the *Skandia* was such that three sister ships followed: the *Nordia* in 1962, the *Botnia* in 1967 and the *Floria* in 1970.

In addition to the *Skandia*-class ships, Siljarederiet acquired the slightly smaller *Holmia* second-hand in 1965, and the larger newbuilt *Fennia* in 1966. The two new ships opened new services for the company: the *Holmia* linked Naantali to Stockholm, while the *Fennia* restored direct Turku-Stockholm sailings to Siljarederiet's portfolio. The *Fennia* was the company's undisputed flagship - while she carried 1,200 passengers (as did her other newbuilt fleetmates), her overnight accommodation was much more extensive and the car deck had space for no less than 265 cars.

SILJAREDERIET BECOMES SILJA LINE

In addition to the Siljarederiet ships, De Samseglande continued their steamer services throughout the 1960s. Toward the decade's end it became clear that these would be gradually phased out, and the birth in 1966 of an aggressive competitor, Viking Line, forced De Samseglande to rethink their marketing strategy. Thus, in 1970, Siljarederiet became Silja Line, a joint marketing venture for De Samseglande's Finland-Sweden routes. During the next two years, the Siljarederiet-owned ships were gradually moved under the ownership of the parent companies.

Already before the formation of Silja Line, Siljarederiet had commissioned three new ferries, one for the Turku-Stockholm line and two to open around-the-year services between Helsinki and Stockholm; hitherto, service on the latter route ceased when the Baltic Sea froze over for the winter. The new Helsinki ship appeared in 1972 as the *Aallotar* (for FÅA) and *Svea Regina* (for Svea). With space for 1,000 passengers, cabin berths for 439 and 180 cars, they were such a resounding success that three larger replacements were contracted within a year of their entering service. The new Turku ship, Bore's *Bore I*, followed in 1973. Essentially an enlarged *Fennia*, she carried 1,200 passengers with 432 cabin berths and space for 359 cars.

The trio of new Helsinki-Stockholm ships were all delivered during 1975: the *Svea Corona* for Svea, *Wellamo* for FÅA and *Bore Star* for Bore. Their capacities were 1,200 passengers, 799 cabin berths and 240 cars. During the summer months, the three ships operated a 'rolling schedule' with both overnight and daytime crossings (hitherto, only an overnight service had been offered), but due to insufficient demand during the winter seasons, the *Bore Star* was initially chartered out for Canary Isles cruising with Finnlines during the winters. The 'rolling schedule' was quickly found inefficient, and the route reverted to an overnight service year-round, with the *Svea Corona* moving to the Turku-Stockholm line.

The classically styled Bore of 1960 joined the Silja Line fleet in 1970s. *(Rami Wirrankoski collection)*

The French-built Wellamo of 1975 and her sisters were quite elegant, despite their high superstructures. *(Bruce Peter collection)*

The Finnjet as she appeared in 1986, already owned by Effoa but not yet incorporation into the Silja fleet. *(Rami Wirrankoski)*

The stylish Svea of 1985 was briefly the largest ferry in the world. *(Krzysztof Brzoza)*

RATIONALISATION

Despite the arrival of new tonnage, Silja Line was struggling to make a profit. Compounding the effects of the oil crisis was the company's inefficient route structure: in addition to the main routes from Helsinki and Turku to Stockholm, it operated a secondary service from Turku to Norrtälje and two steamers from Turku to Stockholm's historic city center (whereas the ferries sailed to the ferry port in Värtan); a total of 11 vessels served these four routes. Silja's new managing director Harry Österberg thus instituted a rationalisation programme on his appointment in 1976: the company would now concentrate on just the Helsinki-Stockholm and Turku-Stockholm routes, which would be operated with just six ships; eventually, these would be replaced with larger and more efficient tonnage, bringing down the number of ships to just four.

The first newbuildings of Österberg's regime were the 'Futurum project', a pair of newbuildings twice as big as the previous Helsinki-Stockholm ships and with unparallelled standard of passenger accommodation. While Österberg convinced Effoa (as FÅA had been renamed in 1976) and Svea of the need for new ships, the Bore company were more sceptical and, following a change in their leadership, withdrew from Silja Line altogether in 1980, selling their ships to Effoa.

Nevertheless, the Futurum ships were delivered in 1981 as the *Finlandia* and *Silvia Regina*. They had a capacity for 2,000 passenger, 1,601 cabin berth and 450 cars, with a gross tonnage of over 25,000. The new ships were, in effect, the first cruise ferries on the Finland-Sweden routes. During the 1980s, the emphasis shifted, in particular on the Helsinki-Stockholm route, permanently from transport to offering short leisure cruises to Finns and Swedes alike. While the ships were otherwise successful, their original buff bow configuration was not, and already in early 1982 both had to return to their builders, where their bows were remodelled with finer lines. Already before this, in the beginning of 1982, Rederi AB Svea had beem taken over by their parent company Johnson Line, who now became the other partner in Silja Line alongside Effoa.

Following the delivery of the Futurum ships, attention turned to the Turku-Stockholm route, now operated by the 1975 *Svea Corona* and *Silja Star* (ex-*Bore Star*), alongside the 1973 *Skandia* (ex-*Bore I*) and 1966 *Fennia*. The first pair operated a leisurely overnight service similar to the Helsinki-Stockholm route, while the older ships both made a complete round trip every 24 hours. While the *Finlandia* and *Silvia Regina* had been designed from the outset to be transferrable to the Turku-Stockholm line, replacing all four pre-existing ships, instead the decision was made to build two brand-new ships for the Turku route, based on the Futurum ships but optimised for the needs of the more hectic service. Particular attention was also paid to the exterior design and bow form; while the *Finlandia* and *Silvia Regina* had received adverse comments for their looks, the 1985-delivered *Svea* and her 1986 sister *Wellamo* were hailed as some of the most beautiful ferries in the world. In 1987, Silja Line's route network extended to Germany, when Effoa took over the loss-making Helsinki-Travemünde ferry *Finnjet* and incorporated her into the Silja Line fleet.

THE SILJA SERENADE AND SILJA SYMPHONY

Simultaneously with the *Svea* and *Wellamo*, Silja's main competitors Viking Line had taken delivery of a pair of new Helsinki-Stockholm ferries, the *Mariella* and *Olympia*, which rivalled and arguably even surpassed the *Finlandia* and *Silvia Regina* in terms of their passenger facilites. Initially, Silja Line's planned response was to lengthen and extensively rebuild the half-decade-old *Finlandia* and *Silvia Regina*, with passenger capacity enlarged to 2,500. Negotiation for the conversion had already been carried out with a Japanese yard, with a price of 200 million Finnish markkaa per ship, when, following Harry Österberg's retirement, the plan was scrapped. Instead, his successor Ralf Sandtröm wanted to build two new ships with unprecedented interior arrangements.

These were delivered in 1990 and 1991 as the *Silja Serenade* and *Silja Symphony*, respectively. At circa 58,000 gross tons, they were the largest ferries in the world, with passenger capacity of 2,500, all with cabin berths, and a car capacity of 450 (subsequent refits, including the conversion of a lower garage into cabins, increased the passenger and cabin berth capacity to 2,800, but decreased the car capacity to 410). More novel than the ships' size, however, was the Promenade, a five-deck-high horizontal atrium running through two thirds of the ship, acting as a centerpoint for all activity onboard and allowing an unprecedentedly high number of cabins with windows, for which a premium could be charged.

However, while the ships were very successful from the passengers' point of view, they were also very expensive: the original contract price had been 700 million markkaa per ship, which rose to one billion markkaa per ship following the bankruptcy of the original builders, Wärtsilä Marine. The high price of the ships, combined with Silja Line's owners – that had merged in 1990 to form EffJohn – ill-adviced expansion to ferry and cruise trades outside the Baltic, would prove near-fatal to the company fortunes in the 1990s. Nevertheless, the *Silja Serenade* and *Silja Symphony* set a new standard for Baltic Sea ferries with their extensive public rooms; in 1992, the *Svea* and *Wellamo* were refitted to match, renamed *Silja Karneval* and *Silja Festival*.

EXPANSION

In 1991, Silja Line thus operated five ships on three routes: Helsinki-Stockholm, Turku-Stockholm and Helsinki-Travemünde. However, already in the late 1980s Silja's owners had acquired the operations of Rederi Ab Sally, which included Baltic Sea ferry operations. To streamline operations, these were merged into Silja Line. First, in 1992, Sally Line and their brand new Helsinki-Tallinn cruise ship *Sally Albatross* joined Silja Line. Then, in the beginning of 1993, the Wasa Line operation, linking Vaasa, Pietarsaari and Kokkola in Finland to Sundsvall, Umeå and Skellefteå in Sweden, followed. This latter merger brought two old Silja Line stalwarts back into the fleet: the *Wasa Queen*, ex-*Bore Star* and *Silja Star*, and the *Fennia*, which had retained its original name despite changes of ownership.

Soon after the takeover of Wasa Line, the news reached Silja Line that Rederi AB Slite, one of the owners of competing Viking Line, was in trouble with their financiers (Nordbanken, who also funded EffJohn) and could not take delivery of their much-publicized Helsinki-Stockholm newbuilding *Europa*. After quick negotiations, the *Europa* was chartered to Silja Line as the *Silja Europa* on completion. With an unprecedented passenger capacity of 3,013 – all with cabin berths – but only 400 cars, the *Silja Europa* took the title of the World's largest ferry from her new running mate *Silja Symphony*, with the *Silja Serenade* moved to the Turku-Stockholm line.

Finally, also during 1993, Silja Line started a joint service with Euroway, a Swedish operator attempting a cruise ferry service between Malmö (Sweden) and Lübeck (Germany). The *Silja Festival*, supplanted from the Turku-Stockholm route, moved to the Malmö-Lübeck service alongside Euroway's *Frans Suell*. This was not a success, and already in early 1994 the service was closed down; the *Frans Suell* was chartered by Silja and renamed *Silja Scandinavia* for the Turku-Stockholm line (replacing the *Silja Karneval*, which was sold), while the *Silja Festival* moved to the routes from Vaasa for the summer season.

DECLINE

Two disasters struck the Baltic Sea ferry scene during 1994: first, the *Sally Albatross* grounded and partially sunk in March, fortunately without loss of life. As a replacement, the *Silja Festival* was moved to the Helsinki-Tallinn route in the Autumn, but returned to Vaasa for the next summer season. Then, in September, the Estline ferry *Estonia* (which had briefly sailed for Silja Line in 1990 as the second *Silja Star*) sunk with the loss of 852 lives. Combined with the ongoing recession, the *Estonia*-disaster plunged the Baltic Sea ferry trades into deep difficulties. To attract more passengers in the new situation, the previously upmarket Silja product was purposefully downgraded and focus was moved more to the Finnish market, which had not been as badly affected as the Swedish one. To improve profits, the *Silja Serenade* – that had been found ill-suited for the Turku-Stockholm run – swapped routes with the *Silja Europa* in early 1995.

Potential for growth was seen on the Helsinki-Tallinn route. Initially this was a one-ship service with the *Silja Festival*, but from autumn 1995 the *Wasa Queen* joined the larger ship for the winter seasons. Future plans were frustrated by the *Silja Scandinavia*'s owners deciding to sell the ship in 1997; as Silja Line could not secure funds to buy her, she was sold to Viking Line. To cope, the *Silja Festival* was moved to the Turku-Stockholm route and the *Wasa Queen* permanently to the Helsinki-Tallinn route. Joining her on the latter for the autumn-to-spring season was the *Finnjet*, which now spent the summers on a new Helsinki-Rostock service.

The revolutionary Silja Serenade under construction at the Turku shipyard. *(Ship Historical Society of Finland collection)*

The Silja Serenade outside the Stockholm archipelago during the difficult winter of 2010. *(Marko Stampehl)*

SILJA LINE

The Silja Festival (originally the Wellamo of 1986) was an enduring member of the Silja fleet until 2008, and then the Tallink fleet until 2013. Today she sails with Corsica Ferries as the Mega Andrea. *(Jukka Huotari)*

The SuperSeaCat Four approaching Helsinki, displaying the dual Silja Line SuperSeaCat livery. *(Sami Koski)*

The magenta-dominated livery of the Baltic Princess, currently Silja Line's newest vessel, is at odds with Silja's traditionally black- or blue-dominated palette. *(Kalle Id)*

THE SEA CONTAINERS ERA

By the second half of the 1990s, EffJohn's Finnish and Swedish owners were looking to rid themselves of the company, which after 1998 owned just Silja Line and their cargo-oriented subsidiary SeaWind Line. A buyer emerged in the form of the Anglo-American conglomerate Sea Containers, whose owner James Sherwood saw much potential in the Sweden-Finland trades after the end of intra-EU tax free sales in 1999. As ships sailing via the Åland Islands, an autonomous Finnish province, could continue to sell tax-free goods, the Helsinki and Turku to Stockholm routes were expected to continue to flourish. The Helsinki-Tallinn route was an added bonus, as Estonia was not yet a part of the EU. In 1999, Silja Line became a part of the Sea Containers empire.

The routes across central Gulf of Bothnia were a different matter after the end of tax-free. The Kokkola-Skellefteå and Vaasa-Sundsvall -routes had already been discontinued, but after 1999, only Vaasa-Umeå was retained, thanks to a state subsidy. As the aged *Fennia* did not fulfill the requirements of the subsidy, she was withdrawn and the *Wasa Queen* returned to her namesake city in her place. This was not a success, and at the end of 2000 the *Wasa Queen* was laid up and subsequently sold. Sea Containers felt there was no need for either her or the *Fennia* on the Helsinki-Tallinn line, on which they had placed their 1999-built fast monohull *SuperSeaCat Four* in 2000, sailing alongside the *Finnjet* outside the summer season.

Sea Containers wanted Silja Line to move back upmarket and concentrate more on the Swedish and emerging Russian markets. At the same time, Silja's Finnish leadership thought profits could only be made with a downmarket product concentrating on the Finnish market. Resulting from this internal strife, neither approach was fully followed; in 2002, when the former *Sally Albatross* returned (having been chartered out after her 1994 grounding, first to Norwegian Cruise Line and then to Star Cruises), she was re-introduced as the upmarket cruise ship *Silja Opera* – but on short cruises from Helsinki. The *Finnjet* was given a large-scale refit in 2004 and moved to a new Saint Petersburg-Tallinn-Rostock service; this was an abysmal failure, and the ship was chartered out in 2005.

However, at the same time Silja's core activities – the Helsinki-Stockholm, Turku-Stockholm and Helsinki-Tallinn routes, the latter now operated by the *SuperSeaCat Three* and *SuperSeaCat Four* – remained lucrative, and in 2005 a letter of intent was signed for new ships for the Turku run. This was not to be: Sea Containers faced difficulties elsewhere in their vast empire and were on the brink of bankruptcy. In late 2005, a plan to sell Silja Line to the highest bidder was made public; to make the company more attractive to potential buyers, the *Finnjet* and *Silja Opera* would not be included in the deal; the former was already chartered out and the latter was withdrawn in early 2006. In June 2006 the Silja Line brand and the company's Finland-Sweden operations were sold to the Baltic Sea's rising star, Tallink. The Helsinki-Tallinn operations were not included, as their takeover would have meant incurred market regulator's wrath on Tallink due to a dominant market position.

THE TALLINK ERA

During Tallink ownership, the Silja Line brand returned to serving only the Helsinki and Turku to Stockholm routes. After the takeover, efforts were made to create a common brand under the combined Tallink Silja Line name, but the overall branding strategy has been inconsistent, with the Tallink name used for the entire operation in some territories, while in Finland and Sweden, the Silja ships have been marketed both under the Silja Line and Tallink Silja names. Reflective of this confusion were the changes to the Turku-Stockholm route, where in 2008 the ex-Tallink ferry *Galaxy* replaced the *Silja Festival*, which moved to the Tallink fleet; both retained their earlier names and only minor changes were made to their exteriors and interiors. The same pattern persisted in 2013, when the *Galaxy*'s sister ship *Baltic Princess* replaced the *Silja Europa*.

Silja Line thus entered its 60th year in 2017 with four ships – the *Silja Serenade, Silja Symphony, Galaxy* and *Baltic Princess* – and an inconsistent brand identity. However, during the same year Tallink Grupp made known that, in an attempt to capitalise on the popularity of the Silja Line brand, two brand identities would again be separated. What exactly this will mean for the onboard product and marketing has not yet been revealed at the time of writing. Rumours have suggested that the *Galaxy* and *Baltic Queen* would be repainted in a livery matching the *Silja Serenade* and *Silja Symphony*, but company representatives have stated there are currently no plans to this effect.

Kalle Id

TALLINN – HELSINKI: FIT FOR THE FUTURE

The development of Tallink's service linking the Estonian and Finnish capitals is one of the most impressive success stories of the ferry industry this century. From humble beginnings in the 1960s, through the fall of communism in the 1990s and into the current millennium, the route is now one of the most well-developed in the world, attracting millions of passengers, vehicles and freight each year.

The service between Tallinn and Helsinki is the company's 'flagship' operation, typically receiving their newest and most impressive ships. For the last fifteen years, the company has introduced a regular stream of newbuildings on the service, each vessel typically representing a significant improvement over the previous vessel. Indeed, no fewer than six brand new vessels have been commissioned by the company for the service since the turn of the millennium, with the very latest, the *Megastar* arriving in January 2017 to critical acclaim.

What makes the route particularly noteworthy however, is that Tallink effectively operate two distinct services: the cruise concept and the fast shuttle service. Whilst the former emerged out of the early days of the route as a tax-free booze and party destination, the latter concept was inaugurated in the later 2000s as the company modernised its eclectic fleet of elderly second hand conventional tonnage and numerous fast craft it had acquired over the years.

Tallink has carved out a striking role for itself in the European ferry industry with its commercial acumen, its bold ambition and its focus on high quality operations. The Tallink Shuttle service celebrates its tenth anniversary this year, fittingly with the arrival of its most impressive ever ship. Additionally, last year saw the introduction of the region's largest ever vessel, the *Silja Europa* which received a major refit and now acts as the sole vessel on the cruise circuit.

A BRIEF HISTORY

The origins of the Tallinn – Helsinki service date back to 1965 when the Estonian Shipping Company (ESCO) started a passenger-only operation between the two ports using the motor vessel *Vanemuine*. The first car ferry was introduced in 1980s, the *Georg Ots*. Shortly before the fall of the Iron Curtain, ESCO teamed up with the Finnish operator Palkkiyhtymä Oy, together with the City and Port of Tallinn, and established a subsidiary called Tallink to commence a new operation on the route. The company purchased the former Silja ferry *Svea Regina* and introduced her as the *Tallink* in January 1990. A little over a year later, Estonia was an independent country and a free market economy and so the stage was set for a tremendous boom in traffic on the service.

By this stage, several other operators had been experimenting with services on the route, including Eckerö Line and Inreko. By 1993, consolidation occurred with both ESCO and Inreko taking shares in Tallink and withdrawing their own operations from the service. At that time, Tallink acquired both the *Georg Ots* and the *Corbière* and the following year the *Vana Tallinn* (ex-*Dana Regina*) was also introduced.

All was not plain saling however and in 1996 Inreko withdrew from the operation and established its own rival service using the *Vana Tallinn* which Tallink replaced with the *Meloodia* (ex-*Mare Balticum*). By the following year, Tallink was in financial difficulties and was taken over by two Estonian businessmen, Enn Pant and Ain Hanschmidt. However, from this crisis, the modern Tallink was born and the seeds sown for the company's success. By 1998, the company was operating four second-hand conventional vessels: the *Georg Ots*, the *Vana Tallinn* (Inreko having previously ceased operations), the *Meloodia* and the newly acquired *Fantaasia* (ex-*Lion King*). All four ships operated one or two round trips a day, catering to both day-trippers, mini-cruisers and regular tourist and freight traffic.

By this stage, both Sila and Viking Lines had successfully established what could best be described as "party" cruises, with large, modern cruiseferries operating a single daily return crossing, typically departing Helsinki in the early evening, allowing passengers to enjoy the facilities before the ship arrived at Tallinn around midnight. Passengers then had the morning to sleep off the previous night's excesses – or enjoy the sights of Tallinn – before the ship returned in the afternoon to Finland. Viking typically utilised their *Cinderella* whilst Silja's *Finnjet* served the market in between regular trips to Travemünde in Germany.

There were also several attempts at fast ferry operations made during the later years of the decade.

Star - Pub Seaport *(Matthew Punter)*

Megastar *(Kalle Id)*

Megastar – Business Class Lounge *(Matthew Punter)*

Megastar – Lobby *(Matthew Punter)*

Viking Line, FRS and Silja all made their own attempts over the years, but it was Tallink's that became dominant with up for four catamarans or monohulls employed on the service by 2004.

The new owners of Tallink were quick to invest in the future of their operation and in 2002, the first of a new generation of ferries arrived in the form of the *Romantika* which replaced the *Fantaasia*, operating a single return crossing per day. She immediately captured the cruise traffic and set new standards of quality on the service. In 2006, she was replaced by an even larger vessel, the *Galaxy*.

Tallink's next move though was even bolder: it took the decision in late 2005 to consolidate all other conventional and fast vessels on the Tallinn – Helsinki route into single "shuttle" operation. A new day ferry was ordered from STX in Rauma which arrived in 2007 as the *Star*. A second ship was ordered from Fincantieri which arrived as the *Superstar* in 2008 – albeit based on an existing design, rather than purpose-built as the *Star* had been. Thanks to their uprated engines and propellors, each vessel could complete a single crossing in two hours and enabled six daily departures from each terminal. Together, these two new ships cleared out all the old 1970s tonnage and the fast ferries and utterly transformed the fortunes of the service.

STAR

The new *Star* inaugurated the Shuttle service on 12 April 2007 and she immediately made a name for herself as a vibrant, modern and capacious vessel, in stark contrast to the vessels she replaced. Shuttle branding was displayed prominently on her lurid, green hull to distinguish the operation from the cruises operated by the *Galaxy*.

At 186 metres in length and measuring 36,249 gross tonnes, the new ship could carry 1,900 passengers with 2,000 lane metres for vehicle or freight traffic. She was a design development of the *SeaFrance Rodin* which STX had constructed for SeaFrance in 2001. Unusually for a day ferry, she offered cabin capacity for 520 passengers. She was powered by four MaK 12M43C medium-speed main engines, each with an output of 12,000kW which provide her 27.5 knot service speed.

She made an immediate impression on the service: passenger accommodation was spread over three main decks – seven, eight and nine – and was decorated to a very high standard, with much use made of wood effect and warm colours. The overall effect was of an attractive, vibrant interior even if it lacks the cool chic of subsequent arrivals in the region.

Deck seven hosts a large duty-free supermarket and other retail spaces in addition to the 'Seaport' Pub. The business class lounge is also situated on this deck, to port. This was a new innovation for the Shuttle service, offering a quieter space for travellers to relax in with complementary food and drinks, including alcohol. All this comes at a price, however, with supplements in the region of €65 per passenger for a single trip.

Deck eight is the restaurant deck, offering the 450-seat Shuttle Buffet forward, an a la carte restaurant to port and a 'Snack Time' cafeteria. The latter was refitted in early 2016 with a Burger King® outlet being installed alongside. Deck nine offers the 'Sunset' bar forward and the 'Quick & Easy' pizzeria amidships. Cabins are situated aft on both decks eight and nine.

Tallink had such confidence in their new service that before the *Star* had been commissioned, it had turned to Fincantieri to secure a second vessel which emerged as the *Superstar* in 2008. This vessel was the fourth in a series that had thus far been constructed for Moby Lines and was a good opportunity for Tallink to quickly procure a similarly-matched vessel for their new route.

Despite having served the route for nine seasons, the *Superstar* never felt quite like a Tallink ship: she arrived complete with standardised Italian interiors and her owners only made superficial changes – largely to her buffet area – to bring her somewhat in line to its standards. What the *Superstar* did offer was the three deck high entertainment venue overlooking the bow of the vessel as well as the two deck conservatory-bar at the stern.

However, it was only a matter of time before the *Superstar* was replaced and so in 2015, a €230 million order was placed at Meyer Turku for a third vessel, the *Megastar* which would replace the *Superstar* as from 2017. It was also decided to convert the *Star* to double-deck loading to speed up turn-around times in port, work that was conducted during winter 2016/7.

MEGASTAR

The order for the new *Megastar* was placed on 27 February 2015. Production started on 4 August that year and her keel was laid on 9 February 2016. After twenty-three months, she entered service on 29 January 2017.

The *Megastar* has capacity for 2,800 passengers and 3,600 lane metres for vehicles, allowing her to carry up to 800 cars on two main freight decks and an upper car-only deck. Unlike the *Star*, she offers very few cabins, with only 94 berths available. She is the first LNG-fuelled vessel in the Tallink fleet and is powered by three 12-cylinder Wärtsilä 12V50DF and two 6-cylinder Wärtsilä 6L50DF dual-fuel engines, enabling her to run on both LNG and marine diesel oil. Her service speed is 27 knots. At 212 metres, she is equal to the *Galaxy* trio of cruiseferries in length. Having given *Star* a fairly classic livery, albeit applied in lime green, and *Superstar* a more dramatic colour scheme featuring orange swirls over a green hull and superstructure, the *Megastar* emerged from the shipyard with a white hull onto which a massive infinity symbol was depicted in red with green shapes surrounding it. The red accenting continues on her forward mast and atop her white funnel. The impression of momentum and modernity is further demonstrated with the application of black stripes along decks eight and nine, the lower of which curves down right at the stern in a rather unconvincing attempt to break up her rather angular profile.

Although Meyer's own naval architects were responsible for the structural design of the ship, the interior design was contracted to dSign Vertti Kivi & Co., whose first maritime commission was the *Viking Grace* of 2013. The design philisophy for the ship was one of moving large numbers of passengers around in a relatively short space of time, requiring long – and appealing – vistas to draw people throughout the ship. The overall effect of the interior design is even more contemporary than the *Viking Grace* with much use made of monochromatic colour schemes throughout. Indeed, there is much – perhaps excessive – use made of blacks throughout the vessel; this looks striking on a bright day but will perhaps look overly dark during an overcast winter's crossing.

Passenger accommodation is arranged over three decks: seven, eight, nine and ten – although the latter only offers a small number of cabins. The main passenger entrances to the vessel are on the port side of deck eight. Almost half of this deck is taken up by the incredible 'Travel Superstore', a retail space like no other in the ferry industry. The outlet is 2,800 square metres with two levels – a first for a ferry. A large central atrium acts as the centrepiece of the shop, towards the stern with a staircase and lift connecting the upper level (which focusses on perfumes, toys, clothing, the deli and other items) with the lower level on deck seven where most of the alcohol is situated. The lower level is adjacent to the upper deck car park and passengers are allowed (thanks to special dispensation that Tallink have obtained) to take their purchases to their vehicles. Indeed, there are some 100 car parking spaces marked out more like a regular supermarket which – for a premium – passengers can use. Décor throughout the superstore is mostly white with black accenting and the whole area is particularly spacious; one could easily spend the two hour crossing browsing the shelves and sampling what's on offer – the whisky area for instance displays a number of books showing the heritage behind various products.

Forward of the superstore on deck eight is the central area which comprises the 'Lobby', a smaller gift shop and news outlet; the 'Coffee & Co.' cafeteria and the information desk, adjacent to which is a large wall of LED screen onto which you can tweet your *Megastar* selfie. Distributed around these outlets are a large number of seats of different styles. The colour scheme throughout this area was dominated by greys, dark beiges and whites with the only contrast provided by coloured ceiling backlighting and the greenery of plants in various places. Passenger flow moves diagonally across this area from each beam, thus opening up further vistas, although also making it a very busy space.

Overlooking the bows of the ship are the two premium lounges: 'Comfort Class' to port and 'Business Class' to starboard, with the former available for €20 per single crossing and the latter €65. 'Comfort Class' includes free snacks, non-alcoholic drinks, newspapers and WIFI whilst 'Business Class' also includes a reasonably comprehensive buffet as well as alcholic drinks, a better WIFI connection and priority disembarkation for drivers. Again, both spaces make heavy use of neutral colours, with 'Business Class' being much darker than 'Comfort Class' overall.

Deck nine is the restaurant deck with the large 'Delight' buffet restaurant forward, adjacent to which is

Megastar *(Matthew Punter)*

Megastar – Fast Lane Cafeteria Server *(Matthew Punter)*

Megastar – Coffee & Co *(Matthew Punter)*

Megastar – Victory Pub *(Matthew Punter)*

Megastar – Traveller Superstore *(Matthew Punter)*

Megastar – Traveller Superstore car parking area *(Matthew Punter)*

Megastar – Grande Buffet *(Matthew Punter)*

Megastar – Burger King *(Matthew Punter)*

the 'Chef's Kitchen' à la carte. The buffet design treatment is unusually muted compared to the rest of the vessel with extensive use of beiges, browns and wood-effect panelling. This space also offers a large, forward-facing, panoramic bay window. This is structurally integrated with the bridge, above, although this effect is lost from an external visual perspective due to the horizontal black stripes along her superstructure. From an interior perspective, the seats are undoubtedly the best in the house but the overall effort is tame when compared to the glorious, forward-facing restaurant on the *Finlandia* and *Silvia Regina* of the early 1980s.

Moving aft, the port side of the vessel is occupied by the galley whilst the starboard offers the 'Fast Lane' cafeteria; there is also a Burger King® restaurant adjacent to this. The aft area of deck nine offers the 'Victory' sports bar to starboard, themed around horse-racing, the centrepiece of which is a large, black horse (the second ferry to do so: Brittany Ferries' *Normandie* pioneered an equine feature in 1992). Hidden behind a bulkhead in the centre of the ship is the teenagers' games room whilst to port is a rather oddly-placed quiet lounge of reclining seats.

At the aft of the accommodation on deck nine is the 'Sea Pub' – a superficially nautical-themed space, where the charcoal design treatment is somewhat broken up with dark turquoise and dark tan furnishings. Beyond this, an attractive veranda deck extends to the end of the deck offering an outside but covered area for drinkers. A central staircase within the veranda leads up to deck ten where there is a sun deck at stern – overall, *Megastar* offers comparatively little outside deck space. The passenger cabins are also situated on deck ten.

Overall, *Megastar* is an incredibly impressive vessel. Externally, she cuts a dynamic profile, visually demonstrating both her speed and the continuous nature of the shuttle service. Internally, she offers the by now customary spread of Baltic ferry facilities and her design treatment is striking and contemporary. However, it would be fair to say that other than the 'Travel Superstore' - which must surely now be the reference point for all future seabourne large retail outlets – there is little about her interior which is ground-breaking.

Both *Star* and *Megastar* are essentially well-matched: the former's interior design is less dramatic but probably makes for an emotionally warmer onboard experience. There were originally plans for a sister vessel to *Megastar* but the option for this was allowed to pass during her construction and *Star* was converted to double-deck loading instead. It is likely that Tallink will be carefully watching how *Megastar* grows traffic on the route before they decide whether to in fact commission a fully matching pair.

SILJA EUROPA

Since 2002, the pattern for the Helsinki – Tallinn cruisferry circuit seemed set in stone: a new ship was constructed and took over the service until a few years later when a new ship arrived. This state of affairs continued for thirteen years and through three iterations (*Romantika*, *Galaxy* and *Baltic Princess*) but the spell was broken in 2016 when Tallink introduced their elderly – and previously redundant – *Silja Europa* back onto the service.

The ship had spent almost its entire career operating between Stockholm and Turku but had become surplus to requirements on that service in 2013 and was added as a second cruisferry onto the Helsinki – Tallinn circuit. However, in 2014, she was chartered out to the Australian company Bridgemans for whom she was to operate as an accommodation vessel: it was reasonably expected that she would not be returning to the Baltic ever again. The following year however, Bridgemans ended the charter, thus leaving Tallink with something of a large white elephant on its hands. The company then took the bold decision to return her to the Helsinki – Tallinn route. She entered service in March 2016, partnering the *Baltic Queen* and having benefitted from a thorough refit. However at the end of the year, Tallink announced that such was the success of the vessel, she would receive a further €16 million investment and replace the *Baltic Queen* (which, through vessel cascade, enabled them to fill a gap in the vessel roster on the Stockholm – Riga service). She re-entered service after this second refit in December 2016.

During the course of the two refurbishment projects, the ship has been utterly transformed and is like an almost new vessel, such is the depth and the quality of the work that has been undertaken. Now, it is fair to say that the work is all essentially cosmetic, and that Tallink have spread €16 million over one of the largest passenger ferries afloat, but one cannot fail to be impressed by the new look nor how much

Silja Europa – Beauty Centre *(Matthew Punter)*

Star *(Matthew Punter)*

Silja Europa *(Matthew Punter)*

commitment Tallink have had to refreshing almost all areas – even the cabin bathrooms are all new.

Public areas on *Silja Europa* occupy two principal decks: seven and eight, with decks five and six plus nine through eleven hosting the vast number of cabins onboard. Centrepiece of the ship is a large atrium, beginning on deck six, through which two glass lifts convey passengers up to deck twelve. At its lower levels, this space works well, acting as a focal point although at higher decks the space gets increasingly boxed in and loses its emphasis.

Forward on deck seven is the Fast Lane Cafeteira which offers a wide range of snacks and hot and cold meals; this area was refurbished in the ship's March 2016 refit and decorated in beech and bright greens. There is also a Coffee & Co. outlet in this vicinity. Moving aft, the main retail space is laid out either side of a wide passenger corridor; this works quite effectively, almost like walking through a shoreside street with different stalls and kiosks selling a range of merchandising. Separate outlets are given over to Perfume, Fashion, Gifts, Toys and of course the vast tax-free superstore selling alcohol, tobacco and huge quantities of confectionery. Beyond the shopping centre, at the very stern of the ship's a small disco.

Deck eight is the restaurant deck: the Grande Buffet is situated forward, which has benefitted from a very comprehensive refit late last year and is now a very impressive space indeed. Thanks to the curved and raked windows that wrap around the front of the space, a large number of tables have sea views and there is an elevated section inboard of this affording even more diners a view. Two large serveries run down the length of the buffet with attractive new electronic visual displays that have been deployed throughout the fleet. Décor is a contrast between neutral-coloured carpets and ceilings and furniture in striking reds and blacks.

Aft of the Grande Buffet are a number of other dining options including the Italian themed 'Tavolata' and 'Grill House', both of which had been refitted although retaining some interesting features from the ship's original guise.

The remainder of deck eight is occupied by the Bars and Nightclub, with an attractive midships 'Corner Bar' providing a more intimate atmosphere before one reaches the Ocean Nightclub, 'Sea Pub' and the 'Windjammer' Bar, overlooking the stern. The Ocean Nightclub is the main entertainment venue for the ship although karaoke is also provided in the Windjammer.

The final public area of note on the *Silja Europa* is on deck twelve. The forward part of this is given over to the conference venue – which had also been thoroughly, and impressively refurbished. The aft area comprises the beauty and fitness centre: a hair salon and masseuse as well as a large sauna and spa complex, complete with bar. It is also worth noting the 'Moulin Rouge' theatre on deck six which is no longer in use although is still in existance.

FIT FOR THE FUTURE

Tallink's Tallinn – Helsinki service is undoubtedly in the best shape it has ever been, with probably its optimal fleet mix. Having travelled the route on *Baltic Queen* in 2015, whilst she is the superior vessel compared to *Silja Europa*, the latter is probably the better ship for the service with her vast capacity for passengers, food, entertainment and fun. Her refit has been very well executed indeed and many operators could learn from the extent to which Tallink have breathed new life into a vessel that was previously viewed as something of a dinosaur.

Elsewhere, *Megastar* represents a swaggeringly contemporary take on the day ferry. She perhaps doesn't quite match the design of *Superspeed 1* with interior design prioritised over a paradigm-shifting interior architecture. She is well-matched, but not perfectly so, with *Star*: they are distinct and different ships and doubtless passengers will have their favourite – and with such frequent departures, will have the luxury of chosing on which to travel.

Tallink of course now leave their competitors far behind: Eckerö Line with their solitary *Finlandia* and Viking Line with the idiosyncratic pairing of *Viking XPRS* and *Express*. Both the *Megastar* and *Silja Europa* offer the industry superb examples of the future of ferry travel and all eyes will undoubtedly be upon them as they operate the route in the years ahead.

Matthew Punter

Silja Europa *(Matthew Punter)*

Silja Europa on passage to Tallinn *(Matthew Punter)*

TO ICELAND IN WIND AND STORM

The smell of fish is only a mild one upon my arrival in the Danish port of Hirtshals. It used to be stronger in the early days, but maybe it's just my memory. I've been here since the late 1980s, sailing to Norway on the likes of Color Line's *Skagen*, *Christian IV* and later *Superspeed I* and Fjord Line's new *Stavangerfjord* which also brought me here this morning. But today, my destination is not Norway. It's Iceland, the farthest north you can get by an international car ferry in Europe. Smyril Line serves the route which stops at Tórshavn on the Faroe Islands on both ways since 1982, calling at Hirtshals each Saturday. The North Atlantic link is exposed to stormy weather for much of the year, but from the beginning on this April morning, the sun is shining over Jutland, and there is hardly any wind. Only some sea fog swallows the fishing boats just outside the breakwater, also hiding the *Norröna* until she arrives at Hirtshals shortly before 10.00 am.

During the following hours until embarkation, the terminal fills up with an astonishing number of German passengers who have booked the roundtrip via coach operators. The sea voyage to Iceland and back is being marketed by Smyril Line as a 'Viking cruise', enabling foot passengers to experience the North Atlantic islands just like the Vikings did, also serving more or less traditional 'Viking' food and offering excursions to local sites of historical interest on both the Faroe Islands and in Iceland. The Viking cruise is on offer in spring and autumn only since the *Norröna* switches to a more intense 'ferry' timetable during summer, carrying out a second weekly roundtrip between Hirtshals and Tórshavn, in addition to the one going up north to Seyðisfjörður.

Embarkation for the 3.00 pm departure starts at 1.30 pm, but there is nothing like the usual 'cruise' reception on this ship – no welcome photo, no disinfection of hands, no grinning of animators willing to turn your holiday into a loud nightmare of permanent 1980s disco music. A crewmember divides the arriving passengers according to the deck their cabin is situated on in order to avoid congestion, and that's it. Of course you also have to carry your luggage yourself. After all, the *Norröna* is still a ferry. The latter also goes for the cabin. Drawer and cupboard space is limited and the suitcase doesn't even fit underneath the bed. There also isn't the usual heap of papers waiting for you to go through in order to find your way or decide what to do on board. Just a file on the desk containing some 'onboard information' and a bible (new Testament only) in Danish, German and English. Not really what the Vikings took with them when they explored the North Atlantic!

However, some of the embarking German passengers start complaining immediately after arriving onboard. 'I'm used to Aida and Arosa, we'll have to come to terms with the situation: This is only a ferry.' Yes, you have to. And you knew in advance. But I don't say it out loud. The *Norröna* makes clear she is no warm weather love boat. Heavy steel doors lead to the outside decks where even the large Kärcher cleaner is safely tied to the wall by means of several thick strings. On the other hand, passengers have free access to the top deck around the funnel, enjoying fine panoramic views, even if the dirt from seagulls here and there spoils the overall impression. But again, this isn't the *Pacific Princess*. Danish (or are they Faroese?) ferry passengers start intoning local folk songs in the ship's Sky Bar, while on the quayside trucks continue to roll into the *Norröna's* hull. With the scheduled time of departure passing, the captain makes an announcement shortly after 3.00 pm that the ship's departure will be delayed by two hours due indeed to cargo still being loaded. And the next bad news arrives shortly afterwards: With the *Norröna* having to avoid an approaching storm front over the North Atlantic, the ship will sail at an accelerated speed in order to arrive in Seyðisfjörður early enough. Which also means that we will arrive at Tórshavn already in the middle of the night on Sunday instead of Monday morning. Those who travel to the Faeroes as 'normal' ferry passengers are thus forced to alter their travel plans while the ship's cruise guests have to accept that all planned bus excursions on the Faeroes are cancelled.

Meanwhile, the three onboard guides (Hardy and Mike for the German guests and Simon, the Dane, for all international passengers) explain to the newly arrived passengers some general terms of their upcoming stay onboard and where to find what on the *Norröna* . The vessel has just returned from a shipyard stay which saw the former 'Saga Café' being transformed into the new 'Naust Bar' and much of the old Naust Bar given to the buffet restaurant to overcome space problems there, when the ship is fully booked. (However, the deck plans on display show the vessel in both her old and her new guise, not really helping orientation.) Regular cruise guests may also miss the daily cruise program, Simon explains. On this ship, all necessary information concerning disembarkation, tour

The Norröna arriving at Hirtshals from Tórshavn on Saturday morning. *(Kai Ortel)*

The Naust Bar has been converted from the old Saga Café. *(Kai Ortel)*

Norröna Buffet Restaurant has been recently extended. *(Kai Ortel)*

Norröna Diner *(Kai Ortel)*

excursions and opening times are on display on a large metal board opposite the reception. So if one needs an update, he or she needs to go there (most cabins don't have telephones either). This a small ship after all, at least compared to the likes of *Aidaprima* & co. With regard to the latter, we also hear that the indoor pool has been closed on this crossing due to bad weather. 'Did you hear about that Aida ship earlier this year where the water from the pool spilled a number of public spaces? You don't want that here as well, do you?' Also onboard payment is not quite what you are used to on your regular cruise ships. There is no such thing as an onboard account on the *Norröna*. Payment is by cash, 'as is, where is'. And although payment in Euro (notes only) is accepted, change is given in Danish crown only. And credit cards? 'Well, you can try, but it depends on satellite access which might be restricted on the North Atlantic.' As is TV in Seyðisfjörður where the surrounding mountains swallow the limited signals that may exist. But no one does the ferry trip to Iceland to watch TV anyway, so that's fine. Onboard entertainment is by means of the unavoidable bingo sessions, a late night troubadour, an onboard cinema and three hot tubs on the outside decks from which you can watch the heavy Atlantic seas (and the occasional sea bird if you're lucky) comfortably sitting in bubbling salty water.

TO TÓRSHAVN

Captain Henrik Hammer, son of the Smyril Line co-founder Óli Hammer, makes a second announcement just after our departure at 5.00 pm. The latter was accompanied by the melody of the Faroese national anthem, something you otherwise only hear when your national soccer team coincidentally plays against the islands in the UEFA European championship qualifications. He expects south-westerly winds with speeds of 5 – 10 m/s (later increasing to 8 – 13 m/s) and wave heights of up to three metres. He also confirms that we will indeed arrive at Tórshavn around 11 pm tomorrow (Sunday) rather than 5 am on Monday. While saying this, he speeds his vessel up to the unusual 19 knots (something normally only required in summertime), and very soon, the Danish coast with the landmark 'Hirtshals fyr' and those familiar sandy North Sea beaches disappears behind us. On this trip, *Norröna* carries a total of 610 passengers and 290 vehicles – not bad for a sailing outside the busy summer season.

At 6.00 pm the first dinner awaits the Viking cruise guests. This is served in form of an opulent buffet. However, the *Norröna* also features the 'Simmer Dim', a nice steak house one deck above. But with no 'cruise card' handed out to the roundtrip guests, check-in at the restaurant is a bit complicated as well. Those belonging to a certain coach travel group have to present their individual meal ticket sent to them in advance (which people regularly forget to bring with them) while all individual cruise guests have to queue in line to have their name crossed through on the passenger list every time they arrive. Together with the remaining ferry guests, that is, who may show up as well to have breakfast or dinner in the same restaurant, paying in cash. Paying for your drinks is even more complicated. Together with your drink comes a small receipt which you are obliged to pay in cash at the cashier at the exit. Sometimes however, you get no receipt at all and have to tell the person in charge your table number and what you had which he/she just has to believe. Funnily, the system somehow works, but it may do so only on a Scandinavian ship, leaving a lot of opportunity for cheating elsewhere.

Once inside at last, the buffet includes various sorts of meat, fish and seafood, not what you would recommend to your newfound vegetarian girlfriend in the first place. The selection is not as wide as for instance on the magnificent *Color Fantasy* and *Color Magic*, but it has a lot to offer to different tastes and also varies from day to day. The dessert buffet is also amazing, including the famous freshly baked Danish pastries and cakes as well as fruits. Only the tiny cups and glasses for coffee, tea and soft drinks are a bit annoying. In fact they are so small that you have to return to the drink station every once in a while and hope that your table hasn't been cleared in the meantime. It's not really Viking portions that these small cups and glasses are made for!

Later the same evening, other parts of the ship convey a typical ferry atmosphere. The Sky Bar for instance looks a bit scruffy with the usual half-empty beer cans and plastic bags left over from the departure party and a few wooden deck chairs not quite in the place and position you would expect them onboard a 'real' cruise ship. But what's worse, the guys just opposite my own cabin have decided to have an open-door cabin party tonight just like they were on *Silja Europa*. In terms of volume, they definitely reach Viking levels, but that surely is not what the Smyril Line marketing

NORRÖNA
WWW.SMYRIL-LINE

Norrona *(Kai Ortel)*

department meant when advertising to 'travel like the Vikings'. Let's hope they disembark in Tórshavn. At least they finish their party around 11.00 pm so our part of the corridor can get some rest after all.

The peach yoghurt the next morning according to the label was 'made in Iceland', although one may wonder where exactly in Iceland peaches can grow. Looking through the restaurant windows, drilling station fill up the horizon while the North Sea remains pretty calm and the windows rise and sink only slowly for the time being. The *Norröna* herself on the other hand is not as noise and vibration-free as the guides had promised yesterday, but it's within the limits. Let's see how she copes with the 'real' North Atlantic once we have reached it tomorrow.

The weather forecast for Tórshavn predicts a fresh breeze for today (9 m/s wind speed), 'near gale' for tomorrow (14 m/s) and gale (18 m/s) for Tuesday, no wonder captain and ship try to get past the Faroe Islands as soon as possible. In extremely harsh weather, *Norröna* can use a different berth than her usual one in Tórshavn or even divert to Klaksvik, the second port on the Faroe Islands capable of accommodating the ferry. At the reception meanwhile, the first passengers let free their anger, arguing they had been deprived of a booked overnight onboard by the change in timetable. Honestly, being stranded on the Faroe Islands on a cold and stormy April night is not exactly what you may have dreamed of when booking the trip, but of course, Smyril Line by contract reserves the right to divert from the published timetable in case of inclement weather conditions. Other (German) passengers spend their forenoon complaining that the Hollywood movies shown in the onboard cinema are not the synchronized German versions, obviously forgetting that they are not onboard the *Mein Schiff 4*, but a Faroese car ferry sailing from Denmark to Iceland. Thankfully for them, the documentary film shown in the Naust Bar at 10.00 am is in German. Among others, it shows the hunt for wild sheep on the islands and how the locals catch and cook sea gulls traditionally. Not your usual uplifting entertainment program, but, as the voice says, 'these are rough islands with rough habits.'

Before we reach the Faroe Islands, the *Norröna* passes the Shetlands. The wind speed at this time is 11 m/s, but with the sun shining, many of the ship's passengers gather on the outside deck spaces around noon to watch the ferry leave the North Sea and enter the North Atlantic. *Norröna* passes the islands in quite close proximity, enabling her passengers to take pictures of Muckle Flugga and Out Stack, the northernmost outposts of the United Kingdom. Behind those rocky islets, the water depth falls to 1.200 metres which admittedly also changes the ship's sea behaviour. The *Norröna* now begins to roll continuously. Also the cabin walls start to squeeze and creak, so on this leg of the journey you realize that you're on the deep blue sea at last. The sky however is not so blue anymore, having turned to grey shortly after the Shetlands. But we may see whales and porpoises now, Simon told us, so anyone going out on the outside decks now should watch out for fountains between the waves. If he or she can stay upright and get a firm grip in the strong wind at all, that is.

At 8.30 pm, Captain Hammer makes another announcement according to which the *Norröna* is indeed forced to use a different berth in Tórshavn due to strong winds. Which not only means that there will be no covered passenger gangway in use, but also that foot passengers will have to wait for the car deck to be cleared before they're allowed to disembark. The passengers concerned, it seems, could not care less. Their male share at least awaits the arrival of the *Norröna* in Tórshavn smoking on the outside decks and wearing only shorts and T-shirts. It's springtime after all! Down around the reception on deck 5 however, things look a bit different with dozens of ferry passengers sitting on their suitcases, waiting for the ferry to arrive. They had been required to vacate their cabins until 10:30 pm and now made themselves more or less comfortable together with their bags, rucksacks, plastic bags and other stuff. The cruise passengers occupy a more convenient retreat in the nearby Naust Bar where the ship's troubadour brings some California vibrations along with his more than solid versions of the Eagles' classics 'Peaceful easy feeling' and 'Tequila Sunrise'.

It is 20 minutes past midnight when the *Norröna* finally docks in Tórshavn, stern first and at the berth normally reserved for the local ferry *Smyril*. The rain blows horizontally over the outside decks and in order to disembark all the vehicles leaving the ship tonight, all coaches have to leave the ship as well, only to wait on the quayside for an hour or so until they're ordered onboard again. It's a long night for everyone, but the *Norröna* herself doesn't even stop her engines, leaving port as soon as disembarkation and embarkation is completed around 2.00 am.

The Norröna during her passage between the Farese islands Eysturoy and Kalsoy. *(Kai Ortel)*

The Norröna safely docked at Seyðisfjörður on Monday evening, having escaped some rough North Atlantic weather. *(Kai Ortel)*

ICELAND

The next day, I wake up before the ringing of my alarm clock, and the *Norröna* is rolling heavily. Brushing one's teeth is only possible with a tight grip to something fix, and dressing should now be done while sitting on the bed. However, the *Norröna's* buffet restaurant is nicely populated despite the ship's motion. But a tray put aside on the bar shelf undertakes a very successful attempt in flying just after I had passed – with the dishes upon it landing quite roughly in a thousand pieces on the floor. Nevertheless, all this does not lead the crew to close the nearby outside decks to passengers; the 'Stormy weather – Closed' sign is still attached to the doorframe. So on this shaky Monday morning, you are allowed to stroll around the *Norröna's* outside decks freely with some really fresh air guaranteed. The ship herself meanwhile continues to proceed northward at 18 – 19 knots with her arrival at Seyðisfjörður now planned for 6.30 pm. The good news is that, according to another announcement from the bridge, despite a wind speed of 13 – 18 m/s and waves of up to 5 metres in height, we are leaving the bad weather behind us and will arrive in Iceland in somewhat more comfortable conditions.

When calling at Tórshavn, the command of the ship had also changed to Captain Petur av Vollanum who had changed to the *Norröna* in 2011 after a career at Maersk Line where he was the master of the giant 9,500 TEU vessel *Gunvor Maersk*. The current change in timetable, by the way, had been agreed upon between the two masters who had been in contact with one another over this subject since the *Norröna's* departure from Hirtshals two days ago.

After a German couple had told this morning on the occasion of another documentary film being shown in the Naust Bar that they had indeed seen whales (or whatever they had identified as such) already yesterday, I try my luck and grab one of the wooden chairs on the sun deck to spot one myself. Fully dressed in raincoat and gloves and with the binoculars from my camera bag in hand, I make myself comfortable for an hour or so between 12.30 and 1.30 pm, only to stare at the waves, but the only marine life visible is a northern gannet that follows the *Norröna* on the port side for ten or fifteen minutes. No dorsal fin, no fluke, but you have to be happy with the small things in life. After all, a northern gannet is a clear sign of (bird) life of the sub-Arctic too, isn't it?

The swell is decreasing the more we approach Iceland in the afternoon, and the massive rocking of the *Norröna* turns into a soft rolling around 5.00 pm. The vessel herself has slowed down to 15 knots now, and a light layer of sea fog is floating above the water. But just when the first mountains of Iceland come in sight, the fog disappears and the sun comes out, only to put a silver shine to that rocky coastline and a huge rainbow across the horizon on starboard. Our arrival in Iceland surely could not have been more magnificent!

Most of the passengers gather on the outside decks again once we approach those mountains and finally enter the fjord that leads us to Seyðisfjörður, the little town and fishery port that is situated at the very end of it. *Norröna* docks there safely, allowing all vehicles to disembark and all cruise passengers to set their feet on Icelandic soil as well. However, unlike our reception by rainbows and mountains in silver light, Seyðisfjörður is not all Scandinavian idyll. All around the port, machines and fishery devices are rusting away, and a number of houses seem to be vacant although the view over the fjord could not be more beautiful. Furthermore, the inevitable smell of fish is in the air. But the snowy mountains form the perfect background to the *Norröna* which will remain here for 48 hours, not bound for Tórshavn and Hirtshals until Wednesday evening. By the way, even the *Norröna* herself smells like fish after my return on board around 9.00 pm on Monday evening. I hadn't noticed that before, but perhaps the embarkation of frozen cargo had already started upon my return.

Thanks to our early arrival in Seyðisfjörður, I can spend two full days in Iceland. On Tuesday, most of the Viking cruise passengers participate in bus tours which take them to the sight of Eastern Iceland, especially Mývatn and lake Lagarfljót (Lögurinn), home of the mythological Lagarfljótwurm – a giant creature not unlike the monster of Loch Ness. But the bus tour to Mývatn is not without problems. Despite having escaped the storm at sea onboard the *Norröna* , the wind remains strong on the mainland. Our bus gets caught by a hurricane gust, being pushed off the road where it subsequently gets stuck on a lava field. Our trip to Mývatn ends there; and instead of seeing the thermal baths, volcanic geology and abundant sea bird life there, we are escorted back to the ship by a number of Icelandic SAR cars, the overland road having been closed due to the storm. Even the

The North Atlantic ferries – Norröna and Smyril together at Tórshavn. *(Kai Ortel)*

The Norröna as seen from the mountains which enclose the port of Seyðisfjörður. *(Kai Ortel)*

The Norröna approaching Iceland in some unexpected afternoon sunlight. *(Kai Ortel)*

The Norröna in Seyðisfjǫrður, loading buses and caravans for Hirtshals. *(Kai Ortel)*

Norröna herself had her fair share of problems during the day, with gusts of wind forcing the officers on duty to keep the vessel at her berth by means of extra engine power.

Instead of going on another bus tour, I spend the next day with lengthy walks along both the northern and the southern arm of the fjord which reward me with terrific photographic opportunities. If one single day of walking in the outskirts of what is one of Iceland's most remote ports provides you with such a number of amazing views, what about a two- or three week stay in the country then? I also spot a seal laying on a rock in the middle of a lake just opposite the ferry herself, not to speak of countless ducks, geese, seagulls and other seabirds.

BACK ON THE NORTH ATLANTIC

On Wednesday evening the *Norröna* departs half an hour early at 8.30 pm. Shortly after leaving Seyðisfjörður and the fjord, the captain makes another announcement regarding the sea weather, this time for our return leg to Tórshavn. He expects south-westerly winds with a speed of 8 – 10 m/s and wave heights of 3 – 4 m. Finest North Atlantic weather, so to speak. We will most likely arrive at Tórshavn on schedule tomorrow at 5.00 pm. However, as soon as the ship has reached the open sea, it starts to roll again. Furthermore, the familiar squeezing and creaking of cabin walls sets in again – we're back on the North Atlantic at last.

Our afternoon arrival at Tórshavn the following day provides me with the welcome opportunity to catch up some sleep, not getting up before 8.00 am. At that time, the *Norröna* still rocks solidly, and the safe transport of trays from the buffet to the table half an hour later requires some balance again. But according to Simon the weather outside is 'most beautiful'. Well, at least for North Atlantic conditions. I also note that the buffet staff drink cans of Red Bull here and there, obviously in order to stay awake and fit to reply enquiries like those from another German guest who complains that unlike the evening seating there were no reserved tables in the morning whatsoever.

At around 12.30 pm, my mobile phone returns to life with an automatic SMS received according to which we had now reached the Faroe Islands. Well, not really yet, but half an hour later, the *Norröna* passes between the archipelago's two biggest islands – Eysturoy und Kalsoy. The passage takes an hour to complete with cloud-covered rocks and mountains on both sides of the ferry and only very infrequent signs of civilized life visible. A single fishing trawler sails close by us for some time, but otherwise the *Norröna* proceeds on her way through a scenery that cannot have looked much different when the Vikings came here 1,200 years ago.

The *Norröna* docks at Tórshavn at 3.00 pm for a six-hour stay at the main port of the Faroe Islands. But again, getting the ship berthed safely appears all but easy in the strong wind, and it takes several attempts until the big ferry is moored and disembarkation can begin. At least the bus excursions don't have to be halted halfway this time, and we are taken to the lovely village of Gjógv which is famous for its massive gorge where the waves of the North Atlantic crush against the walls with a roaring sound. The gorge is also well known for its abundant bird life, although unfortunately we don't see puffins, auks or other sub-arctic birds on our short visit. We are back in Tórshavn at 7.00 pm, in time for me to take pictures of the local ferries *Smyril* and *Ternan* before returning to the ship that is back in 'ferry mode' for the last leg of her roundtrip between Denmark and Iceland. In the terminal at Tórshavn, school classes mix with families travelling with or without children, couples and single travellers who presumably are on a business trip to the continent. Even a dog is about to embark on the *Norröna* , although he has to spend the crossing in a not too luxurious kennel on the top deck of the ferry. And while the buffet restaurant and the Naust Bar had been the public spaces where most of the Viking cruise passengers had met during the day on our way to Iceland and back, it is now the 'Diner' cum cafeteria that enjoys a very healthy occupation. With the difference that unlike the former, the latter hosts a considerable number of baby carriages, pushchairs and walking frames and all demographic groups thinkable. In the restaurant on the other hand, fellow passengers start to wave hands in your direction that you can't remember having met in person at all during the past five days. Which of course is a familiar sign on 'true' cruise ships, so the *Norröna* successfully continues to be the best of both worlds at the same time.

The ship departs half an hour late from Tórshavn at a time of day when it is almost dark outside. But we leave the Faroese full of impressions and memories of a small, but still great country that has an overwhelming landscape and stunning scenery to offer. And yes, 70,000 sheep, of which we also saw a large number during our bus ride to Gjógv and back.

THE VIKING BUFFET

At 8.00 am next morning, while many passengers have breakfast, *Norröna* passes the Shetland Islands again, but this time, the rocky shores are more or less hidden behind a wall of fog and haze. So we're back on the North Sea again. The last day of the Viking cruise begins, a day at sea, in terms of the cruise industry. Thanks to the ever-helpful Simon, I get the opportunity to meet the ship's master Petur av Vollanum for a short interview on the bridge. He tells me that the troubles encountered while docking the vessel in Tórshavn yesterday were related to wind gusts of up to 23 m/s speed, just like the one we had encountered on our ill-fated bus ride to Mývatn. Smyril Line's new cargo ferry *Mykines*, which was scheduled to make her maiden call at Tórshavn the same evening, was not so lucky. The former *Autobaltic* was forced to turn around off Tórshavn and headed for Klaksvik instead. I also learn that on this particular crossing back to Hirtshals, the *Norröna* was sailing with an impressive load of no less than 56 refrigerated lorries and containers full of fish which might partly explain the distinctive smell that the ship conveys. Furthermore, the long route to Iceland enables the ship to sail on two different types of fuel. With the SECA border running (roughly) between Scotland and Aalesund, the *Norröna* sails on low-sulphur diesel oil (LSDO) between Hirtshals and Tórshavn and on heavy fuel oil (HFO) between Tórshavn and Seyðisfjörður. *Norröna* also had a scrubber installed in late 2014, but it didn't quite work, so the crew soon returned to switching the fuel type twice on each round trip.

The last day of the Viking cruise also is the opportunity for the crew and staff to proudly present the Viking buffet. (The chef de cuisine, like 80% of the crew of the *Norröna*, is from the Faroe Islands, by the way.) Which on this day only consists of regional meals and dishes from the Faroe Islands and Iceland, partly even cooked according to original recipes from the Viking era. At least this is what Smyril Line tells you. The buffet features lamb (of course), but also ox tail soup and pork ribs. Moreover, you can have anything that has wings so far north and is not clever or quick enough to escape being caught: duck, chicken, goose and even seagull. And last but not least, the fruits of the sea: shrimps, crabs, lobsters, oysters and, of course, fish, including salmon caught in the waters around the Faroe Islands. There also is 'Knettir', Faroese fish balls filled with lamb tallow. And anything you have for dinner comes with Föroya Bjór (if you like) – beer brewed on the Faroe Islands. Only whale meat has been banned from the Viking buffet quietly a few years ago. In this point at least, political correctness won over Viking traditions.

And if you're too stuffed afterwards to get your suitcase packed, don't worry. *Norröna* is a ferry after all, so you don't need to put your luggage out on the corridor at night to collect it in the terminal building the next morning. Back in Hirtshals at 10.00 am, the following day, it's DIY, just like one week earlier when those adventure-hungry pensioners (and a few other demographics) gathered here to board this remarkable ship. The *Norröna* is as unique as the route she sails on, and anyone who doesn't mind wind and storm and rain should consider taking this trip once in a lifetime. It's absolutely worth it, every single minute of it.

Kai Ortel

■

REVIEW 2016/17 - BRITAIN & IRELAND

The following is a review of passenger and freight ferry activities during 2016 and the first half of 2017. Some events occurring in the first half of 2016 will have also been mentioned in 'Ferries 2017'.

EAST COAST & THAMES

Booming traffic on the Humber - Maas axis led to several of the rival operators chartering extra tonnage to provide extra capacity.

During 2016, CLdN/Cobelfret ordered two new vessels from the Uljanik, shipyard in Croatia - 5,425 lane metre ships - smaller than the two 7,800 lane metre vessels ordered from the Hyundai Mipo yard in South Korea in 2014 . In 2017 four more of the smaller design were ordered, but this time from the Korean yard. The first of larger vessels, the *Celine*, is due to be delivered in the autumn and will probably be placed on the Zeebrugge - Killingholme route.

In February 2016, CLdN launched a new weekly service between Zeebrugge and Hirtshals. As well as serving northern Denmark, the service offers connections to Kristiansand and Larvik via Color Line and Stavanger and Bergen via Fjord Line. In September 2016 the company chartered the *Bore Sea*, a sister vessel of P&O's *Bore Song*, operating initially mainly between Zeebrugge and Purfleet and later on the Iberian routes. The same month, Santander was added to the company's Iberian services. In February 2017, CLdN introduced two Zeebrugge calls per week on its Rotterdam - Santander - Leixoes service.

During the 2016 refit period, DFDS's *Patria Seaways* was chartered to provide freight cover on the Hull - Zeebrugge and Middlesbrough - Zeebrugge routes. She later operated between Vlaardingen and Immingham for her owners before returning to the Baltic in mid March.

In spring 2017 both Hull - Zeebrugge passenger vessels, the *Pride of Bruges* and *Pride of York*, were sent to Gdansk for major refits to extend their lives for at least another five years. Because one of the Zeebrugge vessels covers on the Rotterdam route during the refit period, this meant an extended period when Zeebrugge passenger service operated on alternate days. The cover, in order to provide a daily freight service, in 2017 was the *Neptune Aegli* of Neptune Lines, a specialist car carrying company. Like *L'Audace*, chartered from Lineas Suardiaz in 2015, the *Neptune Aegli* is a dual purpose car carrier or trailer ferry, with each of the two trailer decks having a hoistable mezzanine deck to create two car decks.

In May 2017 the Dutch registered container ship *Elisabeth* was chartered to relieve pressure on the two passenger ships operating between Hull and Zeebrugge .

In March 2016, DFDS announced that the *Petunia Seaways* would be lengthened by 30m to provide an additional 800 lane metres, taking it to 4,600 lane metres (approximately another eighty 13.5m trailers). The lengthening, which is similar to that undertaken on the *Begonia Seaways*, *Freesia Seaways* and *Ficaria Seaways* in 2009, took place in July at MWB Motorenwerke Bremerhaven AG, the yard which undertook the work on the other three vessels. She returned to service in early August.

In May 2016 DFDS placed an order for two 209.6m ro-ro ferries from the Flensburg shipyard. They are long term chartered to DFDS by the yard's owners with an option to purchase. The first of these, the *Gardenia Seaways*, was delivered in July 2017 and entered service on the Rotterdam - Immingham route. The second, the *Tulipa Seaways*, will be delivered in the autumn. Shortly after this order was placed, the company ordered two more ships from the Jinling Shipyard in China. The vessels, due to enter service in 2019, will be the largest ever for DFDS, with 6,800 lane metres of freight capacity and will be operated on DFDS North Sea routes, most likely between Rotterdam (Vlaardingen) and Immingham, enabling the current four ship service to be replaced by a two ship service. In June a further two vessels were ordered, for delivery in 2020.

In April 2016, the *Super-Fast Baleares*, which the company had chartered for their Marseilles - Tunis route, was moved to the North Sea, operating mainly on the Gothenburg - Immingham service. In the autumn, DFDS chartered the *Friedrich Russ* and later the *Finnmaster* in order that there could be two sailings per day each way between Rotterdam and Immingham. The *Finnmaster* remained on charter until early July, some weeks before the delivery of the *Gardenia Seaways* which had been delayed.

Princess Seaways *(Andrew Cooke)*

Spirit of France *(George Holland)*

During 2016 Mann Lines' agreed to charter a new vessel under construction by Italian builder Visentini. Named the *ML Freyja*, she was delivered in June 2017 but was then sub-chartered to SOL Continent Line, replacing the *Ark Forwarder* on the Zeebrugge - Gothenburg route. She is expected to move to Mann Lines in January 2018.

SOL Continent Line continued to expand its North Sea role, especially on the Zeebrugge - Gothenburg route, with the two Wagenborg vessels *Schieborg* and *Slingeborg*, which operated the service when CLdN operated the service for the Stora Enso Paper Group, being supplemented by the chartered *Ark Forwarder* and *Elisabeth Russ*.

In January 2016, SCA Transforest added Sheerness to their schedules and at the end of June Tilbury was dropped from the schedule. At the same time Kiel replaced Lübeck as the German port of call.

Transfennica took on charter the *Bore Bank* in January 2017. An interesting vessel which was built at a conventional trailer ferry, converted to a car carrier and used by UECC and then, in late 2016, converted back.

Finnlines is to lengthen its six Jinling built ships, which will boost capacity by 1,000 lane metres. A 35m long midships section will be added to each vessel, starting this summer.

In late 2016, Sea-Cargo acquired the Rederia AB Atlantic vessel *TransFighter*. Not renamed, she was placed on a new schedule which included Sheerness.

In September 2016, two new vessels were ordered for the historic Woolwich Free Ferry, operated by Briggs Marine, replacing the three existing vessels which date from the 1960s. The vessels, to be delivered in 2018, are being built at the Remontowa Shipyard in Gdansk and will have 210 lane meters of vehicle deck space with dedicated cyclist accommodation separated from foot passengers. The vessels will be licensed to carry 150 passengers. New berths are also being constructed to accommodate the new vessels.

Thames Clippers ordered two further fast ferries in 2016, but this time from a British Yard - Wight Shipyard of Cowes, Isle of Wight (formerly Shemara Refit), which built Red Funnel's *Red Jet 6*. The two new vessels - *Mercury Clipper* and *Jupiter Clipper* - were delivered in June and July 2017.

EASTERN CHANNEL

Ramsgate ferry port saw no ro-ro traffic during 2015 but in January 2016 a ro-ro vessel returned - not a ferry as such but the car carrier *Autopremier* of UECC. A once weekly service from Zeebrugge was started, conveying Citroën and Peugeot cars, in order to relieve pressure on Sheerness. At one time the whole of the ferry port was full of cars. However, later in the year the service ceased and all traffic returned to Sheerness.

Dover enjoyed a much quieter year in 2016 following the mayhem in 2015 caused by striking MyFerryLink workers. In February 2016, following a repaint and a major internal refit, the *Rodin* and *Berlioz* re-entered service for DFDS Seaways between Dover and Calais as the *Côte des Dunes* and *Côte des Flandres* respectively.

In spring 2017, the *Calais Seaways* received a major refit to bring her interior up to the standard of her bigger sisters. She had not received any major work since 1999 when P&O Stena Line had modified her to make her suitable for the Dover - Calais route as the *P&OSL Aquitaine*.

In May 2016 the *Nord Pas-de-Calais* was chartered to FRS Iberia to operate between Spain and Morocco and renamed *Al Andalus Express*. She remains owned by *Eurotunnel*.

P&O maintained their service of five passenger vessels and one freighter, although between May and June 2017 the freighter, *European Seaway*, served in the Irish Sea.

Following a decision by the French courts in March 2016 that the Newhaven - Dieppe route should be put out to tender and that the agreement between DFDS Seaways and the local authorities was invalid, this duly took place. Two applications were made by the due date, 1st May 2017. Meanwhile the three sailings with two ships arrangement continued.

WESTERN CHANNEL AND SOLENT

Early 2016, Brittany Ferries' *Pont Aven* was fitted with scrubbers in order to continue to use lower grade fuel and meet new environmental regulations. This resulted in a very enlarged funnel which was as wide as the ship.

In January 2016, Brittany Ferries chartered the freighter *MN Pelican* from Maritime Nantaise of France. She operates a twice weekly service between Poole and Bilbao. She is the first 12 passenger freighter to be operated by the company since the *Normandie Shipper* was withdrawn in 1995.

In December 2016 Brittany Ferries ordered a new LNG powered 42,000t vessel from Flensburger Schiffbau-Gesellschaft. When delivered in 2019, the *Honfleur* as she is to be called, will operate on the Portsmouth - Caen route, replacing the *Normandie*, which is likely to be moved to the Portsmouth - Le Havre service, replacing the chartered *Etretat*.

Unlike 2015 when the fast ferry *Condor Liberation* operated two round trips per day on some days during summer, only one trip per day was operated throughout 2016. This improved timekeeping and avoided some very early departure times. The service proved more reliable than when the vessel was introduced in 2015 but with one less fast ferry than previously, any mechanical or weather related problems continued to cause disruption. On occasions, the *Condor Rapide* was switched from the St Malo route.

In early 2016 Wightlink published plans for a new generation of Portsmouth - Fishbourne ferries which would incorporate double deck loading from substantially rebuilt terminals. In May an order was placed with the Cemre Shipyard, Yalova, Turkey for a new ship. In February 2016 the *St. Clare* was modified for double deck loading and during 2016 and 2017 major modifications were made to Portsmouth's Gunwharf Terminal to create a two deck marshalling area. The 1980s built *St. Cecilia* and *St. Faith* may be replaced by the new vessel.

Red Jet 6, Red Funnel's new catamaran from Shemara Refit of Cowes entered service in July 2016, replacing the *Red Jet 5*, which was sold.

Hovertravel introduced two new hovercraft on their Southsea - Ryde service in summer 2016. They are 22m Griffon Hoverwork 12000TD/AP models. Both the builder and the operator are subsidiaries of the Gibraltar based Bland Group. The new craft are 88 seaters - slightly less than the 95 seat BHC models they replaced but more efficient. The two older vessels remain in service as the new vessels 'bed in'

Gosport Ferry's *Portsmouth Queen* was sold in February 2016 to Absolute Charters for use as a party cruise boat on the Thames. Sister vessel *Gosport Queen* was also sold in January 2017 to London Party Boats and was due to enter service in July 2017.

Isle of Wight Council's new Cowes Floating Bridge, called *Floating Bridge No 6*, arrived from Pembroke Dock in March 2017. The old vessel ceased to operate at the end of January and was towed away. As infrastructure modifications were necessary, it was not possible for the new vessel to enter service until May. In the interim a passenger only service was operated using a small launch. Problems with the new craft led to her being taken out of service for several weeks and these continued when she re-entered service in June.

The 200 year old Hayling Ferry, which had ceased operation in March 2015 when the operating company filed for administration, resumed in August 2016 under new management. The operator, Baker Trayte Marine Ltd, is supported by the Hayling Ferry Trust.

IRISH SEA

In May 2016, Irish Ferries announced the order of a new 50,000 ton vessel from Flensburger Schiffbau-Gesellschaft, Flensburg, Germany for delivery in 2018. She will replace the chartered *Epsilon*, which operates between Dublin and Holyhead with a weekend trip to Cherbourg.

Seatruck Ferries' third vessel on their Liverpool - Dublin service the *Clipper Ranger* was, in March 2016, replaced by the larger *Seatruck Pace*, transferred from the Heysham - Dublin route. The *Clipper Ranger* was then moved to that route. In September 2016 the *Clipper Point* returned from long-term

Honfleur *(Brittany Ferries)*

New build for Irish Ferries due to enter service in 2018 *(Irish Ferries)*

Ben-my-Chree *(Miles Cowsill)*

Lord of the Isles *(Miles Cowsill)*

charter and took over the Heysham-Dublin service. The smaller *Clipper Ranger* then moved to the Liverpool service as fourth vessel.

From August 2016 until early 2017, Seatruck Ferries operated a weekend car carrying service between Portbury (near Bristol) and Dublin.

IRELAND

Strangford Ferry's new vessel, the *Strangford II* was delivered from Cammell Laird of Birkenhead in December 2016. However, her entry into service was delayed as it was found that, at certain states of the tide, her ramps could not be put down. After modifications, she entered service in February 2017.

When the Lough Foyle Ferry Company ceased their seasonal service from Greencastle to Magilligan in October 2015, they stated that they would not resume in Spring 2016. They sold their vessel, the *Foyle Venture*, to Frazer Ferries, a company seeking to establish a service across Carlingford Lough on the East coast. In July 2016, Frazer Ferries resumed the Greencastle to Magilligan service using the *Foyle Venture*. However in November they announced they would not resume the service in 2017. Instead the vessel, renamed the *Aisling Gabrielle*, was to be deployed on a new service across Carlingford Lough, between Greenore, Co Louth, and Greencastle, Co Down, which started in July 2017. During April and May the *Foyle Venture* was deployed on the Passage East Ferry whilst the regular vessel, the *FBD Tintern*, was undergoing maintenance. Meanwhile in July 2017 Frazer Ferries did restore the Lough Foyle ferry in July, using the former German river ferry, *Berne-Frage*, renamed the *Frazer Mariner*.

The new Rathlin Island vehicle ferry, the *Spirit of Rathlin* built by Arklow Marine Services, to replace the chartered *Canna* was completed in January 2017. However she was not able to enter service until June when necessary infrastructure works and modifications to the vessel's ramp hydraulics were completed.

SCOTLAND

Caledonian MacBrayne's third hybrid vessel, the *Catriona* was delivered in September 2016 and entered service on the summer-only Lochranza - Claonaig service. She resumed on that route in spring 2017.

In summer 2016 Caledonian MacBrayne moved the *Coruisk* from her traditional Mallaig - Armadale roster to operate as second ship on the Oban - Craignure route. Three vessels replaced her - the *Lochinvar*, the *Loch Bhrusda* and the *Lord of the Isles* (between trips to Lochboisdale on South Uist). However, the move proved controversial as it was found the smaller vessels could not operate in some tidal conditions leading to cancellations and the *Lord of the Isles* was sometimes delayed on her service the Outer Hebrides. At one stage, the company considered returning the *Coruisk* to her traditional route, but in the end it was decided to leave things as they were for the current season. The move of the *Lochinvar* to this route meant that the 1977 built *Isle of Cumbrae* came out of retirement to operate on the Tarbert - Portavadie route.

In summer 2017 the larger *Loch Fyne* replaced the *Lochinvar* and *Loch Bhrusda*. However, the *Lochinvar* did not return to the Tarbert - Portavadie (for which she was originally designated) but instead replaced the *Loch Fyne* on the Tobermory service. So the *Isle of Cumbrae* continued to operate.

All Caledonian MacBrayne and Argyll Ferries routes were put out to tender during 2015. There were two contenders - CalMac Ferries and Serco, who operate the Northlink service to Orkney and Shetland. After the Scottish elections in May 2016 it was announced that CalMac Ferries had secured the tender for the Caledonian MacBrayne routes.

In June 2017 it was announced that, following an Internet public consultation, the new ferry for the Ardrossan - Brodick service, due for delivery in 2018, would be called the *Glen Sannox*, reviving the name of one of the earliest Clyde car ferries.

Glen Sannox *(CalMac)*

In July 2017 Caledonian MacBrayne took over the service to the sparsely populated Island of Kerrera, previously privately operated. They chartered the vessel *Gylen Lady* and the operator and his crew became CalMac employees. A new vessel called the *Carvoria* was ordered from a Shetland shipyard.

In May 2015, the operators of the Cromarty - Nigg ferry had announced that this summer only service would not resume as it was not possible to find a suitable places to moor the vessel, the *Cromarty Queen*, overnight. However in June 2016, the service was re-started by Highland Ferries, operators of the Fort William - Camusnagaul service, using the former Strathclyde Transport Renfrew - Yoker ferry *Renfrew Rose*, which they had purchased from Arranmore Fast Ferries of County Donegal.

Orkney operators Pentland Ferries ordered a new 85m catamaran in March 2017 to replace the 10 year old *Pentalina* in 2018. The new vessel, 25m longer than the existing craft, is being built at the Strategic Marine Shipyard, V ng Tàu, Vietnam.

Nick Widdows

www.calmac.co
Caledonian

Isle of Arran *(Andrew Wood)*

SECTION 1 - GB AND IRELAND - MAJOR PASSENGER OPERATORS

BRITTANY FERRIES

THE COMPANY *Brittany Ferries* is the trading name of *BAI SA*, a French private sector company and the operating arm of the *Brittany Ferries Group*. The UK operations are run by *BAI (UK) Ltd*, a UK private sector company, wholly owned by the *Brittany Ferries Group*.

MANAGEMENT CEO Christophe Mathieu, **Commercial Director, Passengers** Mike Bevens, **Commercial Director, Freight** Simon Wagstaff.

ADDRESS Millbay Docks, Plymouth, Devon PL1 3EW.

TELEPHONE **Reservations *All Services*** +44 (0)330 159 7000, **Freight - Administration & Enquiries** +44 (0)330 159 5000, **Reservations** +44 (0)330 159 5000.

INTERNET **Passenger - Website** www.brittanyferries.com *(English, French, Spanish, German)*, **Freight Website** www.brittanyferriesfreight.co.uk *(English)*

ROUTES OPERATED **Conventional Ferries *All year*** Plymouth - Roscoff (6 hrs (day), 7 hrs - 9 hrs (night); *ARMORIQUE, PONT-AVEN*; up to 2 per day (Summer), 1 per day (Winter)), Poole - Cherbourg (4 hrs 15 mins; *BARFLEUR*; 1 per day), Portsmouth - St Malo (8 hrs 45 mins (day), 10 hrs 45 mins (night); *BRETAGNE*; (1 per day), Portsmouth - Caen (Ouistreham) (6 hrs (day), 6 hrs - 8 hrs (night); *NORMANDIE, MONT ST MICHEL*; 3 per day), Portsmouth - Le Havre (5 hrs 30 mins; *BAIE DE SEINE, ETRETAT*, 1 per day), Portsmouth - Santander (Spain) (24 hrs; *BAIE DE SEINE, CAP FINISTERE, ,PONT-AVEN*; up to 3 per week, Portsmouth - Bilbao (Spain) (24/32 hrs; *BAIE DE SEINE, CAP FINISTERE*; up to 3 per week, ***Summer only*** Plymouth - Santander (Spain) (19 hrs 30 mins; *PONT-AVEN*; 1 per week (April - October)), Cork - Roscoff (14 hrs; *PONT-AVEN*; 1 per week (March - November)). **Fast Ferries *Summer only*** Portsmouth – Cherbourg (3 hrs; *NORMANDIE EXPRESS*; up to 2 per day (April-September)). **Freight-only service** Poole - Bilbao (31 hrs; *MN PELICAN*; 2 per week).

Note: The Portsmouth - Le Havre service and sailings to Spain operated by the BAIE DE SEINE and ETRETAT are branded 'économie'.

1	ARMORIQUE	29468t	09	23.0k	167.0m	1500P	470C	65L	BA2	FR	9364980
2	BAIE DE SEINE	22382t	03	22.0k	199.4m	596P	316C	154T	A	FR	9212163
3	BARFLEUR	20133t	92	19.0k	158.0m	1212P	590C	112T	BA2	FR	9007130
4	BRETAGNE	24534t	89	19.5k	151.0m	1926P	580C	84T	BA	FR	8707329
5	CAP FINISTERE	32728t	01	28.0k	203.9m	1608P	1000C	140T	BA	FR	9198927
6	ETRETAT	26500t	08	23.5k	186.5m	800P	185C	120L	A	FR	9420423
7F	MN PELICAN	12076t	99	20.0k	154.5m	12P	-	115T	A2	FR	9170999
8	MONT ST MICHEL	35592t	02	21.2k	173.0m	2200P	880C	166T	BA2	FR	9238337
9	NORMANDIE	27541t	92	20.5k	161.0m	2120P	600C	126T	BA2	FR	9006253
10»	NORMANDIE EXPRESS	6581t	00	40.0k	97.2m	900P	260C	-	A	FR	8814134
11	PONT-AVEN	41748t	04	26.0k	184.3m	2400P	650C	85L	BA	FR	9268708

ARMORIQUE Built by STX Europe, Helsinki, Finland for *Brittany Ferries* to operate between Plymouth and Roscoff.

BAIE DE SEINE Built as the GOLFO DEI DELFINI by Stocznia Szczecinska, Szczecin, Poland for *Lloyd Sardegna* of Italy for service between Italy and Sardinia. However, due to late delivery the order was cancelled. In 2002 purchased by *DFDS Seaways*, and, during Winter 2002/03, passenger accommodation was enlarged and refitted, increasing passenger capacity from 308 to 596. In June 2003, renamed the DANA SIRENA, she replaced unmodified sister vessel, the DANA GLORIA on the Esbjerg – Harwich service. In February 2013 she was renamed the SIRENA SEAWAYS. At the end of September 2014 the route ceased and she moved to the Paldiski (Estonia) - Kapellskär route, replacing the PATRIA SEAWAYS. In December she was replaced by the LIVERPOOL SEAWAYS and laid up. During the early part of 2015 she performed relief work in the Baltic. In April 2015 she was

Barfleur *(Kevin Mitchel)*

Bretagne *(Brian Smith)*

chartered to *Brittany Ferries* for five years and renamed the BAIE DE SEINE. She entered service in May 2015.

BARFLEUR Built as the BARFLEUR by Kvaerner Masa-Yards, Helsinki for the *Truckline* (freight division of *Brittany Ferries*) Poole - Cherbourg service to replace two passenger vessels and to inaugurate a year-round passenger service. In 1999 the *Truckline* branding was dropped for passenger services and she was repainted into full *Brittany Ferries* livery. In 2005 operated partly Cherbourg - Poole and partly Cherbourg - Portsmouth but in 2006 returned to operating mainly to Poole. In February 2010, she was laid up. The conventional car ferry service ended the following month. In February 2011 she resumed service on the Poole - Cherbourg route. In September 2011 she was withdrawn again. In April 2012 chartered to *DFDS Seaways* to operate between Dover and Calais and renamed the DEAL SEAWAYS. In November 2012 returned to *Brittany Ferries* and renamed the BARFLEUR. Resumed the Poole - Cherbourg service in March 2013, replacing the COTENTIN but offering a service for both freight and passengers.

BRETAGNE Built by Chantiers de l'Atlantique, St Nazaire for the Plymouth - Santander and Cork - Roscoff services (with two sailings per week between Plymouth and Roscoff). In 1993 she was transferred to the Portsmouth - St Malo service. In 2004 also operated between Portsmouth and Cherbourg. In 2005 operated between Plymouth and Roscoff. In 2006 returned to the Portsmouth - St Malo route.

CAP FINISTERE Built as the SUPERFAST V by Howaldtswerke Deutsche Werft AG, Kiel, Germany for *Attica Enterprises* (now *Attica Group*) for use by *Superfast Ferries* of Greece. Initially operated between Patras and Ancona and in January 2007 switched to the Patras - Igoumenitsa - Bari route. In 2008 the route became Patras - Igoumenitsa - Ancona. In 2010 sold to *Brittany Ferries*, renamed the CAP FINISTERE and in March placed on the Portsmouth - Santander service, also operating some sailings between Portsmouth and Cherbourg. In 2011 began operating also between Portsmouth and Bilbao and only operated between Portsmouth and Cherbourg during the winter period. Now operates on Portsmouth – Santander and Portsmouth – Bilbao routes only.

ETRETAT Built as the NORMAN VOYAGER by CN Visentini, Porto Viro, Italy for *Epic Shipping* of the UK and chartered to *LD Lines*. Operated between Le Havre and Portsmouth and Le Havre and Rosslare. In September 2009 sub-chartered to *Celtic Link Ferries*. Initially operated between Cherbourg and Portsmouth and Cherbourg and Rosslare but the Portsmouth service was abandoned in November 2009. In October 2011 returned to *LD Lines* and placed on the St Nazaire - Gijon route. In November moved to the Portsmouth - Le Havre service and, following the establishment of the joint *LD Lines/DFDS* venture, the charter was transferred to *DFDS Seaways*. In April 2012 sold to *Stena RoRo*; she continued to be chartered to *DFDS*. In March 2014 chartered to *Brittany Ferries* and placed on the new 'économie' services between Portsmouth and Le Havre and Portsmouth and Santander. Renamed the ETRETAT.

MN PELICAN Built as the TRANS BOTNIA for *SeaTrans ANS* of Norway. Hull constructed by Santierul Naval, Galatz, Romania and vessel completed by Fosen Mekaniske Verksteder, Frengen, Norway. Chartered to *Transfennica* for service between Finland and Western Europe. In June 2006 sold to *Maritime Nantaise* of France. In January 2007 renamed the MN PELICAN. Placed on long term charter to the French MOD. In 2015 placed on the charter market. In January 2016 time chartered to *Brittany Ferries*.

MONT ST MICHEL Built by Van der Giessen-de Noord, Krimpen aan den IJssel, Rotterdam for *Brittany Ferries*. Used on the Portsmouth - Caen route.

NORMANDIE Built by Kvaerner Masa-Yards, Turku, Finland for *Brittany Ferries*. Used on the Portsmouth - Caen route.

NORMANDIE EXPRESS Incat Evolution 10 catamaran built as the INCAT TASMANIA. In November 2000 chartered to *TranzRail* of New Zealand and renamed THE LYNX. Placed on the Wellington – Picton service. In July 2003 replaced by 1997-built Incat 86m craft INCAT 046, given the marketing name 'The Lynx' and laid up. In Spring 2005 chartered to *Brittany Ferries* to operate on their Cherbourg – Portsmouth and Caen – Portsmouth services and renamed the NORMANDIE EXPRESS. In 2007 purchased by *Brittany Ferries*. In 2015 operated to Cherbourg and Le Havre but in 2016 and 2017 only operated to Cherbourg.

PONT-AVEN Built by Jos L Meyer Werft, Papenburg, Germany for *Brittany Ferries* to operate on the Plymouth - Roscoff, Plymouth - Santander and Cork - Roscoff routes.

Under Construction

12	HONFLEUR	42400t	19	22.0k	187.4m	1680P	550C	130T	BA	FR

HONFLEUR Under construction by Flensburger Schiffbau-Gesellschaft, Flensburg, Germany. To operate on the Portsmouth - Caen route, replacing the NORMANDIE. To be LNG powered.

CONDOR FERRIES

THE COMPANY *Condor Ferries Ltd* is a Channel Islands private sector company owned by the *Condor Group*, Guernsey which is owned by *Macquarie European Infrastructure*.

MANAGEMENT **Managing Director** James Fulford, **Executive Director – Commercial** Alicia Andrews, **Marketing Manager** Justin Amey, **Sales Manager** Jonathan Godson.

ADDRESS **Head Office** New Jetty Offices, White Rock, St Peter Port, Guernsey GY1 2LL, **Sales and Marketing** Condor House, New Harbour Road South, Hamworthy, Poole BH15 4AJ.

TELEPHONE **Administration *Guernsey*** +44 (0)1481 728620, ***Poole*** +44 (0)1202 207207, **Passenger Reservations** +44 (0)345 609 1024, **Freight Reservations** +44 (0)1481 728620.

INTERNET **Email *Passenger*** contactcentre@condorferries.co.uk

Freight freight@condorferries.co.uk **Website** www.condorferries.com *(English, French, German)*

ROUTES OPERATED ***Conventional Passenger Ferry*** Portsmouth to Guernsey (from 7 hrs) and Jersey (from 9 hrs) (***COMMODORE CLIPPER***; daily except Sun). ***Fast Ferries*** Poole - Guernsey (from 2 hrs 40 mins) and Jersey (from 4 hrs) (***CONDOR LIBERATION***; 1 per day), Guernsey (2 hrs) and Jersey (1 hr 20 mins) to St Malo (***CONDOR RAPIDE***; 1 per day). ***Freight Ferry*** Portsmouth - Guernsey - Jersey (10 hrs 30 min; ***COMMODORE GOODWILL***; 1 per day), Guernsey - Jersey - St Malo (13 hrs; ***COMMODORE GOODWILL***; 1 per week).

1	COMMODORE CLIPPER	14000t	99	18.0k	129.1m	500P	100C	92T	A	BS	9201750
2F	COMMODORE GOODWILL	11166t	96	17.3k	126.4m	12P	-	92T	A	BS	9117985
3»	CONDOR LIBERATION	6307t	10	39.0k	102.0m	873P	245C	12L	A	BS	9551363
4»	CONDOR RAPIDE	5007t	97	40.5k	86.6m	870P	200C	-	A	BS	9161560

COMMODORE CLIPPER Ro-pax vessel built by Van der Giessen-de Noord, Krimpen aan den IJssel, Rotterdam for *Commodore Ferries* to operate between Portsmouth and the Channel Islands. She replaced the ISLAND COMMODORE, a freight-only vessel. Her passenger capacity is normally restricted to 300 but is increased to 500 when the fast ferries are unable to operate.

COMMODORE GOODWILL Built by Koninklijke Scheldegroep BV, Vlissingen, The Netherlands for *Commodore Ferries*.

CONDOR LIBERATION Austal 102-metre Trimaran built speculatively by Austal Ships Pty, Fremantle, Australia as AUSTAL HULL 270. Laid up. In August 2014 sold to *Condor Ferries*. During autumn and early winter 2014/15 she was modified by Austal Ships in their shipyard at Balamban, Cebu, Philippines and in March 2015 renamed the CONDOR LIBERATION and placed on the Poole - Channel Islands service.

CONDOR RAPIDE Incat 86m catamaran built at Hobart, Tasmania, Australia as the INCAT 045. Chartered to *Transport Tasmania* of Australia and operated between Melbourne (Victoria) and Devonport (Tasmania). In 1999 she was chartered to the *Royal Australian Navy*, renamed the HMAS JERVIS BAY and took part in moving Australian troops from Darwin to Dili (East Timor) as part of the United Nations operation. She operated over 75 trips between the two points carrying personnel and equipment for the United Nations Transitional Administration in East Timor (UNTAET). The charter ended in May 2001 and she was renamed the INCAT 045 and laid up. In Spring 2003 she was chartered to *Traghetti Isole Sarde (TRIS)* of Italy, renamed the WINNER and operated between Genoa and Palau (Sardinia). In Autumn 2003 the charter ended, she resumed the name INCAT 045 and was

MN Pelican *(Kevin Mitchel)*

Normandie Express *(Kevin Mitchel)*

laid up at Portland, Dorset. In 2004 chartered to *SpeedFerries* and renamed the SPEED ONE. In May 2008 purchased by *SpeedFerries*. In November 2008 the services ceased and the company went into administration. She was laid up at Tilbury. In May she was sold at auction to *Epic Shipping* of the UK and renamed the SEA LEOPARD. In April 2010 sold to *Condor Ferries* and renamed the CONDOR RAPIDE. Entered service in May 2010.

DAVID MACBRAYNE GROUP

THE COMPANY *David MacBrayne Limited* is a Scottish registered company, wholly owned by the Scottish Ministers. Its ferry operations are conducted through two subsidiary companies - *Argyll Ferries Ltd* and *CalMac Ferries Ltd* (trading as *Caledonian MacBrayne*). The majority of *CalMac Ferries* vessels are owned by *Caledonian Maritime Assets Limited*, a separate company which is also owned by the Scottish Ministers.

ARGYLL FERRIES

MANAGEMENT **Managing Director** Martin Dorchester, **Public Affairs Manager** David Cannon.

ADDRESS Ferry Terminal, Gourock PA19 1QP.

TELEPHONE **Administration** +44 (0)1475 650100, **Customer services** 0800 066 5000.

FAX **Administration** +44 (0)1475 650336,

INTERNET **Email** info@argyllferries.co.uk **Website** www.argyllferries.co.uk *(English)*

ROUTE OPERATED **All-year passenger-only ferry** Gourock - Dunoon (20 mins; ***ALI CAT, ARGYLL FLYER, CORUISK of Caledonian MacBrayne (winter only)*** 1 or 2 per hour.

1p	**ALI CAT**	**74t**	**99**	**-**	**19.8m**	**250P**	**0C**	**0L**	**-**	**UK**	
2p	**ARGYLL FLYER**	**300t**	**01**	**19.5k**	**29.9m**	**227P**	**0C**	**0L**	**-**	**UK**	**9231016**

ALI CAT Catamaran built for *Solent & Wight Line Cruises* of Ryde, Isle of Wight. She operated a passenger service from Cowes to Hamble and Warsash and cruises from Cowes. At times chartered to *Wightlink* to cover for their fast catamarans. In 2002 chartered to *Red Funnel Ferries* who had contracted with *Caledonian MacBrayne* to operate passenger-only services between Gourock and Dunoon in the morning and evening peaks. In June 2011 purchased by and operated by *Argyll Ferries*.

ARGYLL FLYER Built as the QUEEN OF ARAN II by OCEA, Les Sables d'Olonne, France for *Inis Mór Ferries*. In 2007 sold to *Aran Island Ferries* and renamed the BANRION CHONAMARA. In June 2011 sold to *Argyll Ferries*, renamed the ARGYLL FLYER and replaced the car ferry SATURN on the Gourock - Dunoon service.

CALEDONIAN MACBRAYNE

MANAGEMENT **Managing Director** Martin Dorchester, **Marketing and e.Commerce Manager** Cathy Craig, **Public Affairs Manager** David Cannon.

ADDRESS Ferry Terminal, Gourock PA19 1QP.

TELEPHONE **Administration** +44 (0)1475 650100, **Vehicle Reservations** +44 (0)800 066 5000.

FAX **Administration** +44 (0)1475 650336, **Vehicle Reservations** +44 (0)1475 635235.

INTERNET **Email** enquiries@calmac.co.uk **Website** www.calmac.co.uk *(English)*

ROUTES OPERATED **All-year vehicle ferries** (frequencies are for Summer – services are listed alphabetically by mainland port or larger island port where service is between two islands)

Ardmhor (Barra) - Eriskay (40 mins; ***LOCH ALAINN***; up to 5 per day)

Ardrossan - Brodick (Arran) (55 mins; ***CALEDONIAN ISLES, ISLE OF ARRAN***; up to 6 per day)

Colintraive - Rhubodach (Bute) (5 mins; ***LOCH DUNVEGAN***; frequent service)

Condor Rapide *(Kevin Mitchel)*

Commodore Clipper *(Brian Maxted)*

Kennacraig - Port Askaig (Islay) (2 hrs 5 mins; ***FINLAGGAN, HEBRIDEAN ISLES***; up to 4 per day)

Kennacraig - Port Ellen (Islay) (2 hrs 20 mins; ***FINLAGGAN, HEBRIDEAN ISLES***; service currently suspended due to harbour works)

Largs - Cumbrae Slip (Cumbrae) (10 mins; ***LOCH RIDDON, LOCH SHIRA***; every 30 or 15 mins)

Leverburgh (Harris) - Berneray (1 hr 10 mins; ***LOCH PORTAIN***; 3-4 per day)

Lochaline - Fishnish (Mull) (15 mins; ***LOCHINVAR***; up to 14 per day)

Mallaig - Armadale (Skye) (23 mins; ***LOCHNEVIS*** (Winter) ***LOCH FYNE, LORD OF THE ISLES*** (summer); up to 9 per day (2 in Winter))

Mallaig - Lochboisdale (South Uist) (3 hrs 30 mins; ***LORD OF THE ISLES***; 1per day)

Oban - Castlebay (Barra) (5 hrs); ***ISLE OF LEWIS***; 1 per day)

Oban - Coll - Tiree (2 hrs 45 min to Coll 3 hrs 50 min to Tiree via Coll; ***CLANSMAN***; 1 per day)

Oban - Colonsay (2 hrs 15 mins; ***CLANSMAN***; 5 per week)

Oban - Craignure (Mull) (45 mins; ***CORUISK, ISLE OF MULL***; up to 7 per day)

Oban - Lismore (50 mins; ***LOCH STRIVEN***; up to 5 per day)

Sconser (Skye) - Raasay (15 mins; ***HALLAIG***; up to 11 per day)

Tarbert (Loch Fyne) - Portavadie (25 mins; ***ISLE OF CUMBRAE***; up to 12 per day)

Tayinloan - Gigha (20 mins; ***LOCH RANZA***; up to 10 per day)

Tobermory (Mull) - Kilchoan (35 mins; ***LOCH TARBERT;*** up to 7 per day)

Uig (Skye) - Lochmaddy (North Uist) (1 hr 45 mins; ***HEBRIDES***; 1 or 2 per day)

Uig (Skye) - Tarbert (Harris) (1 hr 40 mins; ***HEBRIDES***; 1 or 2 per day)

Ullapool - Stornoway (Lewis) (2 hrs 45 mins; ***LOCH SEAFORTH***; up to 3 per day (one freight only))

Wemyss Bay - Rothesay (Bute) (35 mins; ***ARGYLE, BUTE***; hourly).

All-year passenger and restricted vehicle ferries (frequencies are for Summer) Gallanach (near Oban) - Kerrera (5 mins; ***GYLEN LADY***; up to 12 per day).

Fionnphort (Mull) - Iona (5 mins; ***LOCH BUIE***; frequent)

Mallaig - Eigg - Muck - Rum - Canna - Mallaig (round trip 7 hrs (all islands); ***LOCHNEVIS***; at least 1 sailing per day - most islands visited daily). **Note** Although these services are operated by vehicle ferries special permission is required to take a vehicle and tourist cars are not normally conveyed.

Summer-only vehicle ferries Ardrossan - Campbeltown (2 hrs 30 mins; ***ISLE OF ARRAN***; 3 per week)

Claonaig - Lochranza (Arran) (30 mins; ***CATRIONA***; up to 9 per day)

Kennacraig - Port Askaig - Colonsay - Oban (3 hrs 35 mins; ***HEBRIDEAN ISLES***; 1 per week).

Winter-only vehicle ferry Tarbert (Loch Fyne) - Lochranza (Arran) (1 hr; ***varies***; 1 per day)

1	ARGYLE	2643t	07	14.0k	69.0m	450P	60C	-	BAS	UK	9365178
2	BUTE	2612t	05	14.0k	69.0m	450P	60C	-	AS	UK	9319741
3	CALEDONIAN ISLES	5221t	93	15.0k	94.3m	1000P	120C	10L	BA	UK	9051284
4	CATRIONA	499t	16	9.0k	43.5m	150P	23C	2L	BA	UK	9759862
5	CLANSMAN	5499t	98	16.5k	99.0m	638P	90C	6L	BA	UK	9158953
6	CORUISK	1599t	03	14.0k	65.0m	250P	40C	-	BA	UK	9274836
7	EIGG	69t	75	8.0k	24.3m	75P	6C	-	B	UK	
8	FINLAGGAN	5626t	11	16.5k	89.9m	550P	88C	-	BA	UK	9482902
9	GYLEN LADY	9t	99	8.0k	10.0m	12P	1C	-	B	UK	
10	HALLAIG	499t	13	9.0k	43.5m	150P	23C	2L	BA	UK	9652832
11	HEBRIDEAN ISLES	3040t	85	15.0k	85.1m	494P	68C	10L	BAS	UK	8404812
12	HEBRIDES	5506t	00	16.5k	99.0m	612P	110C	6L	BA	UK	9211975
13	ISLE OF ARRAN	3296t	84	15.0k	85.0m	446P	68C	8L	BA	UK	8219554
14	ISLE OF CUMBRAE	201t	77	8.5k	37.7m	139P	18C	-	BA	UK	7521625
15	ISLE OF LEWIS	6753t	95	18.0k	101.2m	680P	123C	10L	BA	UK	9085974
16	ISLE OF MULL	4719t	88	15.0k	90.1m	962P	80C	20L	BA	UK	8608339
17	LOCH ALAINN	396t	98	10.0k	43.0m	150P	24C	-	BA	UK	9147722
18	LOCH BHRUSDA	246t	96	8.0k	35.4m	150P	18C	-	BA	UK	9129483
19	LOCH BUIE	295t	92	9.0k	35.5m	250P	9C	-	BA	UK	9031375
20	LOCH DUNVEGAN	549t	91	9.0k	54.2m	200P	36C	-	BA	UK	9006409
21	LOCH FYNE	549t	91	9.0k	54.2m	200P	36C	-	BA	UK	9006411
22	LOCH LINNHE	206t	86	9.0k	35.5m	199P	12C	-	BA	UK	8512308
23	LOCH PORTAIN	950t	03	10.5k	50.0m	200P	32C	-	BA	UK	9274824
24	LOCH RANZA	206t	87	9.0k	35.7m	199P	12C	-	BA	UK	8519887
25	LOCH RIDDON	206t	86	9.0k	35.5m	199P	12C	-	BA	UK	8519875
26	LOCH SEAFORTH	8478t	14	19.2k	116.0m	700P	143C	20L	BA	UK	9665437
27	LOCH SHIRA	1024t	07	13.0k	43.0m	250P	24C	-	BA	UK	9376919
28	LOCH STRIVEN	206t	86	9.0k	35.7m	199P	12C	-	BA	UK	8512293
29	LOCH TARBERT	211t	92	9.0k	34.5m	149P	18C	-	BA	UK	9039389
30	LOCHINVAR	523t	14	9.0k	43.5m	150P	23C	2L	BA	UK	9652844
31	LOCHNEVIS	941t	00	13.0k	49.1m	190P	14C	-	A	UK	9209063
32	LORD OF THE ISLES	3504t	89	16.0k	84.6m	506P	56C	16L	BAS	UK	8710869
33	RAASAY	69t	76	8.0k	24.3m	75P	6C	-	B	UK	

Note In the following list, Gaelic names are shown in parenthesis.

ARGYLE *(EARRA-GHÀIDHEAL)*, BUTE *(EILEAN BHÒID)* Built by Stocznia Remontowa, Gdansk, Poland to operate on the Wemyss Bay - Rothesay route.

CALEDONIAN ISLES *(EILEANAN CHALEDONIA)* Built by Richards Shipyard, Lowestoft, UK for the Ardrossan - Brodick (Arran) service.

CATRIONA Built by Ferguson Marine Engineering, Port Glasgow. Near sister vessel of the HALLAIG and LOCHINVAR. Operates on the Claonaig - Lochranza service during the summer and other routes during the winter.

CLANSMAN *(FEAR-CINNIDH)* Built by Appledore Shipbuilders Ltd, Appledore, UK to replace the LORD OF THE ISLES on the Oban - Coll and Tiree and Oban - Castlebay and Lochboisdale services in the summer. She also serves as winter relief vessel on the Stornoway, Tarbert, Lochmaddy, Mull/Colonsay and Brodick routes.

CORUISK *(COIR' UISG')* Built by Appledore Shipbuilders Ltd, Appledore, UK to operate on the Mallaig - Armadale route during the summer. During the winter operates for *Argyle Ferries* in lieu of the ALI CAT during peak periods and when that vessel cannot sail due to adverse weather. In summer 2016 operated as second vessel on the Oban - Craignure service and this was repeated in 2017.

Hebridean Isles *(Andrew Wood)*

Catriona *(Miles Cowsill)*

Loch Striven *(Miles Cowsill)*

Clansman *(Miles Cowsill)*

Loch Alainn *(Miles Cowsill)*

Loch Portain *(Miles Cowsill)*

EIGG *(EILEAN EIGE)* Built by James Lamont & Co, Port Glasgow, UK. Since 1976 she has been employed mainly on the Oban - Lismore service. In 1996 she was transferred to the Tobermory (Mull) - Kilchoan route, very occasionally making sailings to the Small Isles (Canna, Eigg, Muck and Rum) for special cargoes. In 1999 her wheelhouse was raised to make it easier to see over taller lorries and she returned to the Oban - Lismore route. Now a spare vessel.

FINLAGGAN *(FIONN LAGAN)* Built by Stocznia Remontowa, Gdansk, Poland for the Kennacraig - Islay service.

GYLEN LADY Built by Compact Boatyard, Corpach, UK for *Kerrera Ferry* to inaugurate a vehicle ferry service to the Isle of Kerrera, replacing an open passenger boat. In July 2017 service taken over by *Caledonian MacBrayne* and vessel chartered. To be replaced.

HALLAIG *(HALLAIG)* Built by Ferguson Shipbuilders, Port Glasgow, UK to replace the LOCH STRIVEN on the Sconser - Raasay service. The vessel has both diesel and battery electric propulsion and can be 'plugged in' to a land supply on Raasay overnight.

HEBRIDEAN ISLES *(EILEANAN INNSE GALL)* Built by Cochrane Shipbuilders, Selby UK for the Uig - Tarbert/Lochmaddy service. She was used initially on the Ullapool - Stornoway and Oban - Craignure/Colonsay services pending installation of link-span facilities at Uig, Tarbert and Lochmaddy. She took up her regular role in May 1986. From May 1996 she no longer operated direct services in summer between Tarbert and Lochmaddy, this role being taken on by the new Harris - North Uist services of the LOCH BHRUSDA. In 2001 she was replaced by the HEBRIDES and transferred to the Islay service. In Autumn 2002 she operated between Scrabster and Stromness for *NorthLink Orkney and Shetland Ferries* before port modifications at Scrabster enabled the HAMNAVOE to enter service in Spring 2003. She then returned to the Islay service. She also relieved on the *NorthLink* Pentland Firth service between 2004 and 2007.

HEBRIDES *(INNSE GALL)* Built by Ferguson Shipbuilders Ltd, Port Glasgow, UK for the Uig - Tarbert and Uig - Lochmaddy services.

ISLE OF ARRAN *(EILEAN ARAINN)* Built by Ferguson Ailsa, Port Glasgow, UK for the Ardrossan - Brodick service. In 1993 transferred to the Kennacraig - Port Ellen/Port Askaig service, also undertaking the weekly Port Askaig - Colonsay - Oban summer service. From then until 1997/98 she also relieved on the Brodick, Coll/Tiree, Castlebay/Lochboisdale, Craignure and Tarbert/Lochmaddy routes in winter. In 2001 she was replaced by the HEBRIDEAN ISLES and became a reserve for the larger vessels. She has operated on the two-ship Islay service in summer since 2003; this service is now all-year-round. Following the delivery of the FINLAGGAN in May 2011 she became a spare vessel, and operates extra services between Ardrossan and Brodick and Ardrossan and Campbeltown during the peak summer period.

ISLE OF CUMBRAE *(EILEAN CHUMRAIGH)* Built by Ailsa Shipbuilding Ltd, Troon, UK for the Largs - Cumbrae Slip (Cumbrae) service. In 1986 she was replaced by the LOCH LINNHE and the LOCH STRIVEN and transferred to the Lochaline - Fishnish (Mull) service. She used to spend most of the winter as secondary vessel on the Kyle of Lochalsh - Kyleakin service; however, this ceased following the opening of the Skye Bridge in 1995. In 1997 she was transferred to the Colintraive - Rhubodach service. In Summer 1999 she was transferred to the Tarbert - Portavadie service. In May 2015 replaced by the new LOCHINVAR and laid up. In summer 2016 returned to the Tarbert - Portavadie service.

ISLE OF LEWIS *(EILEAN LEÒDHAIS)* Built by Ferguson Shipbuilders Ltd, Port Glasgow, UK for the Ullapool - Stornoway service. In February 2015 replaced by the new LOCH SEAFORTH. During peak summer period 2015 she operated an additional sailing between Ullapool and Stornoway. In summer 2016 operated between Oban and Castlebay.

ISLE OF MULL *(AN T-EILEAN MUILEACH)* Built by Appledore Ferguson, Port Glasgow, UK for the Oban - Craignure (Mull) service. She also operates some Oban - Colonsay sailings and until 1997/98 was the usual winter relief vessel on the Ullapool - Stornoway service. She has also deputised on the Oban - Castlebay/Lochboisdale and Oban - Coll/Tiree routes.

LOCH ALAINN *(LOCH ÀLAINN)* Built by Buckie Shipbuilders Ltd, Buckie, UK for the Lochaline - Fishnish service. Launched as the LOCH ALINE but renamed the LOCH ALAINN before entering service. After a brief period on the service for which she was built, she was transferred to the Colintraive - Rhubodach route. In 1998 she was transferred to the Largs - Cumbrae Slip service. In 2007 moved to the Ardmhor (Barra) - Eriskay service. She relieves the larger 'Loch' class vessels in the winter, with her own service covered by the LOCH BHRUSDA.

LOCH BHRUSDA *(LOCH BHRÙSTA)* Built by McTay Marine, Bromborough, Wirral, UK to inaugurate a new Otternish (North Uist) - Leverburgh (Harris) service. In 2001 the service became Berneray - Leverburgh. In 2003 she moved to the Eriskay - Barra service, previously operated by *Comhairle Nan Eilean Siar* vessels. In 2007 she became a spare vessel on the Clyde. In summer 2016 operated between Mallaig and Armadale. Note 'Bhrusda' is pronounced "Vroosta".

LOCH BUIE *(LOCH BUIDHE)* Built by J W Miller & Sons Ltd, St Monans, Fife, UK for the Fionnphort (Mull) - Iona service to replace the MORVERN (see *Arranmore Island Ferry Services*) and obviate the need for a relief vessel in the summer. Due to height restrictions, loading arrangements for vehicles taller than private cars are stern-only. Only islanders' cars and service vehicles (eg mail vans, police) are carried; no tourist vehicles are conveyed.

LOCH DUNVEGAN *(LOCH DÙNBHEAGAN)* Built by Ferguson Shipbuilders Ltd, Port Glasgow, UK for the Kyle of Lochalsh - Kyleakin service. On the opening of the Skye Bridge in October 1995 she was withdrawn from service and offered for sale. In Autumn 1997, she returned to service on the Lochaline - Fishnish route. In 1998 she was due to be transferred to the Colintraive - Rhubodach route but this was delayed because of problems in providing terminal facilities. She operated on the Clyde and between Mallaig and Armadale during the early summer and spent the rest of that summer laid up. In 1999 she was transferred to the Colintraive - Rhubodach route.

LOCH FYNE *(LOCH FINE)* Built by Ferguson Shipbuilders Ltd, Port Glasgow, UK for the Kyle of Lochalsh - Kyleakin service (see the LOCH DUNVEGAN). In Autumn 1997, she also served on the Lochaline - Fishnish route and was transferred to this route as regular vessel in 1998. In summer 2017 transferred to the Mallaig - Armadale route.

LOCH LINNHE *(AN LINNE DHUBH)* Built by Richard Dunston (Hessle) Ltd, Hessle, UK. Until 1997 she was used mainly on the Largs - Cumbrae Slip (Cumbrae) service and until Winter 1994/95 she was usually used on the Lochaline - Fishnish service during the winter. Since then she has relieved on various routes in winter. In Summer 1998 she operated mainly on the Tarbert - Portavadie route. In 1999 she was transferred to the Tobermory - Kilchoan service in summer.

LOCH PORTAIN *(LOCH PORTAIN)* Built by McTay Marine, Bromborough, Wirral, UK (hull constructed in Poland) to replace the LOCH BHRUSDA on the Berneray - Leverburgh service.

LOCH RANZA *(LOCH RAONASA)* Built by Richard Dunston (Hessle) Ltd, Hessle, UK for the Claonaig - Lochranza (Arran) seasonal service and used a relief vessel in the winter. In 1992 she was replaced by the LOCH TARBERT and transferred to the Tayinloan - Gigha service.

LOCH RIDDON *(LOCH RAODAIN)* Built by Richard Dunston (Hessle) Ltd, Hessle, UK. Until 1997 she was used almost exclusively on the Colintraive - Rhubodach service. In 1997, she was transferred to the Largs - Cumbrae Slip service. In January 2014 she became regular vessel on the Oban - Lismore service. However, after problems with using the slipways, she became the second vessel on the Largs - Cumbrae Slip service.

LOCH SEAFORTH *(LOCH SHIPHOIRT)* Built by Flensburger Schiffbau-Gesellschaft, Flensburg, Germany for the Stornoway - Ullapool service, replacing the ISLE OF LEWIS and freight vessel CLIPPER RANGER.

LOCH SHIRA *(LOCH SIORA)* Built by Ferguson Shipbuilders, Port Glasgow, UK for the Largs – Cumbrae Slip route.

LOCH STRIVEN *(LOCH SROIGHEANN)* Built by Richard Dunston (Hessle) Ltd, Hessle, UK. Used mainly on the Largs - Cumbrae Slip service until 1997. In Winter 1995/96 and 1996/97 she was used on the Tarbert - Portavadie and Claonaig - Lochranza routes. In 1997 she took over the Sconser - Raasay service. In winter 2014 replaced by the HALLAIG. In summer 2014 transferred to the Oban - Lismore route.

LOCH TARBERT *(LOCH AN TAIRBEIRT)* Built by J W Miller & Sons Ltd, St Monans, Fife, UK for the Claonaig - Lochranza service. She was the winter relief vessel on the Largs - Cumbrae Slip route between 1994/95 and 2007/08.

LOCHINVAR *(LOCH AN BARR)* As the HALLAIG. Initially operated on the Tarbert - Portavadie route. In summer 2016 transferred to Mallaig - Armadale and in summer 2017 to the Lochaline - Fishnish route.

LOCHNEVIS *(LOCH NIBHEIS)* Built by Ailsa Shipbuilding, Troon, UK to replace the LOCHMOR on the Mallaig - Small Isles service and the winter Mallaig - Armadale service. Although a vehicle ferry, cars are not normally carried to the Small Isles; the ro-ro facility is used for the carriage of agricultural machinery and livestock and it is possible to convey a vehicle on the ferry from which goods can be unloaded directly onto local transport rather than transhipping at Mallaig.

LORD OF THE ISLES *(RIGH NAN EILEAN)* Built by Appledore Ferguson, Port Glasgow, UK to replace the CLAYMORE on the Oban - Castlebay and Lochboisdale services and also the COLUMBA (1420t, 1964) on the Oban - Coll and Tiree service. She took over the Mallaig - Armadale and Mallaig - Outer Isles services in July 1998 but returned to her previous routes during the winter period. In Spring 2003 the Mallaig – Armadale service was taken over by the PIONEER standing in for the new CORUISK and she operated services from Oban to South Uist and Barra. In summer 2016 operated between Mallaig and Lochboisdale and also between Mallaig and Armadale.

RAASAY *(EILEAN RATHARSAIR)* Built by James Lamont & Co Ltd, Port Glasgow, UK for and used primarily on the Sconser (Skye) - Raasay service. In 1997 she was replaced by the LOCH STRIVEN, became a spare/relief vessel and inaugurated in October 2003 the winter service between Tobermory (Mull) and Kilchoan (Ardnamurchan). In summer 2016 operates as second vessel on Oban - Lismore route.

Under Construction

34	**CARVORIA**	**9t**	**17**	**8.0k**	**-**	**12P**	**1C**	**-**	**B**	**UK**	
35	**GLEN SANNOX**	**5000t**	**18**	**16.5k**	**102.0m**	**1000P**	**127C**	**16L**	**BA**	**UK**	**-**
36	**NEWBUILDING**	**5000t**	**18**	**16.5k**	**102.0m**	**1000P**	**127C**	**16L**	**BA**	**UK**	**-**

CARVORIA Under construction by Malakoff Limited, Lerwick, Shetland for *Caledonian Maritime Assets* and to be chartered to *Caledonian MacBrayne* to replace the chartered GYLEN LADY on the Gallanach - Kerrera service.

GLEN SANNOX, NEWBUILDING Under construction by Ferguson Marine Engineering, Port Glasgow for *Caledonian Maritime Assets* and to be chartered to *Caledonian MacBrayne*. The GLEN SANNOX will operate on the Ardrossan - Brodick service and the other on the service between Uig and Harris and North Uist.

DFDS SEAWAYS

THE COMPANY *DFDS Seaways* is a business unit within *DFDS A/S*, a Danish private sector company. Services from Dover, Newhaven and Marseilles are operated by *DFDS Seaways France* which was inaugurated in March 2013 following the establishment of a *DFDS Seaways/LD Lines* joint venture in November 2012. It is 82% owned by *DFDS* and 18% by *Louis Dreyfus Armateurs*. The Newhaven - Dieppe route is branded as *Transmanche Ferries*, operating under a franchise awarded by *Syndicat Mixte de L'Activité Transmanche* in Dieppe.

MANAGEMENT President and CEO DFDS A/S Niels Smedegaard, **Executive Vice President Shipping Division** Peder Gellert Pedersen, **Managing Director, DFDS Seaways PLC** Sean Potter, **Senior Vice President South** Kell Robdrup, **Head of English Channel Business Area** Kasper Moos, **Head of Passenger Business Area** Brian Thorsted Hansen.

ADDRESS (UK) DFDS A/S, Whitfield Court, White Cliffs Business Park Whitfield, Dover CT16 3PX.

TELEPHONE Administration +44 (0)1304 874001. **Passenger Reservations** ***Dover- Calais*** 0871 574 7223, +44 (0)208 127 8303, ***Newcastle - Ijmuiden*** 0871 522 9955, +44 330 333 0245, ***Newhaven - Dieppe*** 0844 576 8836, +33 232 144 729 **Freight Reservations** see website.

Calais Seaways *(George Holand)*

Côte des Flandres *(George Holland)*

INTERNET Websites *Passenger* www.dfdsseaways.co.uk *(various)* ***Freight*** freight.dfdsseaways.com *(English)* ***Corporate*** www.dfds.com *(English)*

ROUTES OPERATED ***Passenger ferries*** Newcastle (North Shields) - IJmuiden (near Amsterdam, The Netherlands) (15 hrs; *KING SEAWAYS, PRINCESS SEAWAYS*; daily). ROUTES OPERATED Dover - Dunkerque (2 hrs; *DELFT SEAWAYS, DOVER SEAWAYS, DUNKERQUE SEAWAYS*, 12 per day), Dover - Calais (1 hr 30 mins; *CALAIS SEAWAYS, CÔTE DES FLANDRES, CÔTE DES DUNES*; 15 per day), Newhaven - Dieppe (4 hrs; *CÔTE D'ALBATRE, SEVEN SISTERS*; up to 3 per day, ***Freight ferries*** Zeebrugge (Belgium) - Rosyth (Scotland) (20 hrs; *FINLANDIA SEAWAYS*; 3 per week), Esbjerg - Immingham (18 hrs; *ARK DANIA, ARK GERMANIA*; 6 per week), Cuxhaven - Immingham (19 hrs; *HAFNIA SEAWAYS, JUTLANDIA SEAWAYS*; 4/5 per week), Gothenburg - Immingham (26 hrs (direct), *45 hrs (via Brevik (Fri)); *MAGNOLIA SEAWAYS, PETUNIA SEAWAYS, PRIMULA SEAWAYS*; 7 per week), Brevik - Immingham (25 hrs (direct), 42 hrs (via Gothenburg); *MAGNOLIA SEAWAYS, PETUNIA SEAWAYS, PRIMULA SEAWAYS*; 2 per week), Gothenburg - Brevik (Norway) - Ghent (Belgium) (Gothenburg 32 hrs, Brevik 32 hrs; *BEGONIA SEAWAYS, FIONIA SEAWAYS, FREESIA SEAWAYS*;; 5 per week), Vlaardingen - Immingham (14 hrs; *ANGLIA SEAWAYS, CORONA SEAWAYS, FICARIA SEAWAYS, GARDENIA SEAWAYS*,; 8 per week), Vlaardingen - Felixstowe (7 hrs; *BRITANNIA SEAWAYS, SELANDIA SEAWAYS, SUECIA SEAWAYS*; 3 per day). Note: vessels are often switched between routes.

1F	ANGLIA SEAWAYS	13073t	00	18.5k	142.5m	12P	-	114T	A	DK	9186649
2F	ARK DANIA	33313t	14	20.0k	195.2m	12P	-	206T	A	DK	9609964
3F	ARK FUTURA	18725t	96	19.7k	183.3m	12P	-	164T	AS	DK	9129598
4F	ARK GERMANIA	33313t	14	20.0k	195.2m	12P	-	206T	A	DK	9609952
5F	BEGONIA SEAWAYS	37722t	04	22.5k	230.0m	12P	-	340T	AS	DK	9262089
6F	BRITANNIA SEAWAYS	24196t	00	21.1k	197.5m	12P	-	200T	AS	DK	9153032
7	CALAIS SEAWAYS	28833t	91	21.0k	163.6m	1850P	600C	100L	BA2	FR	8908466
8F	CORONA SEAWAYS	25609t	08	20.0k	184.8m	12P	-	250T	AS	UK	9357597
9	CÔTE D'ALBATRE	18425t	06	22.0k	112.0m	600P	300C	62L	BA	FR	9320128
10	CÔTE DES DUNES	33796t	01	25.0k	186.0m	1500P	700C	120L	BA2	FR	9232527
11	CÔTE DES FLANDRES	33940t	05	25.0k	186.0m	1500P	700C	120L	BA2	FR	9305843
12	DELFT SEAWAYS	35923t	06	25.5k	187.0m	780P	200C	120L	BA2	UK	9293088
13	DOVER SEAWAYS	35923t	06	25.8k	187.0m	780P	200C	120L	BA2	UK	9318345
14	DUNKERQUE SEAWAYS	35923t	05	25.8k	187.0m	780P	200C	120L	BA2	UK	9293076
15F	FICARIA SEAWAYS	37939t	04	22.5k	230.0m	12P	-	340T	AS	DK	9320568
16F	FINLANDIA SEAWAYS	11530t	00	20.0k	162.2m	12P	-	140T	A	LT	9198721
17F	FIONIA SEAWAYS	25609t	09	20.0k	184.8m	12P	-	250T	AS	UK	9395343
18F	FREESIA SEAWAYS	37722t	04	22.5k	230.0m	12P	-	340T	AS	DK	9274848
19F	GARDENIA SEAWAYS	32000t	17	21.0k	209.6m	12P	-	262T	A2	LT	9809095
20F	HAFNIA SEAWAYS	25609t	08	20.0k	184.8m	12P	-	250T	AS	UK	9357602
21F	JUTLANDIA SEAWAYS	25609t	10	20.0k	184.8m	12P	-	250T	AS	UK	9395355
22	KING SEAWAYS	31788t	87	20.0k	161.6m	1400P	600C	104T	BA	DK	8502406
23F	MAGNOLIA SEAWAYS	32289t	03	22.5k	199.8m	12P	-	280T	AS	DK	9259496
24F	PETUNIA SEAWAYS	32289t	04	22.5k	199.8m	12P	-	280T	AS	DK	9259501
25F	PRIMULA SEAWAYS	37985t	04	22.5k	229.8m	12P	-	340T	AS	DK	9259513
26	PRINCESS SEAWAYS	31356t	86	18.5k	161.0m	1600P	600C	100T	BA	DK	8502391
27F	SELANDIA SEAWAYS	24196t	98	21.0k	197.5m	12P	-	206T	A	DK	9157284
28	SEVEN SISTERS	18425t	06	22.0k	112.0m	600P	300C	62L	BA	FR	9320130
29F	SUECIA SEAWAYS	24196t	99	21.0k	197.5m	12P	-	206T	AS	DK	9153020

ANGLIA SEAWAYS Built as the MAERSK ANGLIA by Guangzhou Shipyard International, Guangzhou, China for *Norfolkline*. Entered service as the GUANGZHOU 7130011 (unofficially the 'China II') but renamed shortly afterwards. Operated on the Scheveningen (from 2007 Vlaardingen) - Felixstowe service. In June 2009 moved to the Heysham - Dublin route. In August 2010 renamed the ANGLIA SEAWAYS. In January 2011 service withdrawn. In February 2011 chartered to *Seatruck Ferries* to

inaugurate their new Heysham - Dublin service. In January 2012 returned to *DFDS Seaways* and placed on the Vlaardingen - Immingham route as an extra vessel. In April 2012 moved to the Zeebrugge - Rosyth service but proved too slow. In May chartered to *Seatruck Ferries* to operate between Heysham and Belfast. In August, this service ceased and she was switched to the Heysham - Dublin route and in September to the Heysham - Warrenpoint route. In April 2014 returned to *DFDS Seaways* and placed on Kiel - St Petersburg service. In July 2014 transferred to the Travemünde - Klaipėda route and in September to the Vlaardingen - Immingham service, providing additional capacity. In March 2015 placed on the charter market. In May 2015 returned to the Rotterdam - Felixstowe route.

ARK DANIA, ARK GERMANIA Built by P + S Werften GmbH, Stralsund, Germany. They are used for the German/Danish joint ARK Project providing NATO transport but are also available for *DFDS* use and charter when not required. They have a crane for loading containers on the weather deck. In December 2012 the order for these vessels was cancelled due to late delivery. Following negotiations with the shipyard it was agreed that they would be completed under a new contract which was signed in February 2013. Both vessels were delivered to *DFDS* in April 2014, the ARK GERMANIA almost complete, the ARK DANIA still incomplete. The latter vessel was towed to the Fayard shipyard, Odense, to be completed. The ARK GERMANIA entered service a few days after delivery, the ARK DANIA in November 2014.

ARK FUTURA Built as the DANA FUTURA by C N Visentini di Visentini Francesco & C, Donada, Italy for *DFDS*. In 2001 she was renamed the TOR FUTURA. Initially operated mainly between Esbjerg and Harwich, but latterly operated mainly between Esbjerg and Immingham. In 2004 chartered to *Toll Shipping* of Australia. Later time-chartered to the *Danish MoD* for 5.5 years. However, when not required for military service she has been chartered to other operators such as *P&O Ferries*, *Cobelfret Ferries* and *Van Uden Ro-Ro* and used on *DFDS Tor Line* services. In 2006 sold to *DFDS Lys Line Rederi A/S* of Norway, a *DFDS* subsidiary and chartered back. In April 2011 renamed the ARK FUTURA. Currently operating on the Marseilles - Tunis service.

BEGONIA SEAWAYS Built as the TOR BEGONIA by Flensburger Schiffbau-Gesellschaft, Flensburg, Germany for *DFDS Tor Line*. Operates on the Gothenburg - Immingham/Brevik route. In Summer 2009 lengthened by 30m by MWB Motorenwerke Bremerhaven AG, Germany. In July 2012 renamed the BEGONIA SEAWAYS.

BRITANNIA SEAWAYS Built as the TOR BRITANNIA by Fincantieri-Cantieri Navali Italiani SpA, Ancona, Italy for *DFDS Tor Line*. Operated on the Gothenburg - Immingham route until 2004 when she was transferred to the Esbjerg - Immingham route. In January 2010 chartered to *Norfolkline* to operate between Vlaardingen and Felixstowe. In May 2011 renamed the BRITANNIA SEAWAYS.

CALAIS SEAWAYS Built as the PRINS FILIP by NV Boelwerf SA, Temse, Belgium for *Regie voor Maritiem Transport (RMT)* of Belgium for the Ostend - Dover service. Although completed in 1991, she did not enter service until May 1992. In 1994 the British port became Ramsgate. Withdrawn in 1997 and laid up for sale. In 1998 she was sold to *Stena RoRo* and renamed the STENA ROYAL. In November 1998 she was chartered to *P&O Ferries* to operate as a freight-only vessel on the Dover - Zeebrugge route. In Spring 1999 it was decided to charter the vessel on a long-term basis and she was repainted into *P&O Stena Line* (later *P&O Ferries*) colours and renamed the P&OSL AQUITAINE. In Autumn 1999 she was modified to make her suitable to operate between Dover and Calais and was transferred to that route, becoming a passenger vessel again. In 2002 renamed the PO AQUITAINE and in 2003 the PRIDE OF AQUITAINE. In September 2005 sold to *LD Lines* and renamed the NORMAN SPIRIT. In October, inaugurated a Le Havre - Portsmouth service, replacing that previously operated by *P&O Ferries*. In November 2009 moved to the Dover - Boulogne route. In March 2010 chartered to *TransEuropa Ferries*, placed on the Ostend - Ramsgate service (as part of a joint venture) and renamed the OSTEND SPIRIT. In May 2011 returned to the Portsmouth - Le Havre route and renamed the NORMAN SPIRIT. In November 2011 chartered to *DFDS Seaways* to add extra capacity to their Dover - Dunkerque route. In February 2012 transferred to the new Dover - Calais route, joint with *DFDS Seaways*. Ownership transferred to *DFDS Seaways* in late 2012. In March 2013 refurbished, repainted into *DFDS Seaways* colours and renamed the CALAIS SEAWAYS.

CORONA SEAWAYS Built as the TOR CORONA by Jinling Shipyard, Nanjing, China for *Macoma Shipping Ltd* of the UK and time-chartered to *DFDS Tor Line* for ten years. Used on the Fredericia –

SECTION 1 – GB & IRELAND PASSENGER OPERATIONS

Copenhagen - Klaipėda service. In April 2012 renamed the CORONA SEAWAYS. In December 2015 transferred to the Vlaardingen - Immingham service.

CÔTE D'ALBATRE Built by Astilleros Barreras SA, Vigo, Spain for *Transmanche Ferries* to operate between Newhaven and Dieppe. In February 2009 she was moved to the Boulogne - Dover and Dieppe - Dover routes for *LD Lines*. In September 2009 moved to the Le Havre - Portsmouth route. The vessel has had periods laid up when not required on the Newhaven – Dieppe route.

CÔTE DES DUNES Built as the SEAFRANCE RODIN by Aker Finnyards, Rauma, Finland for *SeaFrance*. Launched in November 2001. In November 2011 laid up. In June 2012 sold to *Eurotransmanche*. In July 2012 renamed the RODIN. In August 2012 chartered to *MyFerryLink* and resumed operation between Calais and Dover. In July 2015 chartered to *DFDS Seaways* and *MyFerryLink* operations ceased. After a prolonged occupation by former *MyFerryLink* workers. *DFDS Seaways* took possession in early September and in November 2015 she was renamed the CÔTE DES DUNES. She re-entered service on the Dover - Calais route in February 2016. In June 2017 purchased by *DFDS Seaways*.

CÔTE DES FLANDRES Built as the SEAFRANCE BERLIOZ by Chantiers de l'Atlantique, St Nazaire for *SeaFrance*. Launched in March 2005. In November 2011 laid up. In June 2012 sold to *Eurotransmanche*, a *Groupe Eurotunnel* company. In July 2012 renamed the BERLIOZ. In August 2012 chartered to *MyFerryLink* and resumed operation between Calais and Dover. In July 2015 chartered to *DFDS Seaways* and *MyFerryLink* operations ceased. After a prolonged occupation by former *MyFerryLink* workers, *DFDS Seaways* took possession in early September and, in November 2015, she was renamed the CÔTE DES FLANDRES. She re-entered service on the Dover - Calais route in February 2016. In June 2017 purchased by *DFDS Seaways*.

DELFT SEAWAYS, DOVER SEAWAYS, DUNKERQUE SEAWAYS Built as the MAERSK DELFT, DOVER SEAWAYS and MAERSK DUNKERQUE by Samsung Heavy Industries, Koje (Geoje) Island, South Korea for *Norfolkline* to operate between Dover and Dunkerque. In July and August 2010 renamed the DELFT SEAWAYS, DOVER SEAWAYS and DUNKERQUE SEAWAYS. In November 2012 the DOVER SEAWAYS was moved to the Dover - Calais route.

FICARIA SEAWAYS Built as the TOR FICARIA by Flensburger Schiffbau-Gesellschaft, Flensburg, Germany for *DFDS Tor Line*. Operated on the Gothenburg - Immingham/Brevik service. In Summer 2009 lengthened by 30m by MWB Motorenwerke Bremerhaven AG, Germany. In July 2011 renamed the FICARIA SEAWAYS. In March 2015 placed on the Vlaardingen - Immingham service.

FINLANDIA SEAWAYS Launched as the FINNMAID but renamed the FINNREEL before delivery. Built by Jinling Shipyard, Nanjing, China for the *Macoma Shipping Group* and chartered to *Finnlines*. In 2008 sold to *DFDS Lisco* and in January 2009 delivered, chartered to *DFDS Tor Line* and renamed the TOR FINLANDIA. Operated on the Immingham - Rotterdam route until January 2011 when she was transferred to the Rosyth - Zeebrugge route. In May 2012 moved to the Cuxhaven - Immingham service but returned in July. In December 2012 renamed the FINLANDIA SEAWAYS. In October 2013 moved to the Kiel - St Petersburg service. In April 2014 returned to the Rosyth - Zeebrugge route.

FIONIA SEAWAYS Built as the TOR FIONIA by Jinling Shipyard, Nanjing, China for *Macoma Shipping Ltd* of the UK. Launched as the JINGLING 3. She was time-chartered to *DFDS Tor Line* for ten years (with an option on a further three). Delivered in May 2009 and initially replaced the TOR BEGONIA, TOR FICARIA and TOR FREESIA while they were being lengthened. In October 2011 renamed the FIONIA SEAWAYS. In March 2015 placed on the Gothenburg - Immingham service.

FREESIA SEAWAYS Built as the TOR FREESIA by Flensburger Schiffbau-Gesellschaft, Flensburg, Germany for *DFDS Tor Line*. Operates on the Gothenburg - Immingham/Brevik service. In Summer 2009 lengthened by 30m by MWB Motorenwerke Bremerhaven AG, Germany. In August 2012 renamed the FREESIA SEAWAYS.

GARDENIA SEAWAYS Built by Flensburger Schiffbau-Gesellschaft, Flensburg, Germany for the Siem Industries Inc (owners of FSG). She is bareboat chartered to *DFDS Seaways* for five years with an option to purchase at the end of the charter period. Operates between Vlaardingen and Immingham.

HAFNIA SEAWAYS Built as the TOR HAFNIA by Jinling Shipyard, Nanjing, China for *Macoma Shipping Ltd* of the UK and time-chartered to *DFDS Tor Line* for ten years. Until 2013, mainly operated on the Immingham - Esbjerg route. In March 2011 renamed the HAFNIA SEAWAYS. In February 2013

Seven Sisters *(Richard Kirkman)*

Gardenia Seaways (*Rob de Visser)*

Dunkerque Seaways *(George Holland)*

transferred to the Vlaardingen - Immingham route. In January 2015 chartered to *Cobelfret Ferries* for four weeks. Currently operates on the Cuxhaven - Immingham service.

JUTLANDIA SEAWAYS Built as the TOR JUTLANDIA by Jinling Shipyard, Nanjing, China for *Macoma Shipping Ltd* of the UK and time-chartered to *DFDS Tor Line* for ten years. In July 2011 renamed the JUTLANDIA SEAWAYS.

KING SEAWAYS Built as the NILS HOLGERSSON by Schichau Seebeckwerft AG, Bremerhaven, Germany for *Rederi AB Swedcarrier* of Sweden for their service between Trelleborg and Travemünde, joint with *TT-Line* of Germany (trading as *TT-Line*). In 1992 purchased by *Brittany Ferries* for entry into service in Spring 1993. After a major rebuild, she was renamed the VAL DE LOIRE and introduced onto the Plymouth - Roscoff, Plymouth - Santander and Cork - Roscoff routes. In 2004 transferred to the Portsmouth - St Malo and Portsmouth – Cherbourg services. In 2005 operated mainly Portsmouth - St Malo. In 2006 sold to *DFDS*, renamed the KING OF SCANDINAVIA and placed on the Newcastle – IJmuiden route. In January 2011 renamed the KING SEAWAYS.

MAGNOLIA SEAWAYS Built as the TOR MAGNOLIA by Flensburger Schiffbau-Gesellschaft, Flensburg, Germany for *DFDS Tor Line*. In July 2011 renamed the MAGNOLIA SEAWAYS.

PETUNIA SEAWAYS Built as the TOR PETUNIA by Flensburger Schiffbau-Gesellschaft, Flensburg, Germany for *DFDS Tor Line*. In July 2011 renamed the PETUNIA SEAWAYS.

PRIMULA SEAWAYS Built as the TOR PRIMULA by Flensburger Schiffbau-Gesellschaft, Flensburg, Germany for *DFDS Tor Line*. In July 2010 renamed the PRIMULA SEAWAYS. In July 2016 lengthened by 30m by MWB Motorenwerke Bremerhaven AG, Germany.

PRINCESS SEAWAYS Built by Schichau Seebeckwerft AG, Bremerhaven, Germany as the PETER PAN for *TT-Line* for the service between Travemünde and Trelleborg. In 1992 sold to *TT Line* of Australia (no connection) for use on their service between Port Melbourne (Victoria) and Devonport (Tasmania) and renamed the SPIRIT OF TASMANIA. In 2002 sold to *Nordsjøferger K/S* of Norway and renamed the SPIR. After modification work she was, in 2003, renamed the FJORD NORWAY and chartered to *Fjord Line*. Placed on the Bergen - Egersund - Hanstholm route. In 2005 placed on the Bergen - Stavanger - Newcastle route, but operated once a week to Hanstholm. In October 2006 sold to *DFDS* and renamed the PRINCESS OF NORWAY, remaining on the Newcastle - Norway service but no longer serving Hanstholm. In May 2007 moved to the Newcastle - IJmuiden route. In February 2011 renamed the PRINCESS SEAWAYS.

SELANDIA SEAWAYS Built as the TOR SELANDIA by Fincantieri-Cantieri Navali Italiani SpA, Ancona, Italy for *DFDS Tor Line*. Operated on the Gothenburg - Immingham route until 2004 when she was moved to the Gothenburg – Ghent route. In 2005 she moved to the Gothenburg – Harwich route. In July the UK terminal moved to Tilbury. In August 2010 renamed the SELANDIA SEAWAYS. Currently operates on the Rotterdam - Felixstowe route.

SEVEN SISTERS Built by Astilleros Barreras SA, Vigo, Spain for *Transmanche Ferries* to operate between Newhaven and Dieppe. In recent years generally held as a reserve vessel. In March 2014 transferred to the *DFDS Seaways* Portsmouth - Le Havre service. She continues to carry *Transmanche Ferries* branding. In 2015 returned to the Newhaven - Dieppe service as second vessel, continuing to operate for *DFDS Seaways*. The vessel has had periods laid up when not required on the Newhaven – Dieppe route.

SUECIA SEAWAYS Built as the TOR SUECIA by Fincantieri-Cantieri Navali Italiani SpA, Ancona, Italy for *DFDS Tor Line*. Operated on the Gothenburg - Immingham route until 2004 when she was transferred to the Esbjerg - Immingham route. Later transferred to the Danish flag. In March 2010 chartered to *Norfolkline* to operate between Vlaardingen and Felixstowe and continued on the route when it was taken over by *DFDS*. In June 2011 renamed the SUECIA SEAWAYS.

Under Construction

30F	**TULIPA SEAWAYS**	**32000t**	**17**	**21.0k**	**209.6m**	**12P**	**-**	**262T**	**A2**	**DK**	**9809100**
31F	**NEWBUILDING 1**	**40000t**	**19**	**21.0k**	**235.0m**	**12P**	**-**	**450T**	**A2**	**-**	**-**
32F	**NEWBUILDING 2**	**40000t**	**19**	**21.0k**	**235.0m**	**12P**	**-**	**450T**	**A2**	**-**	**-**
33F	**NEWBUILDING 3**	**40000t**	**20**	**21.0k**	**235.0m**	**12P**	**-**	**450T**	**A2**	**-**	**-**

34F	NEWBUILDING 4	40000t	20	21.0k	235.0m	12P	-	450T	A2	-	-

TULIPA SEAWAYS Under construction by Flensburger Schiffbau-Gesellschaft, Flensburg, Germany for the Siem Industries Inc (owners of FSG). She will be bareboat chartered to *DFDS Seaways* for five years with an option to purchase at the end of the charter period. She is expected to be delivered in autumn 2017.

NEWBUILDING 1, NEWBUILDING 2 Under construction by Jinling Shipyard, Nanjing, China.

IRISH FERRIES

THE COMPANY *Irish Ferries* is a Republic of Ireland private sector company, part of the *Irish Continental Group*. It was originally mainly owned by the state-owned *Irish Shipping* and partly by *Lion Ferry AB* of Sweden. *Lion Ferry* participation ceased in 1977 and the company was sold into the private sector in 1987. Formerly state-owned *B&I Line* was taken over in 1991 and from 1995 all operations were marketed as *Irish Ferries*.

MANAGEMENT **Irish Continental Group Chief Executive Office** Eamonn Rothwell, **Irish Ferries Limited Managing Director** Andrew Sheen.

ADDRESS PO Box 19, Ferryport, Alexandra Road, Dublin 1, D01 W2F5, Republic of Ireland.

TELEPHONE **Administration** +353 (0)1 607 5700, **Reservations *Ireland*** +353 (0)818300 400, ***Rosslare Harbour*** +353 (0)53 913 3158, ***Holyhead*** +44 (0)8717 300200, ***Pembroke Dock*** +44 (0)8717 300500, ***National*** 44 (0)8717 300400, ***24 hour information*** +353 (0)818300 400 (Ireland) or 44 (0)8717 300400 (UK).

FAX **Administration & Reservations *Dublin*** +353 (0)1 607 5660, ***Rosslare*** +353 (0)53 913 3544.

INTERNET **Email** info@irishferries.com **Website** www.irishferries.com *(English, French, German, Italian)*

ROUTES OPERATED **Conventional Ferries** Dublin - Holyhead (3 hrs 15 mins; ***EPSILON***; ***ULYSSES***; 2-4 per day), Rosslare - Pembroke Dock (4 hrs; ***ISLE OF INISHMORE***; 4 per day), Dublin - Cherbourg (17-19 hrs; ***EPSILON***; 1 per week), Rosslare - Cherbourg (France) (17 hrs 30 mins; ***OSCAR WILDE***; average of 3 per week), Rosslare - Roscoff (France) (16 hrs; ***OSCAR WILDE***; 1 or 2 per week (seasonal)). **Fast Ferry** Dublin - Holyhead (1 hr 49 min; ***JONATHAN SWIFT***; 2 per day) marketed as 'DUBLIN*Swift*'.

1	EPSILON	26375t	11	24.0k	177.5m	500P	500C	190T	A	IT	9539054
2	ISLE OF INISHMORE	34031t	97	21.3k	182.5m	2200P	802C	152T	BA2	CY	9142605
3»	JONATHAN SWIFT	5989t	99	37.0k	86.6m	800P	200C	-	BA	CY	9188881
4	OSCAR WILDE	31914t	87	22.0k	166.3m	1458P	580C	90T	BA	BS	8506311
5	ULYSSES	50938t	01	22.0k	209.0m	1875P	1342C	300T	BA2	CY	9214991
6»	WESTPAC EXPRESS	8403t	01	37.0k	101.0m	900P	182C	-	BA	US	9243227

EPSILON Built as the CARTOUR EPSILON by CN Visentini, Porto Viro, Italy. Chartered to *Caronte & Tourist SPA* of Italy. In November 2013 chartered to *Irish Ferries*. In February 2014 renamed the EPSILON.

ISLE OF INISHMORE Built by Van der Giessen-de Noord, Krimpen aan den IJssel, Rotterdam for *Irish Ferries* to operate on the Holyhead - Dublin service. In 2001 replaced by the ULYSSES and moved to the Rosslare - Pembroke Dock route. She also relieves on the Dublin – Holyhead route when the ULYSSES receives her annual overhaul.

JONATHAN SWIFT Austal Auto-Express 86 catamaran built by Austal Ships Pty, Fremantle, Australia for *Irish Ferries* for the Dublin - Holyhead route.

OSCAR WILDE Built as the KRONPRINS HARALD by Oy Wärtsilä AB, Turku, Finland for *Jahre Line* of Norway for the Oslo - Kiel service. In 1991 ownership was transferred to *Color Line*. In early 2007 sold to *Irish Ferries* for delivery in September 2007. Chartered back to *Color Line* until that date. When

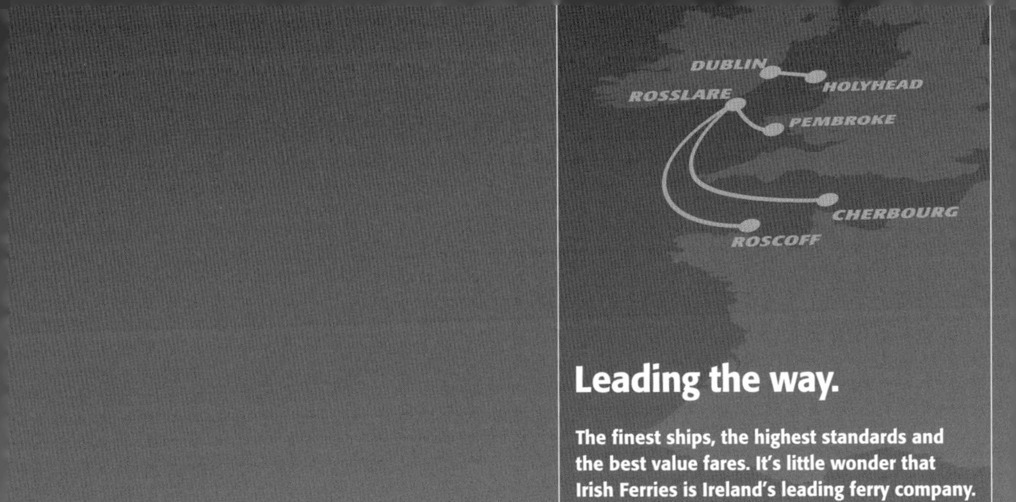
DUBLIN
HOLYHEAD
ROSSLARE
PEMBROKE
CHERBOURG
ROSCOFF
Leading the way.
The finest ships, the highest standards and the best value fares. It's little wonder that Irish Ferries is Ireland's leading ferry company.

IRISH FERRIES
ULYSSES
IRISH FERRIES

Isle of Innishmore *(Gordon Hislip)*

Oscar Wilde *(Brian Maxted*

delivered, renamed the OSCAR WILDE and in November placed on the Rosslare - Roscoff/Cherbourg routes.

ULYSSES Built by Aker Finnyards, Rauma, Finland for *Irish Ferries* for the Dublin - Holyhead service.

WESTPAC EXPRESS Austal Auto-Express catamaran built by Austal Ships Pty, Fremantle, Australia. Chartered through a number of third party companied to the *US Marine Corps* as a support vessel. In 2015 returned to *Austal Ships*. In May 2016 sold to the *Irish Continental Group*. Chartered to *Sealift Inc* of the USA and continues to be operated for the *US Marine Corps*.

Under Construction

7	**NEWBUILDING**	**54975t**	**18**	**22.5k**	**194.8m-**	**1850P**	**1216C**	**165L**	**BA2**	**-**	**-**

NEWBUILDING Under construction by Flensburger Schiffbau-Gesellschaft, Flensburg, Germany. She will replace the chartered EPSILON when delivered in May 2018.

ISLE OF MAN STEAM PACKET COMPANY

THE COMPANY *The Isle of Man Steam Packet Company Limited* is an Isle of Man-registered company.

MANAGEMENT **Chief Executive Officer** Mark Woodward.

ADDRESS Imperial Buildings, Douglas, Isle of Man IM1 2BY.

TELEPHONE **Administration** +44 (0)1624 645645, **Reservations** +44 (0)1624 661661

FAX **Administration** +44 (0)1624 645627.

INTERNET **Email** iom.reservations@steam-packet.com **Website** www.steam-packet.com *(English)*

ROUTES OPERATED **Conventional Ferries** ***All year*** Douglas (Isle of Man) - Heysham (3 hrs 30 mins; *BEN-MY-CHREE*; up to 2 per day), ***November-March*** Douglas - Liverpool (Birkenhead) (4 hrs 15 mins; *BEN-MY-CHREE*; 2 per week). **Fast Ferries** ***March-October*** Douglas - Liverpool (2 hrs 40 mins; *MANANNAN*; up to 2 per day), Douglas - Belfast (2 hrs 55 mins; *MANANNAN*; up to 2 per week), Douglas - Dublin (2 hrs 55 mins; *MANANNAN*; up to 2 per week), Douglas - Heysham (2 hrs; *MANANNAN*; occasional), **Freight Ferry** Douglas - Heysham (3 hrs 30 mins; *ARROW*; as required)

1F	**ARROW**	**7606t**	**98**	**15.0k**	**122.3m**	**12P**	**-**	**84T**	**A**	**IM**	**9119414**
2	**BEN-MY-CHREE**	**12747t**	**98**	**18.0k**	**124.9m**	**630P**	**275C**	**90T**	**A**	**IM**	**9170705**
3»	**MANANNAN**	**5743t**	**98**	**43.0k**	**96.0m**	**820P**	**200C**	**-**	**A**	**IM**	**9176072**

ARROW Built as the VARBOLA by Astilleros de Huelva SA, Huelva, Spain for the *Estonian Shipping Company*. On completion, chartered to *Dart Line* and placed on the Dartford - Vlissingen route. In 1999 she was renamed the DART 6. At the end of August 1999, the charter was terminated and she was renamed the VARBOLA. She undertook a number of short-term charters, including *Merchant Ferries*. In 2000 long-term chartered to *Merchant Ferries* to operate between Heysham and Dublin. In 2003 the charter ended and she was chartered to *Dart Line* to replace the DART 9; she was placed initially on the Dartford - Vlissingen route but later transferred to the Dartford - Dunkerque route. Later sub-chartered to *NorseMerchant Ferries* and placed on the Heysham – Dublin route. In 2004 the charter transferred to *NorseMerchant Ferries*. In 2005 sold to *Elmira Shipping* of Greece and renamed the RR ARROW. In October 2007 sold to *Seatruck Ferries* but the charter to *Norfolkline* continued. Renamed the ARROW. In June 2009 returned to *Seatruck Ferries*. In April 2014 long term chartered to *IOMSP*. When not required she is sub-chartered to other operators.

BEN-MY-CHREE Built by Van der Giessen-de Noord, Krimpen aan den IJssel, Rotterdam for the *IOMSP Co* and operates between Douglas and Heysham. Additional passenger accommodation was added at her spring 2004 refit. In 2005 her passenger certificate was increased from 500 to 630. She operates some sailings between Douglas and Liverpool (Birkenhead) in the winter.

MANANNAN Incat 96m catamaran built at Hobart, Tasmania. Initially chartered to *Transport Tasmania* of Australia and operated between Port Melbourne (Victoria) and Georgetown (Tasmania). In 1999 chartered to *Fast Cat Ferries* of New Zealand and operated between Wellington (North Island) and Picton (South Island) under the marketing name 'Top Cat'. In 2000 she was laid up. In 2001 she

Hamnavoe *(Miles Cowsill)*

Graemsay *(Miles Cowsill)*

was chartered to the *US Navy* and renamed the USS JOINT VENTURE (HSV-X1). In 2008 the charter was terminated and she was renamed the INCAT 050. Later purchased by *IOMSP*. Following conversion back to civilian use she was renamed the MANANNAN and entered service in May 2009.

NORTHLINK FERRIES

THE COMPANY *NorthLink Ferries* is a UK based company, wholly owned *Serco Group plc*. The service is operated on behalf of Scottish Ministers.

MANAGEMENT **Managing Director** Stuart Garrett, **Customer Service Director** Peter Hutchinson.

ADDRESS Ferry Terminal, Ferry Road, Stromness, Orkney KW16 3BH.

TELEPHONE **Customer Services** 0845 6000 449, (International +44 (0)1856 885500), **Freight Reservations** 0845 6060 449.

FAX +44 (0)1856 851795.

INTERNET **Email** info@northlinkferries.co.uk **Website** www.northlinkferries.co.uk *(English)*

ROUTES OPERATED ***Passenger Ferries*** Scrabster - Stromness (Orkney) (1 hr 30 min; ***HAMNAVOE***; up to 3 per day), Aberdeen - Lerwick (Shetland) (direct) (12 hrs; ***HJALTLAND, HROSSEY***; 3 northbound/4 southbound per week), Aberdeen - Kirkwall, Hatston New Pier (Orkney) (5 hrs 45 mins) - Lerwick (14 hrs; ***HJALTLAND, HROSSEY***; 4 northbound/3 southbound per week). ***Freight Ferries*** Aberdeen - Kirkwall (Orkney) (12 hrs; ***HELLIAR, HILDASAY***; 4 per week), Aberdeen - Lerwick (Shetland) (***HELLIAR, HILDASAY***; 4 per week).

1	**HAMNAVOE**	**8780t**	**02**	**19.3k**	**112.0m**	**600P**	**95C**	**20L**	**BA**	**UK**	**9246061**
2F	**HELLIAR**	**7800t**	**98**	**17.0k**	**122.3m**	**12P**	**-**	**86T**	**A**	**IM**	**9119397**
3F	**HILDASAY**	**7606t**	**99**	**17.0k**	**122.3m**	**12P**	**-**	**84T**	**A**	**IM**	**9119426**
4	**HJALTLAND**	**11720t**	**02**	**24.0k**	**125.0m**	**600P**	**150C**	**30L**	**BA**	**UK**	**9244958**
5	**HROSSEY**	**11720t**	**02**	**24.0k**	**125.0m**	**600P**	**150C**	**30L**	**BA**	**UK**	**9244960**

HAMNAVOE Built by Aker Finnyards, Rauma, Finland for *NorthLink Orkney and Shetland Ferries Ltd* to operate on the Scrabster - Stromness route. Did not enter service until Spring 2003 due to late completion of work at Scrabster to accommodate the ship. *Caledonian MacBrayne's* HEBRIDEAN ISLES covered between October 2002 and Spring 2003.

HELLIAR Built as the LEHOLA by Astilleros de Huelva SA, Huelva, Spain for the *Estonian Shipping Company*. Initially used on *ESCO* Baltic services. In 1998 chartered to *Czar Peter Line* to operate between Moerdijk (The Netherlands) and Kronstadt (Russia). In 1999 chartered to *Delom* of France to operate between Marseilles and Sete and Tunis. In 2000 she returned to *ESCO*, operating between Kiel and Tallinn. In 2003 chartered to *Scandlines AG* and transferred to subsidiary *Scandlines Estonia AS*. Operated Rostock - Helsinki – Muuga initially and later Rostock – Helsinki. Service finished at the end of 2004 and in 2005 she was chartered to *P&O Ferries* to operate between Hull and Rotterdam and Hull and Zeebrugge. In 2005 sold to *Elmira Shipping* of Greece. Later renamed the RR TRIUMPH. In 2006 transferred to *P&O Irish Sea* to operate between Liverpool and Dublin. In 2007 chartered to *Balearia* of Spain and operated from Barcelona. In December 2007 purchased by *Seatruck Ferries* and renamed the TRIUMPH. In June 2008 placed on the Liverpool - Dublin route and in July renamed the CLIPPER RACER. In February 2009 replaced by the new CLIPPER PACE. In April 2009 again chartered to *Balearia*. In January 2011 chartered to *NorthLink Ferries* and renamed the HELLIAR. In June 2017 sold to other interests.

HILDASAY Built as the LEILI by Astilleros de Huelva SA, Huelva, Spain for the *Estonian Shipping Company*. Used on Baltic services. In 2002 chartered to *Crowley Maritime* of the USA and renamed the PORT EVERGLADES EXPRESS. In 2004 resumed the name LEILI and chartered to *NorseMerchant Ferries* to operate between Birkenhead and Dublin. In July 2005 moved to the Heysham - Belfast route and at the same time sold to *Elmira Shipping* of Greece and renamed the RR SHIELD. In 2007 sold to *Attica Group* of Greece and renamed the SHIELD. In January 2008 sold to *Seatruck Ferries* but continued to be chartered to *Norfolkline*. In June 2009 returned to *Seatruck Ferries*. In January 2009 chartered to *NorthLink Orkney and Shetland Ferries* and renamed the HILDASAY. In June 2017 sold to other interests.

HJALTLAND, HROSSEY Built by Aker Finnyards, Rauma, Finland for *NorthLink Orkney and Shetland Ferries* to operate on the Aberdeen - Kirkwall - Lerwick route when services started in 2002.

ORKNEY FERRIES

THE COMPANY *Orkney Ferries Ltd* (previously the *Orkney Islands Shipping Company*) is a British company, owned by *Orkney Islands Council*.

MANAGEMENT **Ferry Services Manager** Fraser Murray.

ADDRESS Shore Street, Kirkwall, Orkney KW15 1LG.

TELEPHONE **Administration** +44 (0)1856 872044, **Reservations** +44 (0)1856 872044.

FAX **Administration & Reservations** +44 (0)1856 872921.

INTERNET **Email** info@orkneyferries.co.uk **Website** www.orkneyferries.co.uk *(English)*

ROUTES OPERATED Kirkwall (Mainland) to Eday (1 hr 15 mins), Rapness (Westray) (1 hr 25 mins), Sanday (1 hr 25 mins), Stronsay (1 hr 35 mins), Papa Westray (1 hr 50 mins), North Ronaldsay (2 hrs 30 mins) ('North Isles service') (timings are direct from Kirkwall - sailings via other islands take longer; *EARL SIGURD, EARL THORFINN, VARAGEN*; 1/2 per day except Papa Westray which is twice weekly and North Ronaldsay which is weekly), Pierowall (Westray) - Papa Westray (25 mins; *GOLDEN MARIANA*; up to six per day (Summer service - passenger-only)), Kirkwall - Shapinsay (25 mins; *SHAPINSAY*; 6 per day), Houton (Mainland) to Lyness (Hoy) (35 mins; *HOY HEAD*; 5 per day), and Flotta (35 mins; *HOY HEAD*; 4 per day) ('South Isles service') (timings are direct from Houton - sailings via other islands take longer), Tingwall (Mainland) to Rousay (20 mins; *EYNHALLOW*; 6 per day), Egilsay (30 mins; *EYNHALLOW*; 5 per day) and Wyre (20 mins; *EYNHALLOW*; 5 per day) (timings are direct from Tingwall - sailings via other islands take longer), Stromness (Mainland) to Moaness (Hoy) (25 mins; *GRAEMSAY*; 2/3 per day) and Graemsay (25 mins; *GRAEMSAY*; 2/3 per day) (passenger/cargo service - cars not normally conveyed).

1	EARL SIGURD	771t	90	12.5k	45.0m	190P	26C	-	BA	UK	8902711
2	EARL THORFINN	771t	90	12.5k	45.0m	190P	26C	-	BA	UK	8902723
3	EYNHALLOW	104t	87	10.5k	28.8m	95P	11C	-	BA	UK	8960880
4p	GOLDEN MARIANA	33t	73	9.5k	15.2m	40P	0C	-	-	UK	
5	GRAEMSAY	90t	96	10.0k	20.6m	73P	2C	-	C	UK	
6	HOY HEAD	358t	94	11.0k	53.5m	125P	24C	3L	BA	UK	9081722
7	SHAPINSAY	199t	89	10.0k	32.6m	91P	16C	-	BA	UK	8814184
8	THORSVOE	385t	91	10.6k	35.0m	122P	16C	-	BA	UK	9014743
9	VARAGEN	928t	88	14.5k	49.9m	144P	33C	5L	BA	UK	8818154

EARL SIGURD, EARL THORFINN Built by McTay Marine, Bromborough, Wirral, UK to inaugurate ro-ro working on the 'North Isles service'.

EYNHALLOW Built by David Abels Boat Builders, Bristol, UK to inaugurate ro-ro services from Tingwall (Mainland) to Rousay, Egilsay and Wyre. In 1991 she was lengthened by 5 metres, to increase car capacity.

GOLDEN MARIANA Built by Bideford Shipyard Ltd, Bideford, UK for *A J G England* of Padstow as a dual-purpose passenger and fishing vessel. In 1975 sold to *M MacKenzie* of Ullapool, then to *Pentland Ferries, Wide Firth Ferry* in 1982, and *Orkney Islands Council* in 1986. Passenger-only vessel. Generally operates summer-only feeder service between Pierowall (Westray) and Papa Westray.

GRAEMSAY Built by Ailsa Shipbuilding, Troon UK to operate between Stromness (Mainland), Moaness (Hoy) and Graemsay. Designed to offer an all-year-round service to these islands, primarily for passengers and cargo. Between October 2009 and January 2010 lengthened by 4.4 metres.

HOY HEAD Built by Appledore Shipbuilders Ltd, Appledore, UK to replace the THORSVOE on the 'South Isles service'. During winter 2012/13 extended by 14 metres at Cammell Laird Shiprepairers & Shipbuilders, Birkenhead, England.

Earl Thorfinn *(Miles Cowsill)*

Pride of Hull *(Rob de Visser)*

SHAPINSAY Built by Yorkshire Drydock Ltd, Hull, UK for the service from Kirkwall (Mainland) to Shapinsay. In April 2011 lengthened by 6 metres at the Macduff Shipyards, Macduff, Scotland to increase car capacity from 12 to 16 and re-engined.

THORSVOE Built by Campbeltown Shipyard, Campbeltown, UK for the 'South Isles service'. In 1994 replaced by the new HOY HEAD and became the main reserve vessel for the fleet.

VARAGEN Built by Cochrane Shipbuilders, Selby, UK for *Orkney Ferries*, a private company established to start a new route between Gills Bay (Caithness, Scotland) and Burwick (South Ronaldsay, Orkney). However, due to problems with the terminals it was not possible to maintain regular services. In 1991, the company was taken over by *Orkney Islands Shipping Company* and the VARAGEN became part of their fleet, sharing the 'North Isles service' with the EARL SIGURD and the EARL THORFINN and replacing the freight vessel ISLANDER (494t, 1969).

P&O FERRIES

THE COMPANY *P&O Ferries Holdings Ltd* is a private sector company, a subsidiary of *Dubai World*, owned by the Government of Dubai. In Autumn 2002 *P&O North Sea Ferries*, P&O Irish Sea, *P&O Portsmouth* and *P&O Stena Line* (*Stena Line* involvement having ceased) were merged into a single operation.

MANAGEMENT Chief Executive Officer Helen Deeble, **Fleet Director** John Garner, **Finance Director** Karl Howarth, **Human Resources Director** Lesley Cotton, **Ports Director** Sue Mackenzie, **Chief Commercial Officer** Janette Bell, **Company Secretary** Susan Kitchin.

ADDRESSES ***Head Office and Dover Services*** Channel House, Channel View Road, Dover, Kent CT17 9TJ, ***Hull*** King George Dock, Hedon Road, Hull HU9 5QA, ***Larne*** P&O Irish Sea, Larne Harbour, Larne, Co Antrim BT40 1AW ***Rotterdam*** Beneluxhaven, Rotterdam (Europoort), Postbus 1123, 3180 Rozenburg, Netherlands, ***Zeebrugge*** Leopold II Dam 13, Havendam, 8380 Zeebrugge, Belgium.

TELEPHONE Administration *UK* +44 (0)1304 863000, **Passenger Reservations *UK*** 08716 64 64 64, ***France*** +33 (0)825 12 01 56, ***Belgium*** +32 (0)70 70 77 71, ***The Netherlands*** +31 (0)20 20 08333, ***Spain*** +34 (0)902 02 04 61, ***Luxembourg*** +34 (0)20 80 82 94. **Freight Reservations *UK*** 0870 6000 868, ***Republic of Ireland*** +353 (0)1 855 0522.

FAX Passenger Reservations *UK East and South Coast* +44 (0)1304 863464, ***West Coast*** 44 (0)02828 872195, ***The Netherlands*** +31 (0)118 1225 5215, ***Belgium*** +32 (0)50 54 71 12, **Freight Reservations *Cairnryan*** +44 (0)1581 200282, ***Larne*** +44 (0)28 2827 2477..

INTERNET Email customer.services@poferries.com **Website** www.poferries.com *(English, French, Dutch, German)* www.poirishsea.com *(English)* www.poferriesfreight.com *(English, French, German)*

ROUTES OPERATED Passenger Dover - Calais (1 hr 15 mins - 1 hr 30 mins; ***PRIDE OF BURGUNDY, PRIDE OF CANTERBURY, PRIDE OF KENT, SPIRIT OF BRITAIN, SPIRIT OF FRANCE***; up to 25 per day), Hull - Zeebrugge (Belgium) (from 12 hrs 30 mins; ***PRIDE OF BRUGES, PRIDE OF YORK***; 1 per day), Hull - Rotterdam (Beneluxhaven, Europoort) (The Netherlands) (from 10 hrs; ***PRIDE OF HULL, PRIDE OF ROTTERDAM***; 1 per day), Cairnryan - Larne (1 hr 45 min; ***EUROPEAN CAUSEWAY, EUROPEAN HIGHLANDER***; 7 per day), Liverpool - Dublin (8 hrs; ***EUROPEAN ENDEAVOUR, NORBANK, NORBAY***; up to 3 per day (some sailings are freight only). **Freight-only** Dover - Calais (1 hr 30 mins; ***EUROPEAN SEAWAY***; 2/3 per day (plus services on passenger ferries)), Tilbury - Zeebrugge (8 hrs; ***NORSKY, NORSTREAM***; 10 per week), Middlesbrough (Teesport) - Rotterdam (Beneluxhaven, Europoort) (16 hrs; ***ESTRADEN***; 3 per week), Middlesbrough (Teesport) - Zeebrugge (15 hrs 30 mins; ***BORE SONG, MISTRAL***; 6 per week), **Container service** Hull - Zeebrugge (Belgium) (from 12 hrs 30 mins; ***ELISABETH***; 3 per week)

1F	**BORE SONG**	**25586t**	**11**	**18.5k**	**195.0m**	**12P**	**-**	**210T**	**A2**	**FI**	**9443566**
2F	**ELISABETH**	**5067t**	**00**	**-**	**118.3m**	**0P**		**648teu**	**C**	**NL**	**9219862**
3F	**ESTRADEN**	**18205t**	**99**	**19.0k**	**162.7m**	**12P**	**130C**	**170T**	**A**	**FI**	**9181077**
4	**EUROPEAN CAUSEWAY**	**20646t**	**00**	**22.7k**	**159.5m**	**410P**	**315C**	**84T**	**BA2**	**BS**	**9208394**
5	**EUROPEAN ENDEAVOUR**	**22152t**	**00**	**22.5k**	**180.0m**	**366P**	**-**	**120L**	**BA2**	**BS**	**9181106**
6	**EUROPEAN HIGHLANDER**	**21128t**	**02**	**22.6k**	**162.7m**	**410P**	**315C**	**84T**	**BA2**	**BS**	**9244116**

7F+	EUROPEAN SEAWAY	22986t	91	21.0k	179.7m	200P	-	120L	BA2	UK	9007283
8F	MISTRAL	10471t	98	22.0k	153.5m	12P	-	112T	A	FI	9183788
9	NORBANK	17464t	93	22.5k	166.7m	114P	-	125T	A	NL	9056583
10	NORBAY	17464t	92	21.5k	166.7m	114P	-	125T	A	BM	9056595
11F	NORSKY	19992t	99	20.0k	180.0m	12P	-	194T	A	FI	9186182
12F	NORSTREAM	19992t	99	20.0k	180.0m	12P	-	194T	A	FI	9186194
13	PRIDE OF BRUGES	31598t	87	18.5k	179.0m	1050P	310C	185T	A	NL	8503797
14	PRIDE OF BURGUNDY	28138t	92	21.0k	179.7m	1420P	465C	120L	BA2	UK	9015254
15	PRIDE OF CANTERBURY	30635t	91	21.0k	179.7m	2000P	537C	120L	BA2	UK	9007295
16	PRIDE OF HULL	59925t	01	22.0k	215.4m	1360P	205C	263T	AS	BS	9208629
17	PRIDE OF KENT	30635t	92	21.0k	179.7m	2000P	537C	120L	BA2	UK	9015266
18	PRIDE OF ROTTERDAM	59925t	00	22.0k	215.4m	1360P	205C	263T	AS	NL	9208617
19	PRIDE OF YORK	31785t	87	18.5k	179.0m	1050P	310C	185T	A	BS	8501957
20	SPIRIT OF BRITAIN	47592t	11	22.0k-	212.0m	2000P	194C	180L	BA2	UK	9524231
21	SPIRIT OF FRANCE	47592t	12	22.0k-	212.0m	2000P	194C	180L	BA2	UK	9533816

BORE SONG Built by Flensburger Schiffbau-Gesellschaft, Flensburg, Germany for *Bore Shipowners (Rettig Group Bore)* of Finland. In July 2011 chartered to *Mann Lines* to cover for the ESTRADEN'S refit. In September 2011 chartered to *P&O Ferries* and placed on the Middlesbrough - Zeebrugge route.

ELISABETH Container ship built by J.J. Sietas KG Schiffswerft GmbH & Co for *Holwerda Shipmanagement BV* of The Netherlands. In May 2017 introduced onto the Hull - Zeebrugge route to relive pressure on the two passenger ships.

ESTRADEN Built as the ESTRADEN by Aker Finnyards, Rauma, Finland for *Rederi Ab Engship* (later *Bore Shipowners*) of Finland and chartered to *ArgoMann*. Later in 1999 renamed the AMAZON. In 2001 the charter was taken over by *Mann Lines* and in August she resumed the name ESTRADEN. In 2006 *Rederi AB Engship* was taken over by *Rettig Group Bore* and she remained on charter to *Mann Lines*. In January 2015 chartered to *P&O Ferries* to replace the WILHELMINE of *Cobelfret Ferries* on the Rotterdam - Middlesbrough (Teesport) service.

EUROPEAN CAUSEWAY Built by Mitsubishi Heavy Industries, Shimonoseki, Japan for *P&O Irish Sea* for the Cairnryan - Larne service.

EUROPEAN ENDEAVOUR Built as the MIDNIGHT MERCHANT by Astilleros Españoles SA, Seville, Spain for *Cenargo* (then owners of *NorseMerchant Ferries*). On delivery, chartered to *Norfolkline* to operate as second vessel on the Dover - Dunkerque (Ouest) service. In 2002 modified to allow two-deck loading. In 2006 chartered to *Acciona Trasmediterranea* of Spain and renamed the EL GRECO. Used on Mediterranean and Canary Island services. In 2007 sold to *P&O Ferries* and renamed the EUROPEAN ENDEAVOUR. Operated on The Dover - Calais route and as a re-fit relief vessel on Irish Sea routes. In May 2010 laid up. In February 2011 moved to the Liverpool - Dublin route.

EUROPEAN HIGHLANDER Built by Mitsubishi Heavy Industries, Shimonoseki, Japan for *P&O Irish Sea* for the Cairnryan - Larne service.

EUROPEAN SEAWAY Built by Schichau Seebeckwerft AG, Bremerhaven, Germany for *P&O European Ferries* for the Dover - Zeebrugge freight service. In 2000 a regular twice-daily freight-only Dover-Calais service was established, using this vessel which continued to operate to Zeebrugge at night. In 2001 car passengers (not foot or coach passengers) began to be conveyed on the Dover - Zeebrugge service. In 2003 the Zeebrugge service ended and she operated only between Dover and Calais in a freight-only mode. In 2004 withdrawn and laid up. In January 2005 returned to the Dover - Calais route. In July 2012 chartered to GLID, a joint venture between Centrica Renewable Energy Limited and EIG, for use by technicians working on the North Sea Lynn and Inner Dowsing wind farm array four miles off Skegness. In October 2012 returned to the Dover - Calais service. In April 2013 laid up at Tilbury. In August 2014 chartered as a wind farm accommodation and support vessel near the North German coast. In April 2015 returned to layup at Tilbury. In August 2015 returned to service on the Dover - Calais route.

Pride of Burgundy and Pride of Canterbury *(George Holland)*

Norbay *(George Holland)*

Spirit of France *(George Holland)*

MISTRAL Built by J J Sietas KG, Hamburg, Germany for *Godby Shipping AB* of Finland. Chartered to *Transfennica*. In 2003 chartered to *UPM-Kymmene Oy* of Finland and operated between Rauma and Santander. In 2005 chartered to *Finnlines*. Until the end of 2007 used on a Helsinki - Hamina - Zeebrugge service only available northbound for general traffic. From January 2008 operated on *UPM-Kymmene Seaways'* service from Hamina to Lübeck, Amsterdam and Tilbury. In June 2013 charter ended. During the ensuing period she undertook several short charters. In October 2014 chartered to *P&O Ferries* as second ship on the Zeebrugge - Middlesbrough (Teesport) service; she has also operated between Tilbury and Zeebrugge.

NORBANK Built by Van der Giessen-de Noord, Krimpen aan den IJssel, Rotterdam, The Netherlands for *North Sea Ferries* for the Hull - Rotterdam service. She was originally built for and chartered to *Nedlloyd* but the charter was taken over by *P&O* in 1996 and she was bought by *P&O* in 2003. She retains Dutch crew and registry. In May 2001 moved to the Felixstowe - Europoort route. In January 2002 transferred to *P&O Irish Sea* and operated on the Liverpool – Dublin route.

NORBAY Built by Van der Giessen-de Noord, Krimpen aan den IJssel, Rotterdam, The Netherlands for *North Sea Ferries* for the Hull - Rotterdam service. Owned by *P&O*. In January 2002 transferred to *P&O Irish Sea* and operated on the Liverpool – Dublin route.

NORSKY, NORSTREAM Built by Aker Finnyards, Rauma, Finland for *Bore Line* of Finland and chartered to *P&O North Sea Ferries*. They generally operated on the Teesport - Zeebrugge service. In September 2011, the NORSTREAM was moved to the Tilbury - Zeebrugge route. In January 2013, the NORSKY was also moved to the Tilbury - Zeebrugge route.

PRIDE OF BRUGES Built as the NORSUN by NKK, Tsurumi, Japan for the Hull - Rotterdam service of *North Sea Ferries*. She was owned by *Nedlloyd* and was sold to *P&O* in 1996 but retains Dutch crew and registry. In May 2001 replaced by the PRIDE OF ROTTERDAM and in July 2001, after a major refurbishment, she was transferred to the Hull - Zeebrugge service, replacing the NORSTAR (26919t, 1974). In 2003 renamed the PRIDE OF BRUGES.

PRIDE OF BURGUNDY Built by Schichau Seebeckwerft AG, Bremerhaven, Germany for *P&O European Ferries* for the Dover - Calais service. When construction started she was due to be a sister vessel to the EUROPEAN SEAWAY (see Section 3) called the EUROPEAN CAUSEWAY and operate on the Zeebrugge freight route. However, it was decided that she should be completed as a passenger/freight vessel (the design allowed for conversion) and she was launched as the PRIDE OF BURGUNDY. In 1998, transferred to *P&O Stena Line* and renamed the P&OSL BURGUNDY. In 2002 renamed the PO BURGUNDY and in 2003 renamed the PRIDE OF BURGUNDY. In 2004 she operated mainly in freight-only mode. In 2005 returned to full passenger service.

PRIDE OF CANTERBURY Built as the EUROPEAN PATHWAY by Schichau Seebeckwerft AG, Bremerhaven, Germany for *P&O European Ferries* for the Dover - Zeebrugge freight service. In 1998 transferred to *P&O Stena Line*. In 2001 car/foot passengers were again conveyed on the route. In 2002/03 rebuilt as a full passenger vessel and renamed the PRIDE OF CANTERBURY; now operates between Dover and Calais.

PRIDE OF HULL Built by Fincantieri-Cantieri Navali Italiani SpA, Venice, Italy for *P&O North Sea Ferries* to replace (with the PRIDE OF ROTTERDAM) the NORSEA and NORSUN plus the freight vessels NORBAY and NORBANK on the Hull - Rotterdam service.

PRIDE OF KENT Built as the EUROPEAN HIGHWAY by Schichau Seebeckwerft AG, Bremerhaven, Germany for *P&O European Ferries* for the Dover - Zeebrugge freight service. In 1998 transferred to *P&O Stena Line*. In Summer 1999 she operated full-time between Dover and Calais. She returned to the Dover - Zeebrugge route in the autumn when the P&OSL AQUITAINE was transferred to the Dover - Calais service. In 2001 car/foot passengers were again conveyed on the route. In 2002/03 rebuilt as a full passenger vessel and renamed the PRIDE OF KENT; now operates between Dover and Calais.

PRIDE OF ROTTERDAM Built by Fincantieri-Cantieri Navali Italiani SpA, Venice, Italy. Keel laid as the PRIDE OF HULL but launched as the PRIDE OF ROTTERDAM. Owned by Dutch interests until 2006 when she was sold to *P&O Ferries*. Further details as the PRIDE OF HULL.

PRIDE OF YORK Built as the NORSEA by Govan Shipbuilders Ltd, Glasgow, UK for the Hull - Rotterdam service of *North Sea Ferries* (jointly owned by *P&O* and *The Royal Nedlloyd Group* of The Netherlands until 1996). In December 2001 she was replaced by the new PRIDE OF HULL and, after a two-month refurbishment, in 2002 transferred to the Hull - Zeebrugge service, replacing the NORLAND (26290t, 1974). In 2003 renamed the PRIDE OF YORK.

SPIRIT OF BRITAIN, SPIRIT OF FRANCE Built by STX Europe, Rauma, Finland for the Dover - Calais service. Car capacity relates to dedicated car deck only; additional cars can be accommodated on the freight decks as necessary.

PENTLAND FERRIES

THE COMPANY *Pentland Ferries* is a UK private sector company.

MANAGEMENT **Managing Director** Andrew Banks, **Designated Person Ashore** Kathryn Scollie.

ADDRESS Pier Road, St Margaret's Hope, South Ronaldsay, Orkney KW17 2SW.

TELEPHONE **Administration & Reservations** +44 (0)1856 831226.

FAX **Administration & Reservations** +44 (0)1856 831697.

INTERNET **Email** sales@pentlandferries.co.uk **Website** www.pentlandferries.co.uk *(English)*

ROUTE OPERATED Gills Bay (Caithness) - St Margaret's Hope (South Ronaldsay, Orkney) (1 hour; *PENTALINA*; up to 4 per day).

1	ORCADIA	899t	78	13.0k	69.5m	-	40C	-	AS	UK	7615490
2	PENTALINA	2382t	08	17.1k	59.0m	345P	70C	9L	A	UK	9437969

ORCADIA Built as the SATURN by Ailsa Shipbuilding, Troon for *Caledonian MacBrayne* and initially used on the Wemyss Bay - Rothesay services. Between 1986 and 2005 she usually rotated on this service and services from Gourock; until 2000 this, in summer, included Clyde cruising but this was not repeated in 2001. In the summers 2005 - 2010, she operated additional peak summer sailings between Ardrossan and Brodick with a maximum capacity of 250 passengers. In October 2010 she took over the Gourock - Dunoon service. In June 2011 replaced by *Argyll Ferries* passenger ferries. During Summer 2011 she operated additional sailings between Ardrossan and Brodick. In September returned to the Gourock - Dunoon route to provide additional capacity for the Cowal Games. She was then laid up. In February 2015 sold to *Pentland Ferries* and renamed the ORCADIA.

PENTALINA Catamaran built by FBMA Marine, Cebu, Philippines for *Pentland Ferries*.

Under construction

3	NEWBUILDING	-	18	16.0k	84.5m	430P	98C	12L	A	UK

NEWBUILDING Catamaran under construction by the Strategic Marine Shipyard, Vũng Tàu, Vietnam.

RED FUNNEL FERRIES

THE COMPANY Red Funnel Ferries is the trading name of the Southampton, Isle of Wight and South of England Royal Mail Steam Packet Company Limited, a British private sector company owned by a consortium of British and Canadian pension funds led by the West Midland Pensions Fund and the Workplace Safety and Insurance Board of the Province of Ontario.

MANAGEMENT **Managing Director** Kevin George, **Commercial Director** Colin Hetherington.

ADDRESS 12 Bugle Street, Southampton SO14 2JY.

TELEPHONE **Administration** +44 (0)23 8024 8500, **Reservations *UK*** 0844 844 9988, ***Elsewhere*** +44 (0)23 8001 9192.

FAX **Administration & Reservations *UK*** +44 (0)23 8024 8501.

INTERNET **Email** post@redfunnel.co.uk **Website** www.redfunnel.co.uk *(English)*

Red Falcon *(George Holland)*

Red Jet 6 *(Andrew Cooke)*

ROUTES OPERATED **Conventional Ferries** Southampton - East Cowes (55 mins; *RED EAGLE, RED FALCON, RED OSPREY*; hourly). **Fast Passenger Ferries** Southampton - Cowes (22 mins; *RED JET 3, RED JET 4, RED JET 6*; every hour or half hour).

1	RED EAGLE	3953t	96	13.0k	93.2m	895P	200C	18L	BA	UK	9117337
2	RED FALCON	3953t	94	13.0k	93.2m	895P	200C	18L	BA	UK	9064047
3»p	RED JET 3	213t	98	33.0k	32.9m	190P	0C	0L	-	UK	9182758
4»p	RED JET 4	342t	03	35.0k	39.8m	277P	0C	0L	-	UK	9295854
5»p	RED JET 6	363t	16	35.0k	41.1m	275P	0C	0L	-	UK	9788083
6	RED OSPREY	3953t	94	13.0k	93.2m	895P	200C	18L	BA	UK	9064059

RED EAGLE Built by Ferguson Shipbuilders, Port Glasgow, UK for the Southampton - East Cowes service. During Winter 2004/05 stretched by 10 metres and height raised by 3 metres at Gdansk, Poland.

RED FALCON Built by Ferguson Shipbuilders, Port Glasgow, UK for the Southampton - East Cowes service. In 2004 stretched by 10 metres and height raised by 3 metres at Gdansk, Poland. In spring 2014 she received a £2m upgrade.

RED JET 3 FBM Marine catamaran built at Isle of Wight, UK.

RED JET 4 North West Bay Ships Pty Ltd catamaran built in Hobart, Tasmania, Australia.

RED JET 6 Built by Shemara Refit LLP, Venture Quays, Cowes, Isle of Wight, UK.

RED OSPREY Built by Ferguson Shipbuilders, Port Glasgow, UK for the Southampton - East Cowes service. In 2003 stretched by 10 metres and height raised by 3 metres at Gdansk, Poland. In spring 2015 she received a £2m upgrade (as RED FALCON).

SHETLAND ISLANDS COUNCIL

THE COMPANY *Shetland Islands Council* is a British local government authority.

MANAGEMENT **Ferry Services Manager** Craig Robertson, **Marine Superintendent** Ian Pearson.

ADDRESS Port Administration Building, Sella Ness, Mossbank, Shetland ZE2 9QR.

TELEPHONE **Administration** +44 (0)1806 244234, 244266, **Reservations** ***Yell Sound & Bluemull*** +44 (0)1595 745804, ***Fair Isle*** +44 (0)1595 760363, ***Whalsay*** +44(0)1595 745804, ***Skerries*** +44 (0)1595 745804, ***Papa Stour*** +44 (0)1595 745804.

FAX +44 (0)1806 244232.

INTERNET **Email** ferries@shetland.gov.uk **Website:** www.shetland.gov.uk/ferries *(English)*

ROUTES OPERATED **Yell Sound Service** Toft (Mainland) - Ulsta (Yell) (20 mins; *DAGALIEN, DAGGRI*; up to 26 per day), **Bluemull Sound Service** (Gutcher (Yell) - Belmont (Unst) (10 mins; *BIGGA, FIVLA, GEIRA*; up to 28 per day), Gutcher – Hamars Ness (Fetlar) (25 mins; *BIGGA, FIVLA, GEIRA*; up to 8 per day), **Bressay** Lerwick (Mainland) - Maryfield (Bressay) (5 mins; *LEIRNA*; up to 23 per day), **Whalsay** Laxo/Vidlin (Mainland) - Symbister (Whalsay) (30-45 mins; *HENDRA, LINGA*; up to 18 per day), **Skerries** Vidlin (Mainland) – Out Skerries (1 hr 30 mins; *FILLA*; up to 10 per week), Out Skerries – Lerwick (3 hours; *FILLA*; 2 per week), **Fair Isle** (Grutness (Mainland) - Fair Isle (3 hrs; *GOOD SHEPHERD IV*; 2 per week), **Papa Stour** West Burrafirth (Mainland) – Papa Stour (40 mins; *SNOLDA*; up to 7 per week).

1	BIGGA	274t	91	11.0k	33.5m	96P	21C	2L	BA	UK	9000821
2	DAGALIEN	1861t	04	12.0k	65.4m	144P	30C	4L	BA	UK	9291626
3	DAGGRI	1861t	04	12.0k	65.4m	144P	30C	4L	BA	UK	9291614
4	FILLA	356t	03	12.0k	35.5m	30P	10C	2L	BA	UK	9269192
5	FIVLA	230t	85	11.0k	29.9m	95P	15C	2L	A	UK	8410237
6	GEIRA	226t	88	10.8k	29.9m	95P	15C	2L	BA	UK	8712489
7	GOOD SHEPHERD IV	76t	86	10.0k	18.3m	12P	2C	0L	C	UK	

8	HENDRA	248	82	11.0k	30.2m	95P	18C	2L	BA	UK	8200254
9	LEIRNA	420t	92	9.0k	35.1m	124P	20C	2L	BA	UK	9050199
10	LINGA	658t	01	11.0k	36.2m	100P	16C	2L	BA	UK	9242170
11	SNOLDA	130t	83	9.0k	24.4m	12P	6C	1L	A	UK	8302090

BIGGA Built by JW Miller & Sons Ltd, St Monans, Fife, UK. Used on the Toft - Ulsta service. In 2005 moved to the Bluemull Sound service.

DAGALIEN, DAGGRI Built by Stocznia Polnócna, Gdansk, Poland to replace the BIGGA and HENDRA on Toft - Ulsta service.

FILLA Built by Stocznia Polnócna, Gdansk, Poland for the Lerwick /Vidlin - Out Skerries service. She looks like an oil rig supply vessel and is capable of transporting fresh water for replenishing the tanks on the Skerries in case of drought.

FIVLA Built by Ailsa Shipbuilding, Troon, UK. Now a spare vessel, though often used on the Bluemull service.

GEIRA Built by Richard Dunston (Hessle), Hessle, UK. Formerly used on the Laxo - Symbister route. Replaced by the HENDRA in 2005 and moved to the Bluemull Sound service.

GOOD SHEPHERD IV Built by JW Miller & Sons Ltd, St Monans, Fife, UK. Used on the service between Grutness (Mainland) and Fair Isle. This vessel is not roll-on roll-off; vehicles are conveyed by special arrangement and generally consist of agricultural vehicles. She is pulled up on the marine slip on Fair Isle at the conclusion of each voyage.

HENDRA Built by McTay Marine, Bromborough, Wirral, UK for the Laxo - Symbister service. In 2002 transferred to the Toft - Ulsta service. In 2004 replaced by new vessels DAGGRI and DAGALIEN and moved to the Bluemull Sound service. In May 2005 returned to the Laxo - Symbister service as second vessel.

LEIRNA Built by Ferguson Shipbuilders, Port Glasgow, UK. Used on the Lerwick - Maryfield (Bressay) service.

LINGA Built by Stocznia Polnócna, Gdansk, Poland. Used on the Laxo - Symbister service.

SNOLDA Built as the FILLA by Sigbjorn Iversen, Flekkefjord, Norway. Used on the Lerwick (Mainland) - Out Skerries and Vidlin (Mainland) - Out Skerries services. At other times she operated freight and charter services around the Shetland Archipelago. She resembles a miniature oil rig supply vessel. Passenger capacity was originally 20 from 1st April to 31st October inclusive but is now 12 all year. In 2003 renamed the SNOLDA; replaced by the new FILLA and, in 2004, transferred to the West Burrafirth - Papa Stour route.

STENA LINE

MANAGEMENT **Chief Executive** Niclas Mårtensson, **Route Manager North Sea** Annika Hult, **Route Manager Irish Sea North** Paul Grant, **Route Manager Irish Sea South** Ian Davies.

ADDRESS ***UK*** Stena House, Station Approach, Holyhead, Anglesey LL65 1DQ, ***The Netherlands*** PO Box 2, 3150 AA, Hook of Holland, The Netherlands.

TELEPHONE **Administration** ***UK*** +44 (0)1407) 606631, ***The Netherlands*** +31 (0)174 389333, **Reservations** ***UK*** 0844 7707070 (from UK only), ***The Netherlands*** +31 (0)174 315811.

FAX **Administration & Reservations** ***UK*** +44 (0)1407 606811, ***The Netherlands*** +31 (0)174 387045, **Telex** 31272.

INTERNET **Email** info@stenaline.com **Website** www.stenaline.co.uk *(English)*

ROUTES OPERATED **Conventional Ferries** Cairnryan - Belfast (2 hrs 15 mins; *STENA SUPERFAST VII, STENA SUPERFAST VII*; up to 6 per day, Port of Liverpool (Twelve Quays River Terminal, Birkenhead) - Belfast (8 hrs; *STENA PERFORMER (freight only), STENA LAGAN, STENA MERSEY*; 1 per day (Mon), 2 per day (Sun, Tue-Sat)), Holyhead - Dublin (3 hrs 15 mins; *STENA ADVENTURER, STENA SUPERFAST X*; 4 per day), Fishguard - Rosslare (3 hrs 15 mins on day sailings *STENA*

EUROPE; 2 per day), Rosslare - Cherbourg (17 - 20 hrs; *STENA HORIZON*; 3 per week), Harwich - Hook of Holland (The Netherlands) (7 hrs 30 mins; *STENA BRITANNICA, STENA HOLLANDICA*; 2 per day), **Freight Ferries** Heysham - Belfast (7 hrs; *STENA HIBERNIA, STENA PRECISION*; 2 per day), Harwich - Rotterdam (8 hrs; *CAPUCINE, SEVERINE*; 11 per week), Killingholme - Hook of Holland (11 hrs; *STENA TRANSIT, STENA TRANSPORTER*; 1 per day), Killingholme - Rotterdam (13 hrs; *CAROLINE RUSS, STENA SCOTIA*; 6 per week).

1F	CAPUCINE	16342t	11	16.0k	150.0m	12P	-	140T	A	UK	9539066
2F	CAROLINE RUSS	10488t	99	21.0k	153.5m	12P	-	134T	A2	PT	9197533
3F	SEVERINE	16342t	12	16.0k	150.0m	12P	-	140T	A	NL	9539078
4	STENA ADVENTURER	43532t	03	22.0k	210.8m	1500P	-	210L	BA2	UK	9235529
5	STENA BRITANNICA	63600t	10	22.0k	240.0m	1200P	-	300T	BA2	UK	9419175
6	STENA EUROPE	24828t	81	20.5k	149.0m	2076P	456C	60T	BA	UK	7901760
7F	STENA HIBERNIA	13017t	96	18.6k	142.5m	12P	-	114T	A	UK	9121637
8	STENA HOLLANDICA	63600t	10	22.5k	240.0m	1200P	-	300T	BA2	NL	9419163
9	STENA HORIZON	26500t	06	23.5k	186.5m	720P	160C	135L	A	IT	9332559
10	STENA LAGAN	27510t	05	23.5k	186.5m	720P	160C	135T	A	UK	9329849
11	STENA MERSEY	27510t	05	23.5k	186.5m	720P	160C	135T	A	UK	9329851
12F	STENA PERFORMER	19722t	12	21.0k	142.0m	12P	-	151T	A	IM	9506227
13F	STENA PRECISION	19722t	12	21.0k	142.0m	12P	-	151T	A	IM	9506239
14F	STENA SCOTIA	13017t	96	18.6k	142.5m	12P	-	114T	A	NL	9121625
15	STENA SUPERFAST VII	30285t	01	22.0k	203.3m	1200P	660C	110L	BA2	UK	9198941
16	STENA SUPERFAST VIII	30285t	01	22.0k	203.3m	1200P	660C	110L	BA2	UK	9198953
17	STENA SUPERFAST X	30285t	02	22.0k	203.3m	1200P	660C	110L	BA2	UK	9211511
18F+	STENA TRANSIT	34700t	11	22.2k	212.0m	300P	-	290T	A2	NL	9469388
19F+	STENA TRANSPORTER	34700t	11	22.2k	212.0m	300P	-	290T	A2	NL	9469376

CAPUCINE, SEVERINE Built by the Kyokuyo Shipyard, Shimonoseki, Japan for *CLdN*. Initially operated on their Ipswich - Rotterdam service. This service was suspended in August 2012. In September, they were chartered to *Stena Line* and placed on the Harwich - Rotterdam service.

CAROLINE RUSS Built by J J Sietas KG, Hamburg, Germany for *Ernst Russ* of Germany and chartered to *Transfennica*. In January 2016, chartered to Corsica Linea of France and transferred to the Portuguese flag. Operated between Corsica - Marseille. In February 2016 renamed the CORSICA LINEA DUI. In March 2016 she was laid up and in September she resumed the name CAROLINE RUSS. In October chartered to *Stena Line* and placed as second vessel on the Hook of Holland - Killingholme route.

STENA ADVENTURER Ro-pax vessel built by Hyundai Heavy Industries, Ulsan, South Korea, for *Stena RoRo* and chartered to *Stena Line* to operate between Holyhead and Dublin.

STENA BRITANNICA Built by Waden Yards in Wismar and Warnemünde, Germany, for *Stena Rederi* (bow sections constructed at Warnemünde and stern and final assembly at Wismar). Replaced the 2003 built STENA BRITANNICA on the Harwich - Hook of Holland service.

STENA EUROPE Built as the KRONPRINSESSAN VICTORIA by Götaverken Arendal AB, Gothenburg, Sweden for *Göteborg-Frederikshavn Linjen* of Sweden (trading as *Sessan Linjen*) for their Gothenburg - Frederikshavn service. Shortly after delivery, the company was taken over by *Stena Line* and services were marketed as *Stena-Sessan Line* for a period. In 1982 she was converted to an overnight ferry by changing one vehicle deck into two additional decks of cabins and she was switched to the Gothenburg - Kiel route (with, during the summer, daytime runs from Gothenburg to Frederikshavn and Kiel to Korsør (Denmark)). In 1989 she was transferred to the Oslo - Frederikshavn route and renamed the STENA SAGA. In 1994, transferred to *Stena Line BV*, renamed the STENA EUROPE and operated between Hook of Holland and Harwich. She was withdrawn in June 1997, transferred to the *Lion Ferry* (a *Stena Line* subsidiary) Karlskrona - Gdynia service and renamed the LION EUROPE. In 1998 she was transferred back to *Stena Line* (remaining on the same route) and renamed the STENA EUROPE. In early 2002 the cabins installed in 1982 were removed and other modifications made and she was transferred to the Fishguard - Rosslare route.

Stena Lagan *(George Holland)*

Stena Performer *(George Holland)*

Stena Superfast VIII *(Gordon Hislip)*

Stena Britannica *(Rob de Visser)*

Capucine *(John Bryant)*

Stena Mersey *(George Holland)*

Stena Euope *(Andrew Wood)*

STENA HIBERNIA Built as the MAERSK IMPORTER by Miho Shipyard, Shimizu, Japan for *Norfolkline*. Used on the Scheveningen (from 2007 Vlaardingen) - Felixstowe service. In October 2009 moved to the Heysham-Belfast service. In July 2010 renamed the HIBERNIA SEAWAYS. In July 2011 renamed the STENA HIBERNIA. In September 2012 transferred to *Stena RoRo*. In November chartered to *Stena Line* and placed on the Birkenhead - Belfast service. In September 2015 moved to the Heysham - Belfast route.

STENA HOLLANDICA Built by Nordic Yards in Wismar and Warnemünde, Germany, for *Stena Rederi* (bow sections constructed at Warnemünde and stern and final assembly at Wismar) to replace the previous STENA HOLLANDICA on the Harwich - Hook of Holland service. Entered service May 2010.

STENA HORIZON Built as the CARTOUR BETA by CN Visentini, Porto Viro, Italy for Levantina Trasporti of Italy. Chartered to *Caronte & Tourist* of Italy and operated between Messina and Salerno (Sicily). In October 2011 chartered to *Celtic Link Ferries*, renamed the CELTIC HORIZON and placed on the Rosslare - Cherbourg route. In March 2014 service and charter taken over by *Stena Line*. Renamed the STENA HORIZON.

STENA LAGAN, STENA MERSEY Built as the LAGAN VIKING and MERSEY VIKING by CN Visentini, Donada, Italy for *Levantina Trasporti* of Italy. Chartered to *NorseMerchant Ferries* and placed on the Birkenhead - Belfast route. In 2008 sold to *Norfolkline*, then resold to *Epic Shipping* and chartered back. In August 2010, following *Norfolkline's* purchase by *DFDS Seaways*, they were renamed the LAGAN SEAWAYS and MERSEY SEAWAYS respectively. Between January and July 2011 they were operated by *Stena Line Irish Sea Ferries*, a 'stand-alone' company pending consideration of a take-over by *Stena Line* by the UK and Irish competition authorities. In July 2011 the take-over was confirmed and in August 2011 they were renamed the STENA LAGAN and STENA MERSEY. In April 2012 they were sold to *Stena RoRo* and chartered back by *Stena Line*.

STENA PERFORMER Built as the SEATRUCK PERFORMANCE by Flensburger Schiffbau-Gesellschaft, Flensburg, Germany for *Seatruck Ferries*. In September 2012 chartered to *Stena Line* to operate between Heysham and Belfast and renamed the STENA PERFORMER. In September 2015 moved to the Birkenhead - Belfast route.

STENA PRECISION Built as the SEATRUCK PRECISION by Flensburger Schiffbau-Gesellschaft, Flensburg, Germany for *Seatruck Ferries*. In September 2012 chartered to *Stena Line* to operate between Heysham and Belfast and renamed the STENA PRECISION.

STENA SCOTIA Built as the MAERSK EXPORTER by Miho Shipyard, Shimizu, Japan for *Norfolkline*. Used on the Scheveningen (from 2007 Vlaardingen) - Felixstowe service until March 2009 when she was moved to the Heysham - Belfast route. In July 2010 renamed the SCOTIA SEAWAYS. In July 2011 renamed the STENA SCOTIA. In September 2013 transferred to *Stena RoRo* and placed on the charter market. In September 2014 chartered to *Stena Line* and inaugurated a new service between Rotterdam and Killingholme.

STENA SUPERFAST VII, STENA SUPERFAST VIII Built as the SUPERFAST VII and SUPERFAST VIII by Howaldtswerke Deutsche Werft AG, Kiel, Germany for *Attica Enterprises* (now *Attica Group*) for use by *Superfast Ferries* between Rostock and Hanko. In 2006 sold to *Tallink*. The Finnish terminal was transferred to Helsinki and daily return trips between Helsinki and Tallinn were introduced. These ceased in September 2008. The operation was ceased for the winter season in December 2009 and 2010. Service resumed at the end of April 2010 and 2011. In August 2011 chartered to *Stena Line* and renamed the STENA SUPERFAST VII, STENA SUPERFAST VIII. In November 2011, after a major refit, they were placed on a service between Cairnryan and Belfast (replacing the Stranraer - Belfast service). In December 2017 to be purchased by Stena Ropax

STENA SUPERFAST X Built as the SUPERFAST X by Howaldtswerke Deutsche Werft AG, Kiel, Germany for *Attica Enterprises* (now *Attica Group*) for use by *Superfast Ferries*. In May 2002 she and the SUPERFAST IX (see ATLANTIC VISION, *Tallink*, Section 6) began operating between Rosyth (Scotland) and Zeebrugge. In 2004 fitted with additional cabins and conference/seating areas. In 2007 sold to *Veolia Transportation* and renamed the JEAN NICOLI. Chartered to *CoTuNav* of Tunisia and operated between France/Italy and Tunisia. Later chartered to *ANEK Lines* of Greece and operated on the Patras - Corfu - Igoumenitsa - Venice route. In July 2008 chartered to *SeaFrance* and renamed the SEAFRANCE MOLIERE. After modifications she was placed on the Dover - Calais route. In November

2011 laid up. In January 2012 offered for sale or charter. In July 2012 sold to *Scapino Shipping Ltd* of Monaco and renamed the MOLIERE. In October 2012 chartered to the *DFDS/LD Lines* joint venture and, in November, renamed the DIEPPE SEAWAYS and introduced onto the Dover - Calais service. In May 2014 sold to *Stena Line North Sea Ltd*. In December 2014 charter ended. Refurbished and, in March 2015, chartered to *Stena Line*, renamed the STENA SUPERFAST X and placed on the Holyhead - Dublin route.

STENA TRANSIT, STENA TRANSPORTER Built by Samsung Heavy Industries, Koje, South Korea. Used on the Hook of Holland - Killingholme service.

Under Construction

20	**NEWBUILDING 1**	**42000t**	**19**	**22k**	**214.5m**	**927P**	**300C**	**180L**	**BA2**	**-**	**-**
21	**NEWBUILDING 2**	**42000t**	**20**	**22k**	**214.5m**	**927P**	**300C**	**180L**	**BA2**	**-**	**-**
22	**NEWBUILDING 3**	**42000t**	**20**	**22k**	**214.5m**	**927P**	**300C**	**180L**	**BA2**	**-**	**-**
23	**NEWBUILDING 4**	**42000t**	**20**	**22k**	**214.5m**	**927P**	**300C**	**180L**	**BA2**	**-**	**-**

NEWBUILDING 1, NEWBUILDING 2, NEWBUILDING 3, NEWBUILDING 4 Under construction by AVIC International Maritime Holdings, Weihai, China. They are designed to run on either methanol or LPG. They are expected to operate on the Liverpool - Belfast and Cairnryan - Belfast routes. There are options on more vessels.

WESTERN FERRIES

THE COMPANY *Western Ferries (Clyde) Ltd* is a British private sector company.

MANAGEMENT **Managing Director** Gordon Ross.

ADDRESS Hunter's Quay, Dunoon, Argyll PA23 8HJ.

TELEPHONE **Administration** +44 (0)1369 704452, **Reservations** Not applicable.

INTERNET **Email** enquiries@western-ferries.co.uk **Website** www.western-ferries.co.uk *(English)*

ROUTE OPERATED McInroy's Point (Gourock) - Hunter's Quay (Dunoon) (20 mins; *SOUND OF SCARBA, SOUND OF SEIL, SOUND OF SHUNA, SOUND OF SOAY*; every 20 mins (15 mins in peaks)).

1	**SOUND OF SCARBA**	**489t**	**01**	**11.0k**	**49.95m**	**220P**	**40C**	**4/5L**	**BA**	**UK**	**9237424**
2	**SOUND OF SEIL**	**497t**	**13**	**11.0k**	**49.95m**	**220P**	**40C**	**4/5L**	**BA**	**UK**	**9665217**
3	**SOUND OF SHUNA**	**489t**	**03**	**11.0k**	**49.95m**	**220P**	**40C**	**4/5L**	**BA**	**UK**	**9289441**
4	**SOUND OF SOAY**	**497t**	**13**	**11.0k**	**49.95m**	**220P**	**40C**	**4/5L**	**BA**	**UK**	**9665229**

SOUND OF SCARBA, SOUND OF SHUNA Built by Ferguson Shipbuilders, Port Glasgow, UK for *Western Ferries*.

SOUND OF SEIL, SOUND OF SOAY Built by Cammell Laird Shiprepairers & Shipbuilders, Birkenhead, UK for *Western Ferries*.

Sound of Shuna *(Miles Cowsill)*

Wight Ryder II *(Andrew Cooke)*

WIGHTLINK

THE COMPANY *Wightlink* is a British private sector company, owned by *Basalt Infrastructure Partners LLP*, formerly known as *Balfour Beatty Infrastructure Partners (BBIP)*. The routes and vessels were previously part of *Sealink (British Rail)* but were excluded from the purchase of most of the *Sealink* operations by *Stena Line AB* in 1990. They remained in *Sea Containers'* ownership until purchased by *CINVen* Ltd, a venture capital company in 1995. The company was the subject of a management buy-out financed by the *Royal Bank of Scotland* in 2001 and was sold to the *Macquarie Group* of Australia in 2005. It was purchased by *Balfour Beatty Infrastructure Partners LLP* in February 2015.

MANAGEMENT **Interim Chief Executive** John Burrows, **Head of Marketing** Mark Persad, **Commercial Director** Clive Tilley.

ADDRESS Gunwharf Road, Portsmouth PO1 2LA.

TELEPHONE **Administration and Reservations** +44 (0)333 999 7333.

INTERNET **Email** bookings@wightlink.co.uk **Website** www.wightlink.co.uk *(English, Dutch, French, German)*

ROUTES OPERATED **Conventional Ferries** Lymington - Yarmouth (Isle of Wight) (approx 35 mins; ***WIGHT LIGHT, WIGHT SKY***, hourly), Portsmouth - Fishbourne (Isle of Wight) (approx 35 mins; ***ST. CECILIA, ST. CLARE, ST. FAITH, WIGHT SUN***; half-hourly or hourly depending on time of day). **Fast Passenger Ferries** Portsmouth - Ryde (Isle of Wight) (passenger-only) (under 20 mins; ***WIGHT RYDER I, WIGHT RYDER II***; 2 per hour).

1	ST. CECILIA	2968t	86	12.0k	77.0m	771P	142C	12L	BA	UK	8518546
2	ST. CLARE	5359t	01	13.0k	86.0m	878P	186C	-	BA2	UK	9236949
3	ST. FAITH	3009t	89	12.5k	77.0m	771P	142C	12L	BA	UK	8907228
4	WIGHT LIGHT	2546t	08	11.0k	62.4m	360P	65C	-	BA	UK	9446972
5»p	WIGHT RYDER I	520t	09	20.0k	40.9m	260P	0C	-	-	UK	9512537
6»p	WIGHT RYDER II	520t	09	20.0k	40.9m	260P	0C	-	-	UK	9512549
7	WIGHT SKY	2456t	08	11.0k	62.4m	360P	65C	-	BA	UK	9446984
8	WIGHT SUN	2546t	09	11.0k	62.4m	360P	65C	-	BA	UK	9490416

ST. CECILIA, ST FAITH Built by Cochrane Shipbuilders, Selby, UK for *Sealink British Ferries* for the Portsmouth - Fishbourne service.

ST. CLARE Built by Stocznia Remontowa, Gdansk, Poland for the Portsmouth - Fishbourne service. She is a double-ended ferry with a central bridge. During winter 2015/16 modified for double deck loading.

WIGHT LIGHT, WIGHT SKY, WIGHT SUN Built by Brodogradilište Kraljevica, Croatia for the Lymington - Yarmouth route. One of these ships now operates on the Portsmouth - Fishbourne route.

WIGHT RYDER I, WIGHT RYDER II Catamarans built by FBMA Marine, Balamban, Cebu, Philippines. Operate on the Portsmouth - Ryde service.

Note: When one of the 'Wight Ryders' is unavailable a replacement vessel is usually chartered. This is generally the SOLENT CAT of *Solent & Wightline Cruises* - 74t, 2000, 13k, 20.1m, 250 passengers, catamaran.

Under Construction

9	NEWBUILDING	8200t	18	-	89.7m	1208P	178C	-	BA2	UK	-

NEWBUILDING Under construction by the Cemre Shipyard, Yalova, Turkey. She will be hybrid diesel/battery electric vessel.

St Cecilia *(Brian Smith)*

White Sun *(Brian Maxted)*

SECTION 2 - MINOR FERRY OPERATORS

ARGYLL AND BUTE COUNCIL

THE COMPANY *Argyll and Bute Council* is a British local government authority.

Head of Economic Development and Strategic Transportation Jim Smith,

Marine Operations Manager Stewart Clark.

ADDRESS 1A Manse Brae, Lochgilphead, Argyll PA31 8RD.

TELEPHONE **Administration** +44 (0)1546 604673.

FAX **Administration** +44 (0)1546 604738.

INTERNET **Email** stewart.clark@argyll-bute.gov.uk **Website** www.argyll-bute.gov.uk/transport-and-streets/ferry-travel

ROUTES OPERATED **Vehicle ferries** Seil - Luing (5 mins; *BELNAHUA*; approx half-hourly), Port Askaig (Islay) - Feolin (Jura) (5 mins; *EILEAN DHIURA*; approx half-hourly). **Passenger-only ferries** Port Appin – Lismore (10 mins; *THE LISMORE*; approx hourly), Ellenabeich – Easdale (5 mins; *EASDALE*; approx quarter-hourly).

1	BELNAHUA	35t	72	8.0k	17.1m	40P	5C	1L	BA	UK
2p	EASDALE	-	93	6.5k	6.4m	11P	0C	0L	-	UK
3	EILEAN DHIURA	86t	98	9.0k	25.6m	50P	13C	1L	BA	UK
4p	THE LISMORE	12t	88	8.0k	9.7m	20P	0C	0L	-	UK

BELNAHUA Built by Campbeltown Shipyard, Campbeltown, UK for *Argyll County Council* for the Seil - Luing service. In 1975, following local government reorganisation, transferred to *Strathclyde Regional Council*. In 1996, transferred to *Argyll and Bute Council*.

EASDALE Built for *Strathclyde Regional Council* for the Ellenabeich - Easdale passenger-only service. In 1996, following local government reorganisation, transferred to *Argyll and Bute Council*.

EILEAN DHIURA Built by McTay Marine, Bromborough, Wirral, UK for *Argyll and Bute Council* to replace the *Western Ferries (Argyll)* SOUND OF GIGHA on the Islay - Jura route. *ASP Ship Management* manage and operate this vessel on behalf of *Argyll and Bute Council*.

THE LISMORE Built for *Strathclyde Regional Council* for the Port Appin – Lismore passenger-only service. In 1996, following local government reorganisation, transferred to *Argyll and Bute Council*.

ARRANMORE FAST FERRIES

THE COMPANY *Arranmore Fast Ferries*, trading as *Arranmore Blue Ferry*, is a Republic of Ireland private sector company.

MANAGEMENT **Managing Director** Seamus Boyle.

ADDRESS Blue Ferry Office, Burtonport, Letterkenny, Co. Donegal, Republic of Ireland.

TELEPHONE **Administration & Reservations** +353 (0)87 3171810.

INTERNET **Email:** info.fastferry@gmail.com **Website** www.arranmorefastferry.com *(English)*. App can be downloaded from Twitter - @Arranmore Ferry

ROUTE OPERATED Burtonport (County Donegal) - Leabgarrow (Arranmore Island) (20 mins; *MORVERN*; up to 8 per day).

1	MORVERN	83t	73	8.0k	26.6m	96P	10C	-	B	IR
2p	OCEAN WARRIOR	18t	89	18.0k	14.3m	12P	0C	-	-	IR

MORVERN Built by James Lamont & Co Ltd, Port Glasgow, UK for *Caledonian MacBrayne*. After service on a number of routes she was, after 1979, the main vessel on the Fionnphort (Mull) - Iona service.

Eilean Dhiura *(Brian Maxted)*

Morvern *(Nick Widdows)*

In 1992 she was replaced by the LOCH BUIE and became a spare vessel. In 1995 sold to *Arranmore Island Ferry Services*. In 2001 sold to *Bere Island Ferries*. In February 2010 refurbished by Bere Island Boatyard and sold to *Arranmore Charters* (now *Arranmore Fast Ferries*). Extended in June 2012.

OCEAN WARRIOR Built by FBM Marine, Cowes, Isle of Wight as an RNLI Tyne class lifeboat ALEXANDER COUTANACHE (No1157) and operated at St Helier, Channel Islands until June 2009 when she became a relief vessel. Bought by *Arranmore Fast Ferries* in December 2014 and renamed the OCEAN WARRIOR.

ARRANMORE ISLAND FERRY SERVICES

THE COMPANY *Arranmore Island Ferry Services (Bád Farrantoireacht Arainn Mhór)*, trading as *Arranmore Red Ferry*, is a Republic of Ireland company, supported by *Roinn na Gaeltachta (The Gaeltacht Authority)*, a semi-state-owned body responsible for tourism and development in the Irish-speaking areas of The Republic of Ireland. They also operate the summer only Lough Swilly service.

MANAGEMENT **Managing Director** Dominic Sweeney.

ADDRESS Cara na nOilean, Burtonport Pier, Letterkenny, Co. Donegal, Republic of Ireland.

TELEPHONE **Administration & Reservations** ***Arranmore Island Service*** +353 (0)7495 20532, +353 (0)7495 42233, ***Lough Swilly Service*** +353 (0)87 2112331.

INTERNET **Email** arranmoreferry@gmail.com loughswillyferry@gmail.com **Websites** www.arranmoreferry.com swillyferry.com *(English)*

ROUTES OPERATED ***Arranmore Island Service*** Burtonport (County Donegal) - Leabgarrow (Arranmore Island) (15 mins; ***COLL or RHUM***; up to 8 per day (Summer), 6 per day (Winter)), ***Lough Swilly Service (summer only)*** Buncrana (County Donegal) - Rathmullan (County Donegal) (20 mins; ***COLL or RHUM***; up to 8 per day).

1	COLL	69t	74	8.0k	25.3m	96P	6C	-	B	IR
2	RHUM	69t	73	8.0k	25.3m	96P	6C	-	B	IR

COLL Built by James Lamont & Co Ltd, Port Glasgow, UK for *Caledonian MacBrayne*. For several years she was employed mainly in a relief capacity. In 1986 she took over the Tobermory (Mull) - Kilchoan service from a passenger-only vessel; the conveyance of vehicles was not inaugurated until 1991. In 1996 she was transferred to the Oban - Lismore route. In 1998 she was sold to *Arranmore Island Ferry Services*.

RHUM Built by James Lamont & Co Ltd, Port Glasgow, UK for *Caledonian MacBrayne*. Until 1987, she was used primarily on the Claonaig - Lochranza (Arran) service. After that time she served on various routes. In 1994 she inaugurated a new service between Tarbert (Loch Fyne) and Portavadie. In 1997 she operated between Kyles Scalpay and Scalpay until the opening of the new bridge on 16th December 1997. In 1998 she was sold to *Arranmore Island Ferry Services*.

BERE ISLAND FERRIES

THE COMPANY *Bere Island Ferries Ltd* is a Republic of Ireland private sector company.

MANAGEMENT **Operator** Colum Harrington.

ADDRESS Ferry Lodge, West End, Bere Island, Beara, County Cork, Republic of Ireland.

TELEPHONE **Administration** +353 (0)27 75009, **Reservations** Not applicable, **Mobile** +353 (0)86 2423140.

FAX **Administration** +353 (0)27 75000, **Reservations** Not applicable.

INTERNET **Email** biferry@eircom.net **Website** www.bereislandferries.com *(English)*

1	HOUTON LASS	58t	60	9.0k	22.9m	12P	10C	1L	B	IR
2F	KIRSTY M	109t	66	10.5k	23.7m	0P	-	1L	B	IR
3	OILEAN NA H-OIGE	69t	80	7.0k	18.6m	75P	4C	-	B	IR

4	SANCTA MARIA	67t	83	7.0k	18.6m	75P	4C	-	B	IR

HOUTON LASS Built by Magnaport Marine Ltd, Poole, UK for Flotta Oil Terminals, Stromness, Orkney Islands. Later sold for use as an antipollution vessel on the Black Isle, near Inverness. In November 2013 delivered to *Bere Island Ferries Ltd*. During 2014-2016 refurbished and lengthened in Galway. Mainly in use for transporting lorries but is also used for taking (up to) 10 cars during busy times.

KIRSTY M Landing craft (Klasse 521) built as the LCM 12 SPROTTE by Rheinwerft Walsum, Walsum, Germany for the German Navy. In 1993 withdrawn and sold to a German firm and converted to a civilian ferry. She was later sold to *Mainstream Salmon Farm (Aquascot Seafarms Ltd)*, Orkney, renamed the KIRSTY M and used as a work boat. In December 2009 sold to *Bere Island Ferries* and converted back to ferry operation. She is used in a freight-only mode and has no licence to carry passengers.

OILEAN NA H-OIGE Built as the EILEAN NA H-OIGE by Lewis Offshore Ltd, Stornoway, UK for *Western Isles Islands Council* (from 1st April 1996 the *Western Isles Council* and from 1st January 1998 *Comhairle Nan Eilean Siar*) for their Ludaig (South Uist) - Eriskay service. From 2000 operated from a temporary slipway at the Eriskay causeway. This route ceased in July 2001 following the full opening of the causeway and she was laid up. In 2002 she was moved to the Eriskay - Barra service. In 2003 replaced by the LOCH BHRUSDA of *Caledonian MacBrayne* and laid up. Later sold to *Bere Island Ferries* and renamed the OILEAN NA H-OIGE (same name - "The Island of Youth" - in Irish rather than Scots Gaelic).

SANCTA MARIA Built as the EILEAN BHEARNARAIGH by George Brown & Company, Greenock, UK for *Western Isles Islands Council* for their Otternish (North Uist) - Berneray service. From 1996 until 1999 she was operated by *Caledonian MacBrayne* in conjunction with the LOCH BHRUSDA on the service between Otternish and Berneray and during the winter she was laid up. Following the opening of a causeway between North Uist and Berneray in early 1999, the ferry service ceased and she became reserve vessel for the Eriskay route. This route ceased in July 2001 following the opening of a causeway and she was laid up. In 2002 operated between Eriskay and Barra as reserve vessel. In 2003 sold to *Transalpine Redemptorists Inc*, a community of monks who live on Papa Stronsay, Orkney. Used for conveying supplies to the island - not a public service. In 2008 sold to *Bere Island Ferries*. Entered service in May 2009.

BK MARINE

THE COMPANY *BK Marine* is a UK company.

MANAGEMENT **Managing Director** Donald Gordon Fraser Ross.

ADDRESS Herrislea House Hotel, Veensgarth, Tingwall, Shetland ZE2 9SB.

TELEPHONE **Administration & Reservations** +44 (0)1595 840208.

INTERNET **Website** www.bkmarine.co.uk *(English)*

ROUTE OPERATED ***All year*** Foula - Walls (Mainland) (2 hours; *NEW ADVANCE*; 2 per week (Winter), 3 per week (Summer)), ***Summer only*** Foula - Scalloway (3 hrs 30 mins; *NEW ADVANCE*; alternate Thursdays).

1	NEW ADVANCE	25t	96	8.7k	9.8m	12P	1C	0L	C	UK

NEW ADVANCE Built by Richardson's, Stromness, Orkney, UK for *Shetland Islands Council* for the Foula service. Although built at Penryn, Cornwall, she was completed at Stromness. She has a Cygnus Marine GM38 hull and is based on the island where she can be lifted out of the water. Vehicle capacity is to take residents' vehicles to the island - not for tourist vehicles. In 2004 it was announced that the vessel and service would be transferred to the *Foula Community*. However, it was then found that under EU rules the route needed to be offered for competitive tender. In July 2006 the contract was awarded to *Atlantic Ferries Ltd* who began operations in October 2006. In August 2011 replaced by *BK Marine*.

CLARE ISLAND FERRY COMPANY

THE COMPANY *Clare Island Ferry Company* is owned and operated by the O'Grady family, natives of Clare Island, Republic of Ireland, who have been operating the Clare Island Mail Boat Ferry service since 1880.

MANAGEMENT Managing Director Chris O'Grady.

ADDRESS Clare Island Ferry Co Ltd, Clare Island, Co Mayo, F28 AT04, Republic Of Ireland.

TELEPHONE/FAX ***May-September*** +353 (0)98 23737 ***Winter*** +353 (0)98 25212, +353 (0)86 8515003.

INTERNET Email clareislandferry@anu.ie **Website** www.clareislandferry.com *(English)*

ROUTE OPERATED Roonagh (Co Mayo) - Clare Island (15 mins; ***CLEW BAY QUEEN, PIRATE QUEEN***; ***Winter*** 1 to 2 trips per day, ***Summer*** up to 5 per day, Roonagh - Inishturk (50 mins; ***CLEW BAY QUEEN, PIRATE QUEEN***; ***Winter*** 1 per day ***Summer*** up to 2 per day. Tourist vehicles are not normally carried.

1	**CLEW BAY QUEEN**	**64t**	**72**	**10.0k**	**21.9m**	**96P**	**6C**	**-**	**B**	**IR**
2p	**PIRATE QUEEN**	**73t**	**96**	**10.5k**	**19.8m**	**96P**	**0C**	**-**	**-**	**IR**

CLEW BAY QUEEN Built as the KILBRANNAN by James Lamont & Co Ltd, Port Glasgow, UK for *Caledonian MacBrayne*. Used on a variety of routes until 1977, she was then transferred to the Scalpay (Harris) - Kyles Scalpay service. In 1990 she was replaced by the CANNA and, in turn, replaced the CANNA in her reserve/relief role. In 1992 sold to *Arranmore Island Ferry Services* and renamed the ÁRAINN MHÓR. She was subsequently sold to *Údarás na Gaeltachta* and leased back to *Arranmore Island Ferry Services*. In 2008 she was sold to *Clare Island Ferry Company* and renamed the CLEW BAY QUEEN. She operates a passenger and heavy freight service to both Clare Island and Inishturk all year round. In winter passenger capacity is reduced to 47 with 3 crew. Fitted with crane for loading and unloading cargo.

PIRATE QUEEN Built by Arklow Marine Services in 1996 for *Clare Island Ferry Company*. She operates a daily passenger and light cargo service to Clare Island and Inishturk all year round. In winter passenger capacity is reduced to 47 with 3 crew. Fitted with crane for loading and unloading cargo.

CROSS RIVER FERRIES

THE COMPANY *Cross River Ferries Ltd* is a Republic of Ireland company, part of the *Doyle Shipping Group*.

MANAGEMENT Operations Manager Eoin O'Sullivan.

ADDRESS Westlands House, Rushbrooke, Cobh, County Cork, P24 H940, Republic of Ireland.

TELEPHONE Administration +353 (0)21 481 1485 **Reservations** Not applicable.

INTERNET Website crossriverferries.ie *(English)*

ROUTE OPERATED Carrigaloe (near Cobh, on Great Island) - Glenbrook (Co Cork) (4 mins; ***CARRIGALOE, GLENBROOK***; frequent service 07.00 - 00.15 (one or two vessels used according to demand)).

1	**CARRIGALOE**	**225t**	**70**	**8.0k**	**49.1m**	**200P**	**27C**	**-**	**BA**	**IR**	**7028386**
2	**GLENBROOK**	**225t**	**71**	**8.0k**	**49.1m**	**200P**	**27C**	**-**	**BA**	**IR**	**7101607**

CARRIGALOE Built as the KYLEAKIN by Newport Shipbuilding and Engineering Company, Newport (Gwent), UK for the *Caledonian Steam Packet Company* (later *Caledonian MacBrayne*) for the Kyle of Lochalsh - Kyleakin service. In 1991 sold to *Marine Transport Services Ltd* and renamed the CARRIGALOE. She entered service in March 1993. In Summer 2002 chartered to the *Lough Foyle Ferry Company*, returning in Spring 2003.

GLENBROOK Built as the LOCHALSH by Newport Shipbuilding and Engineering Company, Newport (Gwent), UK for the *Caledonian Steam Packet Company* (later *Caledonian MacBrayne*) for the Kyle of Lochalsh - Kyleakin service. In 1991 sold to *Marine Transport Services Ltd* and renamed the GLENBROOK. She entered service in March 1993.

FRAZER FERRIES

THE COMPANY *Frazer Ferries Ltd*, is a Republic of Ireland company. In June 2016 it took over *Passage East Ferries* and *Lough Foyle Ferry Service*. The *Carlingford Ferry* started in June 2017. The *Lough Foyle Ferry Service* will not be operated by the company in 2017.

MANAGEMENT **Director** John Driscol, **Chief Executive** Pamela Houston **Manager, Passage East Ferry** Gary O Hanlon.

ADDRESSES **Registered Office** Riverfront, Howley's Quay, Limerick, V94 WTK7, Republic of Ireland, **Lough Foyle Ferry** The Pier, Greencastle, Co Donegal, Republic of Ireland, **Carlingford Ferry** Greenore Port, The Harbour, Greenore, Co. Louth, A91 A0V1, Republic of Ireland. **Passage East Ferry** Barrack Street, Passage East, Co Waterford, X91 C52E, Republic of Ireland.

TELEPHONE **Passage East Ferry** +353 (0)51 382480.

FAX **Passage East Ferry** +353 (0)51 382598.

INTERNET **Carlingford Ferry Website** carlingfordferry.com *(English)* **Lough Foyle Ferry** www.loughfoyleferry.com *(English)* **Passage East Ferry Email** passageferry@eircom.net **Website** www.passageferry.ie *(English)*

ROUTES OPERATED ***All Year Service*** **Carlingford Ferry** Greenore, Co Louth, Republic of Ireland - Greencastle, Co Down, Northern Ireland (15 minutes; Caledonian MacBraynecarvor; hourly), **Passage East Ferry** Passage East (County Waterford) - Ballyhack (County Wexford) (7 mins; *FBD TINTERN*; frequent service), ***Summer Service*** **Lough Foyle Ferry** ***July - September*** Greencastle (Inishowen, Co Donegal, Republic of Ireland) - Magilligan (Co Londonderry, Northern Ireland) (15 mins; *FRAZER MARINER*; frequent service),

1	AISLING GABRIELLE	324t	78	10.0k	47.9m	300P	44C	-	BA	IR	7800033
2	FBD TINTERN	236t	71	9.0k	54.8m	130P	30C	-	BA	IR	
3	FRAZER MARINER	-	83	.7.2k	43.0m	100P	20C	-	BA	IR	

AISLING GABRIELLE Built as the SHANNON WILLOW by Scott & Sons (Bowling) Ltd, Bowling, Glasgow, UK for *Shannon Ferry Ltd*. In 2000 replaced by the SHANNON BREEZE and laid up for sale. In 2003 sold to the *Lough Foyle Ferry Company Ltd* and renamed the FOYLE VENTURE. In November 2015 sold to *Frazer Ferries*. In July 2016 re-opened the *Lough Foyle Ferry;* this ceased in October. In February 2017 renamed the AISLING GABRIELLE. In July 2017 inaugurated a new Carlingford Lough service.

FBD TINTERN Built as the STADT LINZ by Schiffswerft Oberwinter, Oberwinter/Rhein, Germany for *Rheinfähre Linz - Remagen GmbH* of Germany and operated on the Rhine between Linz and Remagen. In 1990 renamed the ST JOHANNES. In 1997 sold to *Fähren Bremen-Stedingen GmbH*, renamed the VEGESACK and operated across the Weser between Lemwerder and Vegesack. In 2003 she became a reserve vessel and in 2004 was renamed the STEDINGEN. Later sold to *Schraven BV* of The Netherlands and refurbished. In Autumn 2005 sold to *Passage East Ferry* and renamed the FBD TINTERN.

FRAZER MARINER Built as the BERNE-FARGE for *Schnellastfähre Berne-Farge GmbH* (from 1993 *Fähren Bremen-Stedingen GmbH*) to operate across the River Weser (Vegesack - Lemwerder and Berne - Farge). In January 2017 sold to *Frazer Ferries*. In July 2017 renamed the FRAZER MARINER and began operating between Greencastle and Magilligan.

Rhum *(Nick Widdows)*

Corran *(Brian Maxted)*

THE HIGHLAND COUNCIL

THE COMPANY *The Highland Council* is a Scottish local authority.

MANAGEMENT **Area Roads Operations Manager** Richard Porteous, **Ferry Foremen** Allan McCowan and Donald Dixon.

ADDRESS ***Area Office*** Lochybridge Depot, Carr's Corner Industrial Estate, Fort William PH33 6TQ, ***Ferry Office*** Ferry Cottage, Ardgour, Fort William PH33 7AA.

TELEPHONE **Administration *Area Office*** +44 (0)1397 709000, ***Corran*** +44 (0)1855 841243.

INTERNET **Email** communityservices@highland.gov.uk **Website** www.highland.gov.uk/info/1526/public_and_community_transport/111/public_transport/3 *(English)*

ROUTES OPERATED **Vehicle Ferries** Corran - Ardgour (5 mins; ***CORRAN, MAID OF GLENCOUL***; half-hourly).

1	CORRAN	351t	01	10.0k	42.0m	150P	30C	2L	BA	UK	9225990
2	MAID OF GLENCOUL	166t	75	8.0k	32.0m	116P	16C	1L	BA	UK	7521613

CORRAN Built by George Prior Engineering Ltd, Hull, UK for *The Highland Council* to replace the MAID OF GLENCOUL as main vessel.

MAID OF GLENCOUL Built by William McCrindle Ltd, Shipbuilders, Ardrossan, UK for *Highland Regional Council* for the service between Kylesku and Kylestrome. In 1984 the ferry service was replaced by a bridge and she was transferred to the Corran - Ardgour service. In April 1996, ownership transferred to *The Highland Council*. In 2001 she became the reserve vessel.

The *Highland Council* also supports both services operated by *Highland Ferries*.

HIGHLAND FERRIES

THE COMPANY *Highland Ferries* is a UK private sector operation. Services are operated under contract to *The Highland Council*.

MANAGEMENT **Operator** Dougie Robertson.

TELEPHONE **Administration** +44(0)7468 417137 **Reservations** Not applicable.

INTERNET **Email** southuist24@hotmail.co.uk

Facebook www.facebook.com/CamusnagaulFerry

1p	BHOY TAYLOR	-	80	7.5k	9.8m	26P	0C	0L	-	UK
2	RENFREW ROSE	65t	84	7.6k-	17.5m	12P	3C	0L	B	UK

ROUTES OPERATED **Vehicle Ferry *1st June - 30th September*** Cromarty - Nigg (Ross-shire) (10 mins; ***RENFREW ROSE***; half-hourly), **Passenger-only Ferry** Fort William - Camusnagaul (10 mins; ***BHOY TAYLOR***; up to 5 per day).

BHOY TAYLOR Built as the CAILIN AN AISEAG by Buckie Shipbuilders Ltd, Buckie, UK for *Highland Regional Council* and used on the Fort William - Camusnagaul passenger-only service. In 2006 the service transferred to *Geoff Ward* under contract with a different vessel. In 2013 the CAILIN AN AISEAG resumed service with *Highland Ferries* as contractor. In April 2013 renamed the BHOY TAYLOR.

RENFREW ROSE Built by MacCrindle Shipbuilding Ltd, Ardrossan for *Strathclyde PTE* (later *Strathclyde Partnership for Transport*). Built as a small car ferry but operated passenger only between Renfrew and Yoker (apart from occasionally carrying ambulances in earlier days before they became too heavy). In March 2010 laid up. In June 2012 sold to *Arranmore Fast Ferries* for use as a passenger/car ferry. In June 2016 sold to *Highland Ferries* to reopen the Cromarty - Nigg service.

ISLES OF SCILLY STEAMSHIP COMPANY

THE COMPANY *Isles of Scilly Steamship Company* is a British private sector company.

MANAGEMENT **Chief Executive** Robert Goldsmith, **Marketing & Communications Manager** Sharon Sandercock.

ADDRESS ***Scilly*** PO Box 10, Hugh Town, St Mary's, Isles of Scilly TR21 0LJ, ***Penzance*** Steamship House, Quay Street, Penzance, Cornwall, TR18 4BZ.

TELEPHONE **Administration & Reservations** +44 (0) 1736 334220.

INTERNET **Email** sales@islesofscilly-travel.co.uk **Website** www.islesofscilly-travel.co.uk *(English)*

ROUTES OPERATED ***Passenger services:*** Penzance - St Mary's (Isles of Scilly) (2 hrs 40 mins; ***SCILLONIAN III***; 1 per day), St Mary's - Tresco/St Martin's/St Agnes/Bryher; ***LYONESSE LADY, SWIFT LADY (inter-island boats)***; irregular), ***Freight service***: ***GRY MARITHA***; Freight from Penzance Monday, Wednesday and Fridays (weather dependant, all year round).

1F	GRY MARITHA	590t	81	10.5k	40.3m	6P	5C	1L	C	UK	8008462
2	LYONESSE LADY	40t	91	9.0k	15.5m	4P	1C	0L	AC	UK	
3F	MALI ROSE	768t	92	-	50.2m	6P	10C	1L	SC	NO	9065144
4	SCILLONIAN III	1346t	77	15.5k	67.7m	485P	5C	-	C	UK	7527796
5F	SWIFT LADY	-	04	30.0k	8.4m	0P	0C	0L	-	UK	

GRY MARITHA Built by Moen Slip AS, Kolvereid, Norway for *Gjofor* of Norway. In design she is a coaster rather than a ferry. In 1990 she was sold to the *Isles of Scilly Steamship Company*. She operates a freight and passenger service all year (conveying most goods to and from the islands). During the winter she provides the only sea service to the islands, the SCILLONIAN III being laid up.

LYONESSE LADY Built Lochaber Marine Ltd of Corpach, Fort William, Scotland, for inter-island ferry work.

MALI ROSE Pallet and deck cargo carrier built by Halsnøy Verft, Halsnøy, Norway. Passed through various hands until June 2016 when she was sold to *Isles of Scilly Steamship Company* to replace the GRY MARITHA.

SCILLONIAN III Built by Appledore Shipbuilders Ltd, Appledore, UK for the Penzance - St Mary's service. She operates from late March to November and is laid up in the winter. She is the last major conventional passenger/cargo ferry built for UK waters and probably Western Europe. Extensively refurbished during Winter 1998/99 and 2012/13. She can carry cars in her hold and on deck, as well as general cargo/perishables, boats, trailer tents and passenger luggage.

SWIFT LADY Stormforce 8.4 RIB (Rigid Inflatable Boat) built by Redbay Boats of Cushendall, Co Antrim, Northern Ireland for inter-island ferry work conveying mail and as back-up to the LYONESSE LADY.

MURPHY'S FERRY SERVICE

THE COMPANY *Murphy's Ferry Service* is privately operated.

MANAGEMENT **Operator** Brendan Murphy.

ADDRESS Lawrence Cove, Bere Island, Co Cork, Republic of Ireland.

TELEPHONE **Administration** +353 (0)87 2386095.

INTERNET **Email** edel@bereislandlodge.com **Website** www.murphysferry.com *(English)*

ROUTE OPERATED Castletownbere (Pontoon - 3 miles to east of town centre) - Bere Island (Lawrence Cove, near Rerrin) (20 mins; ***IKOM K***; up to 8 per day).

1	IKOM K	55t	99	10.0k	16.0m	60P	4C	1L	B	IR

IKOM K Built by Arklow Marine Services, Arklow, Republic of Ireland for *Murphy's Ferry Service*.

RATHLIN ISLAND FERRY

THE COMPANY *Rathlin Island Ferry Ltd* is a UK private sector company owned by Ciarán and Mary O'Driscoll of County Cork, Republic of Ireland.

MANAGEMENT **Managing Director** Ciarán O'Driscoll.

ADDRESS Ballycastle Ferry Terminal, 18 Bayview Road, Ballycastle, County Antrim BT54 6BT.

TELEPHONE **Administration & Reservations** +44 (0)28 2076 9299.

INTERNET **Email** info@rathlinballycastleferry.com **Website** www.rathlinballycastleferry.com *(English)*

ROUTE OPERATED **Vehicle Ferry** Ballycastle - Rathlin Island (45 min; ***SPIRIT OF RATHLIN***; up to 4 per day). **Passenger-only Fast Ferry** (20 min; *RATHLIN EXPRESS*; up to 6 per day). The service is operated on behalf of the *Northern Ireland Department of Regional Development*.

1»p	RATHLIN EXPRESS	31t	09	18.0k	17.7m	98P	0C	0L	-	UK	
2	SPIRIT OF RATHLIN	105t	17	-	25.0m	125P	5C	1L	B	UK	9780122

RATHLIN EXPRESS Built by Arklow Marine Services, Arklow, Republic of Ireland for *Rathlin Island Ferry Ltd.*

SPIRIT OF RATHLIN Built by Arklow Marine Services, Arklow, Irish Republic for *DRD (Northern Ireland)*, UK to replace the CANNA. Chartered to *Rathlin Island Ferry Ltd.*

SHANNON FERRY

THE COMPANY *Shannon Ferry Group Ltd* is a Republic of Ireland private company owned by eighteen shareholders on both sides of the Shannon Estuary.

MANAGEMENT **Managing Director** Eugene Maher.

ADDRESS Ferry Terminal, Killimer, County Clare, V15 FK09, Republic of Ireland.

TELEPHONE **Administration** +353 (0)65 9053124, **Reservations** Phone bookings not available; Online booking available at www.shannonferries.com

FAX **Administration** +353 (0)65 9053125, **Reservations** Fax bookings not available; Online booking available at www.shannonferries.com

INTERNET **Email** enquiries@shannonferries.com **Website** www.shannonferries.com *(English)*

ROUTE OPERATED Killimer (County Clare) - Tarbert (County Kerry) (20 mins; *SHANNON BREEZE, SHANNON DOLPHIN*; hourly (half-hourly during June, July, August and September)).

1	SHANNON BREEZE	611t	00	10.0k	80.8m	350P	60C	-	BA	IR	9224910
2	SHANNON DOLPHIN	501t	95	10.0k	71.9m	350P	52C	-	BA	IR	9114933

SHANNON BREEZE, SHANNON DOLPHIN Built by Appledore Shipbuilders, Appledore, UK for *Shannon Ferry Group Ltd.*

SHERKIN ISLAND FERRY

THE COMPANY The *Sherkin Island Ferry* is privately operated in the Republic of Ireland

MANAGEMENT **Operator:** Vincent O'Driscoll.

ADDRESS Sherkin Ferry, The Cove, Baltimore, Skibbereen, Co Cork, P81 RW71, Republic of Ireland.

TELEPHONE **Administration** +353 (0)87 244 7828. **Ferry Boat** +353 (0)87 911 7377.

INTERNET **Email** info@sherkinferry.com **Website** www.sherkinferry.com *(English)*

ROUTE OPERATED **Passenger only** Baltimore (Co Cork) - Sherkin Island (10 minutes; ***MYSTIC WATERS***; up to 10 per day). **Note:** No vehicle service advertised.

01p	MYSTIC WATERS	100t	72		19.8m	99P	0C	0L	-	IR	8943038
02	YOKER SWAN	65t	84		21.9m	50P	3C	0L	B	IR	-

MYSTIC WATERS Built by Ryton Marine Ltd, Wallsend, UK as the FREDA CUNNINGHAM for *Tyne & Wear PTE* and operated between North Shields and South Shields. Withdrawn in 1993 and sold to *Tyne Towage Ltd*, Newcastle and renamed the ANYA DEV. Later sold and renamed the LADY LAURA. In 2006 sold to *Sherkin Island Ferry* and renamed the MYSTIC WATERS.

YOKER SWAN Built by MacCrindle Shipbuilding Ltd, Ardrossan for *Strathclyde PTE* (later *Strathclyde Partnership for Transport*). Built as a small car ferry but operated passenger only between Renfrew and Yoker (apart from carrying ambulances in earlier days before they became too heavy). In March 2010 laid up. Later sold to *Sherkin Island Ferry* for use as a passenger/car ferry. She is used as required to convey vehicles and freight to and from the island, and sometimes conveys passengers. No public vehicle service is advertised.

SKYE FERRY

THE COMPANY The *Skye Ferry* is owned by the *Isle of Skye Ferry Community Interest Company*, a company limited by guarantee.

MANAGEMENT Ferry Development Manager Jo Crawford.

ADDRESS 6 Coulindune, Glenelg, Kyle, Ross-shire, IV40 8JU.

TELEPHONE Administration +44 (0)7881 634726.

INTERNET Email info@skyeferry.co.uk **Website** skyeferry.co.uk *(English)*

ROUTE OPERATED ***Easter - October only*** Glenelg - Kylerhea (Skye) (10 mins; ***GLENACHULISH***; frequent service).

1	GLENACHULISH	44t	69	9.0k	20.0m	12P	6C	-	BSt	UK

GLENACHULISH Built by Ailsa Shipbuilding Company, Troon, UK for the *Ballachulish Ferry Company* for the service between North Ballachulish and South Ballachulish, across the mouth of Loch Leven. In 1975 the ferry was replaced by a bridge and she was sold to *Highland Regional Council* and used on a relief basis on the North Kessock - South Kessock and Kylesku - Kylestrome routes. In 1983 she was sold to *Murdo MacKenzie*, who had operated the Glenelg – Skye route as ferryman since 1959. The vessel was eventually bought by *Roddy MacLeod* and the service resumed in September 1990. The *Isle of Skye Ferry Community Interest Company* reached agreement with *Mr MacLeod* that he would operate the ferry in 2006. In 2007 she was sold to the Company. During winter 2012 she was chartered to *The Highland Council* to operate between North and South Strome following a road closure due to a rock fall. She is the last turntable ferry in operation.

STRANGFORD LOUGH FERRY SERVICE

THE COMPANY The *Strangford Lough Ferry Service* is operated by the *DFI Transport NI*, a Northern Ireland Government Department (formerly operated by *Department of the Environment (Northern Ireland)*

.

MANAGEMENT Ferry Manager Tim Tew.

ADDRESS Strangford Lough Ferry Service, The Slip, Strangford, Co Down BT30 7NE.

TELEPHONE Administration +44 0300 200 7898, **Reservations** Not applicable.

INTERNET Website www.nidirect.gov.uk/strangford-ferry-timetable *(English)*

ROUTE OPERATED Strangford - Portaferry (County Down) (10 mins; ***PORTAFERRY II, STRANGFORD II***; half-hourly).

1	PORTAFERRY II	312t	01	12.0k	38.2m	260P	28C	-	BA	UK	9237436
2	STRANGFORD II	405t	16	12.0k	64.0m	260P	28C	-	BA	UK	9771561

PORTAFERRY II Built by McTay Marine, Bromborough, Wirral, UK for *DRD (Northern Ireland)*.

STRANGFORD II Built by Cammell Laird, Birkenhead for *DRD (Northern Ireland)*, UK to replace the STRANGFORD FERRY. Entered service February 2017.

C TOMS & SON LTD

THE COMPANY *C Toms & Son Ltd* is a British private sector company.

MANAGEMENT **Managing Director** Allen Toms.

ADDRESS East Street, Polruan, Fowey, Cornwall PL23 1PB.

TELEPHONE **Administration** +44 (0)1726 870232.

INTERNET **Email** enquiries@ctomsandson.co.uk **Website** www.ctomsandson.co.uk *(English)*

ROUTE OPERATED *Car Ferry* Fowey - Bodinnick (Cornwall) (5 mins; *GELLAN, JENACK*; frequent), *Passenger Ferry* Fowey - Polruan (Cornwall) (5 mins; *KALEY, LADY DIANA, LADY JEAN, TAMSIN, THREE COUSINS*; frequent).

1	GELLAN	50t	03	4.5k	36.0m	50P	10C	-	BA	UK
2	JENACK	60t	00	4.5k	36.0m	50P	15C	-	BA	UK
3p	KALEY	7.6t	03	-	9.5m	48P	0C	-	-	UK
4p	LADY DI	-	81	-	8.2m	36P	0C	-	-	UK
5p	LADY JEAN	-	-	-	-	12P	0C	-	-	UK
6p	THREE COUSINS	-	14	-	-	12P	0C	-	-	UK

GELLAN, JENACK Built by C Toms & Sons Ltd, Fowey, UK.

KALEY, LADY DIANA, LADY JEAN, THREE COUSINS Built by C Toms & Sons Ltd, Fowey, UK.

VALENTIA ISLAND CAR FERRY

THE COMPANY *Valentia Island Car Ferry* is the trading name of *Valentia Island Ferries Ltd*, a Republic of Ireland private sector company.

MANAGEMENT **Manager** Richard Foran.

ADDRESS Valentia Island, County Kerry, Republic of Ireland.

TELEPHONE **Administration** +353 (0)66 76141, **Reservations** Not applicable.

FAX **Administration** +353 (0)66 76377, **Reservations** Not applicable.

INTERNET **Email** reforan@indigo.ie **Website** www.facebook.com (search for Valentia Island Car Ferry *(English)*

ROUTE OPERATED Reenard (Co Kerry) - Knightstown (Valentia Island) (5 minutes; *GOD MET ONS III*; frequent service, 1st April - 30th September).

1	GOD MET ONS III	95t	63	-	43.0m	95P	18C	-	BA	IR

GOD MET ONS III Built by BV Scheepswerven Vh HH Bodewes, Millingen, The Netherlands for *FMHE Res* of The Netherlands for a service across the River Maas between Cuijk and Middelaar. In 1987 a new bridge was opened and the service ceased. She was latterly used on contract work in the Elbe and then laid up. In 1996 acquired by *Valentia Island Ferries* and inaugurated a car ferry service to the island. **Note** This island never had a car ferry service before. A bridge was opened at the south end of the island in 1970; before that a passenger/cargo service operated between Reenard Point and Knightstown.

SECTION 2 – MINOR FERRY OPERATORS

WOOLWICH FREE FERRY

THE COMPANY The *Woolwich Free Ferry* is operated by *Briggs Marine*, a British private sector company on behalf of *Transport for London*.

ADDRESS New Ferry Approach, Woolwich, London SE18 6DX.

TELEPHONE **Administration** +44 (0)20 8853 9400, **Reservations** Not applicable.

FAX **Administration** +44 (0)20 8316 6096, **Reservations** Not applicable.

INTERNET **Website** www.tfl.gov.uk/modes/river/woolwich-ferry *(English)*

ROUTE OPERATED Woolwich - North Woolwich (free ferry) (5 mins; *ERNEST BEVIN, JAMES NEWMAN, JOHN BURNS*; every 10 mins (weekdays - two ferries in operation), every 15 mins (weekends - one ferry in operation)). **Note** One ferry is always in reserve/under maintenance.

1	ERNEST BEVIN	1194t	63	8.0k	56.7m	310P	32C	6L	BA	UK	5426998
2	JAMES NEWMAN	1194t	63	8.0k	56.7m	310P	32C	6L	BA	UK	5411905
3	JOHN BURNS	1194t	63	8.0k	56.7m	310P	32C	6L	BA	UK	5416010

ERNEST BEVIN, JAMES NEWMAN, JOHN BURNS Built by Robb Caledon Shipbuilders Ltd, Dundee, UK for the *London County Council* who operated the service when the vessels were new. In 1965 ownership was transferred to the *Greater London Council*. Following the abolition of the *GLC* in April 1986, ownership was transferred to the *Department of Transport* and in 2001 to *Transport for London*. The *London Borough of Greenwich* operated the service on their behalf. In 2008 the operation of the service was transferred to Serco. An alternative loading is 6 x 18m articulated lorries and 14 cars; lorries of this length are too high for the nearby northbound Blackwall Tunnel.

Under Construction

4	BEN WOOLLACOTT	-	18	8.0k	56.7m	150P	42C	12L	BA	UK	-
5	DAME VERA LYNN	-	18	8.0k	56.7m	150P	42C	12L	BA	UK	-

BEN WOOLLACOTT, DAME VERA LYNN Under construction by Remontowa Shipbuilding, Gdansk, Poland. They will be battery hybrid vessels.

John Burns *(Nick Widdows)*

Wight Sky *(Andrew Cooke)*

SECTION 3 - GB & IRELAND - FREIGHT ONLY FERRIES

CLDN/COBELFRET FERRIES

THE COMPANIES *CLdN Cobelfret SA* is a Luxembourg private sector company. There are a number of subsidiary companies. *CLdN* stands for *Compagnie Luxembourgouise de Navigation*.

MANAGEMENT **CLdN Ro-Ro SA (Luxembourg)** Caroline Dubois, **Cobelfret Waterways SA (Vlissingen)** Geert Bogaerts, **CLdN ro-ro Agencies Ltd (UK)** Karla Fairway.

ADDRESSES ***Luxembourg*** **CLdN Cobelfret SA & CLdN ro-ro SA**, 3-7 rue Schiller, 2519 Luxembourg, ***UK*** CLdN ro-ro UK Ltd, Long Reach House, London Road, Purfleet, Essex RM19 1RP UK, ***UK - Irish Republic*** CLdN ro-ro SA, Port Centre, 2nd Floor, Alexandra Road, Dublin Port, Dublin 1, D01 H4C6, Republic of Ireland.

TELEPHONE ***Luxembourg*** **CLdN Cobelfret SA** +352 (0)26 44 631, **CLdN ro-ro SA** +352 (0)26 44 661 ***UK*** +44 (0)1708 865522, ***Irish Republic*** +353 (0)1 856 1608.

FAX ***Luxembourg*** **CLdN Cobelfret SA** +352 (0)26 44 63 298, **CLdN ro-ro SA** +352 (0)26 44 66 299 ***UK*** +44 (0)1708 866419, ***Irish Republic*** +353 (0)1 704 0164.

INTERNET **Email** admin.roro@cldn.com **Websites** www.cldn.com *(English)*

ROUTES OPERATED ***Cobelfret Ferries Services*** Zeebrugge - Purfleet (9 hrs; ***ADELINE, WILHELMINE, CELESTINE CLASS, MAZARINE CLASS***; 2/3 per day), Zeebrugge - Killingholme (13 hrs; ***PAULINE, YASMINE***; 6 per week), ***CLdN Services*** Rotterdam - Purfleet (14 hrs 30 mins; ***CEMIL BAYULGEN, MAZARINE CLASS***); 6 per week), Rotterdam - Killingholme (14 hrs; ***OPALINE CLASS*** and ***MAZARINE CLASS***; 6 per week), Zeebrugge - Esbjerg (24hrs; ***CELESTINE CLASS***; 1 per week), Zeebrugge - Dublin (36 hrs; ***MAZARINE CLASS*** and ***OPALINE CLASS***; 4 per week), Rotterdam - Dublin (38 hrs; ***CELESTINE CLASS, MAZARINE CLASS, OPALINE CLASS***; 3 per week), Rotterdam - Zeebrugge - Santander (Spain) - Leixoes (Portugal) (64-69 hrs; ***CATHERINE, BORE SEA, VARIES***; 3 per week), Zeebrugge - Gothenburg (32-33 hrs; ***CELESTINE CLASS, SOMERSET***; 3 per week (1 weekly call at Hirtshals in both directions), (CELESTINE CLASS = CELESTINE, CELANDINE, CLEMENTINE, MELUSINE, VALENTINE and VICTORINE, MAZARINE CLASS = MAZARINE, PALATINE, PEREGRINE and VESPERTINE; OPALINE CLASS = AMANDINE and OPALINE). ***CLdN Container service*** Rotterdam - Dublin (43/47 hrs; ***ARX*** ; 1 per week).

Contract Services for Ford Motor Company Vlissingen - Dagenham (11 hrs; ***CELESTINE, CYMBELINE, UNDINE***; 2 per day).

1	ADELINE	21020t	12	15.8k	150.0m	12P	-	170T	A	MT	9539092
2	AMANDINE	33960t	11	18.5k	195.4m	12P	-	270T	A	MT	9424871
3	ARX	6901t	05	13.8k	139.8m	0P		707 TEU	C	MT	9328625
4	BORE SEA	25586t	11	18.5k	195.0m	12P	-	210T	A2	FI	9443554
5	CATHERINE	21287t	02	18.0k	182.2m	12P	-	200T	A2	MT	9209453
6	CELANDINE	23987t	00	17.9k	162.5m	12P	630C	157T	A	MT	9183984
7	CELESTINE	23986t	96	17.8k	162.5m	12P	630C	157T	A	MT	9125372
8	CEMIL BAYULGEN	29004t	10	17.8k	193.3m	12P	-	270T	A	TR	9422134
9	CLEMENTINE	23986t	97	17.8k	162.5m	12P	630C	157T	A	BE	9125384
10	CYMBELINE	11866t	92	17.0k	147.4m	8P	350C	100T	A2	MT	9007764
11	FADIQ	29429	12	21.5k	193.0m	12P	-	270T	A	MT	9503639
12	MASSIMO MURA	23235t	03	17.1k	193.0m	12P	-	180T	A	IT	9234094
13	MAZARINE	25593t	09	18.5k	195.4m	12P	-	180T	A	MT	9376696
14	MELUSINE	23987t	99	17.8k	162.5m	12P	630C	157T	A	BE	9166637
15	OPALINE	33960t	10	18.5k	195.4m	12P	-	270T	A	MT	9424869
16	PALATINE	25593t	09	18.5k	195.4m	12P	-	180T	A	MT	9376701
17	PAULINE	49166t	06	21.7k	200.0m	12P	656C	258T	A	MT	9324473
18	PEREGRINE	25235t	10	18.5k	195.4m	12P	-	180T	A	MT	9376725

19	SOMERSET	21005t	00	18.0k	183.4m	12P	-	180T	A	MT	9188221
20	UNDINE	11854t	91	15.0k	147.4m	8P	350C	100T	A2	MT	9006112
21	VALENTINE	23987t	99	18.0k	162.5m	12P	630C	157T	A	BE	9166625
22	VESPERTINE	25235t	10	18.5k	195.4m	12P	-	180T	A	MT	9376713
23	VICTORINE	23987t	00	17.8k	162.5m	12P	630C	157T	A	BE	9184029
24	WILHELMINE	21020t	12	15.8k	150.0m	12P	-	170T	A	MT	9539080
25	YASMINE	49166t	07	21.7k	200.0m	12P	656C	258T	A	MT	9337353

ADELINE Built by the Kyokuyo Shipyard, Shimonoseki, Japan. After competition, a additional deck and sponsons were retro-fitted at the Chengxi Shipyard, Jiangyin, China.

AMANDINE Built by Flensburger Schiffbau-Gesellschaft, Flensburg, Germany. Operates mainly between Rotterdam and Killingholme and Rotterdam/Zeebrugge and Dublin.

ARX Container ship built as the LUPUS I by Detlef Hegemann Rolandwerft, Berne, Germany. In June 2005 chartered to *C2C Line* operating between Zeebrugge and Dublin and renamed the C2C LUPUS. In July 2007 renamed the C2C AUSTRALIS. In June 2010 purchased by an associated company of *CLdN* and renamed the ARX.

BORE SEA Built by Flensburger Schiffbau-Gesellschaft, Flensburg, Germany for *Bore Shipowners (Rettig Group Bore)* of Finland. In May 2011 chartered to *Transfennica* and operated between Zeebrugge and Bilbao. In January 2013 chartered for three years to *Fret Cetam* of France and used for the conveyance of parts for Airbus aircraft. In September 2016 chartered to *CLdN/Cobelfret Ferries*. Initially used mainly on the Zeebrugge - Purfleet service but later also used on the Iberian routes.

CATHERINE Built as the ROMIRA by Zhonghua Shipyard, Zhonghua, China for *Dag Engström Rederi* of Sweden. For six months engaged on a number of short-term charters, including *Cobelfret Ferries* who used her on both the Rotterdam - Immingham and Zeebrugge - Purfleet routes. In September 2002 purchased by *Cobelfret Ferries* and, in November 2002, renamed the CATHERINE and placed on the Rotterdam - Immingham service. In Spring 2003 chartered to the *US Defense Department* to convey materials to the Persian Gulf. Returned in late summer and operated thereafter on the Rotterdam - Immingham service. In January 2009 chartered to *CoTuNav* of Tunisia. In February 2010 returned to *Cobelfret* service and operated on the Rotterdam - Purfleet service. In March 2010 again chartered to *CoTuNav*. In March 2011 chartered to *RMR Shipping* to operate between Western Europe and Antwerp, Eemshaven, Harwich and Dublin to Lagos (Nigeria). In May 2011 returned to *Cobelfret Ferries* and used on the Zeebrugge - Gothenburg service until January 2013 when she began operating on the Purfleet route during the week and the Gothenburg route at weekend (one round trip). From April 2013 operated full-time on the Purfleet service. In March 2014 transferred to the Rotterdam - Leixoes route.

CELANDINE, VALENTINE, VICTORINE Built by Kawasaki Heavy Industries, Sakaide, Japan for *Cobelfret*. The CELANDINE was originally to be called the CATHERINE and the VICTORINE the CELANDINE. The names were changed before delivery. Generally used on the Zeebrugge - Purfleet route. In May 2011 the CELANDINE was chartered to *RMR Shipping*. Returned in November 2013.

CELESTINE Built by Kawasaki Heavy Industries, Sakaide, Japan as the CELESTINE. In 1996 chartered to the *British MoD* and renamed the SEA CRUSADER. She was originally expected to return to *Cobelfret Ferries* in early 2003 and resume the name CELESTINE; however, the charter was extended because of the Iraq war. Returned in September 2003 and placed on the Zeebrugge - Immingham service. In November 2006 moved to the Zeebrugge - Purfleet route. In November 2008 moved to the Ostend - Dartford service. In April 2009 the route became Ostend - Purfleet. In April 2010 chartered to *RMR Shipping*. In May 2014 returned to *Cobelfret Ferries* and in May 2016 transferred to the Dagenham - Vlissingen service.

CEMIL BAYULGEN Built by Flensburger Schiffbau-Gesellschaft, Flensburg, Germany for UN Ro-Ro of Turkey for service between Turkey and Italy. In June 2015 chartered to *CLdN*.

CLEMENTINE Built by Kawasaki Heavy Industries, Sakaide, Japan for *Cobelfret Ferries*. Mainly used on the Zeebrugge - Immingham service. In 2007 moved to the Zeebrugge - Purfleet route. In March 2013 chartered to *RMR Shipping*. In July 2013 chartered to *DFDS Seaways* and placed on the Immingham

SECTION 3 – FREIGHT ONLY FERRIES

Cuxhaven service. In November 2014 returned to *Cobelfret Ferries*. In January 2015 she retuned to charter with *DFDS Seaways* for four weeks.

CYMBELINE, UNDINE Built by Dalian Shipyard, Dalian, China for *Cobelfret Ferries*. Currently mainly used on the Dagenham - Vlissingen route. They were occasionally used on a weekend Southampton - Vlissingen service but this ceased in 2012 following the closure of the Southampton Ford Transit factory. Occasional weekend trips are made to Middlesbrough (Teesport).

FADIQ Built as the BERING STRAIT by Odense Staalskibsværft A/S, Odense, Denmark for *Pacific Basin Shipping Ltd Hong Kong* of the UK. In September 2012 sold to *Atlantica Di Navigation (Grimaldi)* of Italy and, in October, renamed the EUROCARGO BRINDISI. In March 2015 sold to *CLdN* and chartered to *Ekol Logistik AS* of Turkey and renamed the FADIQ.

MASSIMO MURA Built as the BEACHY HEAD by Flensburger Schiffbau-Gesellschaft, Flensburg, Germany for *AWSR Shipping*. On delivery, chartered to *Transfennica* and operated between Hanko (Finland) and Lübeck (Germany). In July 2006 chartered to *Stora Enso* and placed on the Kotka - Gothenburg route. In late August transferred to the Antwerp - Gothenburg service. In 2007 chartered to *Transfennica*. In January 2009 chartered to *Finnlines* and normally used on the Helsinki - Aarhus route. In January 2012 chartered to *North Sea RoRo*. In March 2013 the service ceased and she was chartered to *DFDS Seaways*. In April 2014 sold to *C Bulk NV* of Belgium, an associated company of *CLdN/Cobelfret Ferries* and renamed the WILLIAMSBORG. In July she was chartered to *Nordana Line A/S* of Denmark operating from Mediterranean ports to the USA and Latin America. In January 2016 chartered to *Grimaldi Lines* of Italy and renamed the MASSIMO MURA.

MAZARINE, PALATINE, PEREGRINE, VESPERTINE Built by Flensburger Schiffbau-Gesellschaft, Flensburg, Germany.

MELUSINE Built by Kawasaki Heavy Industries, Sakaide, Japan for *Cobelfret*. Similar to the CLEMENTINE.

OPALINE Built by Flensburger Schiffbau-Gesellschaft, Flensburg, Germany. Operates mainly between Rotterdam and Killingholme and Rotterdam and Dublin.

PAULINE, YASMINE Built by Flensburger Schiffbau-Gesellschaft, Flensburg, Germany to operate on the Zeebrugge - Killingholme route.

SOMERSET Built as the SPAARNEBORG by Flender Werft AG, Lübeck, Germany for *Wagenborg* of The Netherlands and time-chartered to *Stora-Enso* to operate between Zeebrugge and Gothenburg in conjunction with *Cobelfret Ferries*. She also operated between Tilbury and Gothenburg during 2010. In August 2011 chartered to the *Canadian MoD* to operate between Montreal and Cyprus in connection with the Libyan 'no fly zone'. On return in November she was laid up in Zeebrugge and in January 2012 moved to Gothenburg. In August 2012 chartered to *LD Lines* to operate between Marseilles and Tunis. In March 2013 returned to the *Stora Enso/Cobelfret Ferries* Zeebrugge - Gothenburg service. In November 2014 the arrangement between *Stora Enso* and *Cobelfret Ferries* ended and she was chartered to *SOL Continent Line* who took over the operation of the service, operating between Finland, Germany, Belgium and the UK. In January 2015 sold to *CLdN* and renamed the SOMERSET. Generally operates between Zeebrugge and Gothenburg.

WILHELMINE Built by the Kyokuyo Shipyard, Shimonoseki, Japan for *CLdN*. After completion, a additional deck and sponsons were retro-fitted at the Chengxi Shipyard, Jiangyin, China. Initially used on the Zeebrugge - Purfleet service. In January 2013 chartered to *P&O Ferries* to operate between Tilbury and Zeebrugge. After three weeks moved to the Middlesbrough - Rotterdam service. In November 2014 the charter ended and she was placed on the Zeebrugge - Purfleet service. She returned to *P&O Ferries* for five weeks during the refit period in January and February 2015 and again operated Middlesbrough - Rotterdam.

Under construction

26	**CELINE**	**60000t**	**17**	**17.9k**	**235.0m**	**12P**	**8000C**	**580T**	**A2**	**MT**	**9789233**
27	**NEWBUILDING 1**	**60000t**	**17**	**17.9k**	**235.0m**	**12P**	**8000C**	**580T**	**A2**	**MT**	
28	**NEWBUILDING 2**	**50000t**	**17**	**17.6k**	**211.6m**	**12P**	**-**	**400T**	**A2**	**-**	**-**
29	**NEWBUILDING 3**	**50000t**	**18**	**17.6k**	**211.6m**	**12P**	**-**	**400T**	**A2**	**-**	**-**

Bore Sea *(Nick Widdows)*

Wilhelmine *(Nick Widdows)*

30	NEWBUILDING 4	50200t	18	18.0k	212.0m	12P	-	400T	A	-	-
31	NEWBUILDING 5	50200t	18	18.0k	212.0m	12P	-	400T	A	-	-
32	NEWBUILDING 6	50200t	19	18.0k	212.0m	12P	-	400T	A	-	-
33	NEWBUILDING 7	50200t	19	18.0k	212.0m	12P	-	400T	A	-	-

CELINE, NEWBUILDING 1 Under construction by Hyundai Mipo Dockyard, Ulsan, South Korea. She is convertible to LPG propulsion and designed to be useable on deep sea ro-ro services as well as *CLdN's* current short sea routes. The CELINE is expected to enter service in September.

NEWBUILDING 2, NEWBUILDING 3 Under construction by Uljanik Shipyard, Pula, Croatia. To operate on North Sea routes.

NEWBUILDING 4, NEWBUILDING 5, NEWBUILDING 6, NEWBUILDING 7, Under construction by Hyundai Mipo Dockyard, Ulsan, South Korea. To operate on North Sea routes.

CLdN also own the CAPUCINE and SEVERINE, on charter to *Stena Line*.

FINNLINES

THE COMPANY *Finnlines PLC* is a Finnish private sector company. Services to the UK are marketed by *Finnlines UK Ltd*, a British private sector company. From 1st January 2001, *Finncarriers* was merged into the parent company, trading as *Finnlines Cargo Service*.

MANAGEMENT President & CEO Emanuele Grimaldi, **Head of Group Marketing North Sea ro-ro** Staffan Herlin.

ADDRESS *Finland* PO Box 197, 00181 Helsinki, Finland, ***UK*** Finnlines UK Ltd, Finhumber House, Queen Elizabeth Dock, Hedon Road, HULL HU9 5PB.

TELEPHONE Administration & Reservations *Finland* +358 (0)10 343 50, ***UK*** +44 (0)1482 377 655.

FAX *Administration Finland* +358 (0)10 343 5200, ***UK*** +44 (0)1482 787 229.

INTERNET *Email Finland* info.fi@finnlines.com ***UK*** info.uk@finnlines.com ***Website*** www.finnlines.com *(English, Finnish, German, Polish, Swedish)*

ROUTES OPERATED Irregular service from St Petersburg, Helsinki, Rauma and Kotka to Hull, Immingham, Amsterdam, Antwerp and Bilbao. For details see website. In view of the fact that ships are liable to be transferred between routes, the following is a list of all Finnlines Cargo Service ro-ro vessels, including those which currently do not serve the UK. Ro-pax vessels on Baltic services are listed in Section 6.

1	FINNBREEZE	28002t	11	20.0k	184.8m	12P	600C	200T	A	FI	9468889
2	FINNCARRIER	12251t	98	20.0k	154.5m	12P	-	124T	A2	FI	9132002
3	FINNHAWK	11530t	01	20.0k	162.2m	12P	-	140T	A	FI	9207895
4	FINNKRAFT	11530t	00	20.0k	162.2m	12P	-	140T	A	FI	9207883
5	FINNMASTER	12251t	98	20.0k	154.5m	12P	-	124T	A2	FI	9132014
6	FINNMERCHANT	23235t	03	21.0k	193.0m	12P	-	180T	A	FI	9234082
7	FINNMILL	25732t	02	20.0k	184.8m	12P	-	190T	A	FI	9212656
8	FINNPULP	25732t	02	20.0k	184.8m	12P	-	190T	A	FI	9212644
9	FINNSEA	28002t	11	21.0k	184.8m	12P	600C	200T	A	FI	9468891
10	FINNSKY	28002t	12	21.0k	184.8m	12P	600C	200T	A	FI	9468906
11	FINNSUN	28002t	12	21.0k	184.8m	12P	600C	200T	A	FI	9468918
12	FINNTIDE	28002t	12	21.0k	184.8m	12P	600C	200T	A	FI	9468920
13	FINNWAVE	28002t	12	21.0k	184.8m	12P	600C	200T	A	FI	9468932

FINNBREEZE, FINNSEA, FINNSKY, FINNSUN, FINNTIDE, FINNWAVE Built by Jinling Shipyard, Nanjing, China for *Finnlines*. To be lengthened by 30 metres at Remontowa Shipyard, Gdansk, Poland starting September 2017.

FINNCARRIER Built as the UNITED CARRIER by Fosen Mekaniske Verksteder A/S, Rissa, Norway for *United Shipping* (a subsidiary of *Birka Shipping*) of Finland and chartered to *Transfennica*. During 2000 she was used on their Kemi - Oulu - Antwerp - Felixstowe service. In 2001 the route was transferred to *Finnlines* and the vessel used sub-chartered to them (charter later transferred to *Finnlines*). In 2002 *United Shipping* was renamed *Birka Cargo* and the ship was renamed the BIRKA CARRIER. In 2006 the service ceased. In 2008 the charter was extended a further four years. In January 2013 chartered to *Transfennica*. In June 2013 she was renamed the CARRIER. In January 2015 sold to *Finnlines* but not delivered until the end of the year, when the charter ended. In January 2016 renamed the FINNCARRIER.

FINNHAWK Built by Jinling Shipyard, Nanjing, China for the *Macoma Shipping Group* and chartered to *Finnlines*. In April 2008 purchased by *Finnlines*. Currently operates used on service between Finland and The Netherlands, Belgium, the UK and Spain.

FINNKRAFT Built by Jinling Shipyard, Nanjing, China for the *Macoma Shipping Group* and chartered to *Finncarriers*. In April 2008 purchased by *Finnlines*. Currently operates on services between Finland and Germany.

FINNMASTER Built as the UNITED TRADER by Fosen Mekaniske Verksteder A/S, Rissa, Norway for *United Shipping* (a subsidiary of *Birka Shipping*) of Finland and chartered to *Transfennica*. During 2000 used on their Kemi - Oulu - Antwerp - Felixstowe service. In 2001 the route was transferred to *Finnlines* and the vessels used sub-chartered to them (charter later transferred to *Finnlines*). In 2002 *United Shipping* was renamed *Birka Cargo* and she was renamed the BIRKA TRADER. In 2006 the service ceased and she was transferred to other *Finnlines* routes. In 2008 the charter was extended a further four years. In January 2013 chartered to *Transfennica*. In July 2013 renamed the TRADER. In January 2015 sold to *Finnlines* but not delivered until the end of the year, when the charter ended. In January 2016 renamed the FINNMASTER. In November 2016 chartered to *DFDS Seaways*. Operated mainly between Immingham and Rotterdam. In July 2017 charter ended and she returned to *Finnlines*, operating on a new service between Oxelösund (Sweden) and Naantali (Finland).

FINNMERCHANT Built as the LONGSTONE by Flensburger Schiffbau-Gesellschaft, Flensburg, Germany for *AWSR Shipping* (later Foreland Shipping). Chartered to *Transfennica* and operated between Hanko (Finland) and Lübeck (Germany). In January 2009 chartered to *Finnlines* and placed on the Helsinki - Aarhus route. In January 2012 chartered to *North Sea RoRo*. In March 2013 the operation ceased and the charter was taken over by *DFDS Seaways* and she was placed on the Immingham - Cuxhaven route. In May took over the Zeebrugge - Rosyth route. In October 2013 sold to *C Bulk NV* of Belgium, an associated company of *CLdN/Cobelfret Ferries*. In April 2014 charter to *DFDS* ended and she was chartered to an Australian operator. In November 2014 renamed the DORSET. In December 2014 the charter ended and she returned to *CLdN*. In early January 2015 placed on the Zeebrugge - Purfleet service. Later in the month sold to *Finnlines* and renamed the FINNMERCHANT.

FINNMILL, FINNPULP Built by Jinling Shipyard, Nanjing, China for the *Macoma Shipping Group* and chartered to *Finnlines*. In 2008 purchased by *Finnlines*. During Winter 2008/09 extra ramps were added at STX Europe Helsinki shipyard to enable ro-ro traffic to be conveyed on the weather deck.

MANN LINES

THE COMPANY *Mann Lines* are owned by *Mann & Son (London) Ltd* of Great Britain. They replaced in 2001 *ArgoMann Ferry Service*, a joint venture between *Argo Reederei* of Germany and *Mann & Son*.

MANAGEMENT Managing Director Bill Binks, **Commercial Manager** David Brooks.

ADDRESS Mann & Son (London) Ltd, The Naval House, Kings Quay Street, Harwich CO12 3JJ.

TELEPHONE Administration & Reservations ***UK*** +44 (0)1255 245200, ***Germany*** +49 (0)40 25499070-0, ***Finland*** +358 (0)2 275 0000, ***Estonia*** +372 (0)679 1450.

FAX Administration & Reservations ***UK*** +44 (0)1255 245219, ***Germany*** + 49 (0)40 25499070-10, ***Finland*** +358 (0)2 253 5905, ***Estonia*** +372 (0)679 1455.

INTERNET **Email** enquiry@manngroup.co.uk **Website** www.mannlines.com *(English, Finnish, Estonian, German, Russian)*

ROUTES OPERATED Harwich (Navyard) - Cuxhaven - Paldiski - Turku - Bremerhaven (Germany) – Harwich (*STENA FORETELLER*; weekly).

1	STENA FORETELLER	24688t	02	22.0k	195.3m	12P	-	210T	A2	SE	9214666

STENA FORETELLER Built as the STENA FORETELLER by Dalian Shipyard Co Ltd, Dalian, China for *Stena RoRo*. Initially chartered to *Cetam* of France to operate between Marseilles and Tunis and renamed the CETAM MASSILIA. In November 2003 the charter ended and she resumed her original name. A number of short-term commercial and military charters followed until June 2006 when she was chartered to *StoraEnso* paper group to operate between Gothenburg and Finnish ports. In September 2009 she was chartered to *Rederi AB Transatlantic* who took over responsibility to operate all *StoraEnso's* Baltic services. In February 2012 she was chartered to *Transfennica*. In January 2015 chartered to *Mann Lines*. This charter is due to end in December 2017.

Mann Lines also have on charter the ML FREYJA which is currently on sub-charter to *SOL Continent Line*. She is expected to replace the STENA FORETELLER in January 2018.

SEA-CARGO

THE COMPANY *Sea-Cargo AS* of Norway is a subsidiary of *Seatrans AS* of Norway.

MANAGEMENT **Managing Director** Ole Saevild, **Director Business Development** Erik A Paulsen, **General Manager (Immingham)** Mark Brighton, **General Manager (Aberdeen)** Ian Shewan.

ADDRESS ***Norway*** Wernersholmvegen 5, 5232 Paradis, Norway, ***Immingham*** Sea-Cargo UK, West Riverside Road, Immingham Dock, Immingham DN40 2NT, ***Aberdeen*** Sea-Cargo Aberdeen Ltd, Matthews Quay, Aberdeen Harbour, Aberdeen, AB11 5PG.

TELEPHONE **Administration & Bookings *Bergen*** +47 55 10 84 84, ***Immingham*** +44 (0)1469 577119, ***Aberdeen*** +44 (0)1224 596481.

FAX **Administration & Reservations *Bergen*** +47 85 02 82 16, ***Immingham*** 44 (0)1469 577708, ***Aberdeen*** +44 (0)1224 582360.

INTERNET **Email** mail@sea-cargo.no **Website** www.sea-cargo.no *(English)*

ROUTES OPERATED *Sea-Cargo* operate a network of services from West Norway to Amsterdam, Aberdeen, Immingham and Esbjerg. The schedule varies from week to week and is shown on the company website. The SC ASTREA and NORRLAND are generally used on the twice-weekly Immingham - Tanager, Haugesund, Bergen and Odda service and the SEA-CARGO EXPRESS on the weekly Aberdeen - Tanager, Haugesund, Bergen, Florø, Aalesund, Kristiansund, Trondheim and Molde service.

1	NORRLAND	5562t	90	14.5k	107.5m	0P	-	28T	A	AG	8818764
2	SC AHTELA	8610t	91	14.8k	139.5m	12P	-	92T	AS	MT	8911736
3	SC ASTREA	9528t	91	13.5k	129.1m	0p	-	58T	A	BS	8917895
4	SC CONNECTOR	12251t	97	15.0k	154.5m	12P	-	124T	AS	MT	9131993
5	SEA-CARGO EXPRESS	6693t	12	16.0k	117.4m	0P	-	35T	A	MT	9358060
6	TRANS CARRIER	9953t	94	14.5k	145.2m	0P	-	94T	AS	BS	9007879
7	TRANSFIGHTER	20851t	01	14.5k	178.6m	0P	-	100T	AS	MT	9216626

NORRLAND Built by J J Sietas KG, Hamburg, Germany for *Trailer Link* of Sweden. Chartered to *Sea-Cargo*.

SC AHTELA Built as the AHTELA by Brodogradiliste "Sava", Macvanska Mitrovica, Yugoslavia, completed by Fosen Mekaniske Verksteder, Rissa, Norway for *Rederi AB Gustav Erikson* of Finland. Chartered to *Transfennica*. In 1995 chartered to *DFDS Tor Line*. In 1996 chartered to *Finncarriers Oy* of Finland and in 1997 renamed the FINNOAK. In 2007 sold to *Hollming Oy* of Finland and in 2008 the charter ended and she was renamed the AHTELA. Chartered to *Navirail* of Estonia to operate between

Helsinki and Muuga (Estonia). Between February and May 2011 chartered to *Sea-Cargo* to operate between Esbjerg (Denmark) and Egersund (Norway). In October 2012 purchased by *Sea-Cargo* and renamed the SC AHTELA.

SC ASTREA Built as the ASTREA by Tangen Verft Kragerø A/S, Kragerø, Norway for *Finncarriers* of Finland. Operated between Finland and Spain - Portugal via Antwerp. In 2006 chartered to *Danish MoD*. In 2007 chartered to *Sea-Cargo*. In August 2011 purchased by *Sea-Cargo* and renamed the SC ASTREA. Until early 2016 used primarily for moving windfarm equipment. In February placed on the Norway - Immingham service.

SC CONNECTOR Built as the UNITED EXPRESS by Fosen Mekaniske Verksteder A/S, Rissa, Norway for *United Shipping* (a subsidiary of *Birka Shipping*) of Finland and chartered to *Transfennica*. During 2000 used on their Kemi - Oulu - Antwerp - Felixstowe service. In 2001 the route was transferred to *Finnlines* and the vessel used sub-chartered to them (charter later transferred to *Finnlines*). In 2002 *United Shipping* was renamed *Birka Cargo* and she was renamed the BIRKA EXPRESS. In 2008 the charter was extended a further four years. In June 2013 renamed the EXPRESS. In November 2013 chartered to *Transfennica*. In April 2014 sold to *Sea-Cargo* but initially continued to operate for *Transfennica*. During winter 2015 re-engined and modified to allow to side loading. In February 2015 renamed the SC CONNECTOR. Entered service in late April.

SEA-CARGO EXPRESS One of two vessels ordered in 2005 from Bharati Ratnagiri Ltd, Mumbai, India for *Sea-Cargo*. The order for the second ship was cancelled. Trailers are carried on the main deck only. Containers are carried on the weather deck and pallets on the lower decks. A crane is provided for the containers and a side door for pallets. She operates on the Aberdeen - Norway service.

TRANS CARRIER Built as the KORSNÄS LINK by Brodogradiliste Kraljevica, Kraljevica, Croatia for *SeaLink AB* of Sweden and due to be time-chartered to *Korsnäs AB*, a Swedish forest products company. However, due to the war in Croatia, delivery was seriously delayed and she was offered for sale. In 1994 sold to the *Swan Group* and renamed the SWAN HUNTER. She was placed on the charter market. In 1997 she was chartered to *Euroseabridge* and renamed the PARCHIM. In 1999 the charter ended and she resumed the name SWAN HUNTER. In 1999 she was sold to *SeaTrans* and renamed the TRANS CARRIER. She operated for *Sea-Cargo*. In 2005 chartered to *Finnlines* and used on the Finland to Spain/Portugal service. In 2006 returned to *Sea-Cargo*. In January and February 2009 lengthened by 18.9 metres in Poland.

TRANSFIGHTER Built as the FINNFIGHTER by Stocznia Gdynia, S.A. Gdynia, Poland for *B & N Nordsjöfrakt* of Sweden and chartered to F-Ships to operate between Finland and the USA. In 2004 Sold to *Gorthons Lines* of Sweden and in 2005 chartered to *Rederi AB Transatlantic* of Sweden. She continued to be operated between Scandinavia and North America. In 2006 extended by Blohm & Voss, Hamburg, Germany. In February 2009 she was renamed the TRANSFIGHTER. In November 2016 sold to *Seatrans AS* of Norway and chartered to *Sea-Cargo*. Operates between Norwegian ports, Rotterdam and Sheerness.

SEATRUCK FERRIES

THE COMPANY *Seatruck Ferries Ltd* is a British private sector company. It is part of the *Clipper Group*.

MANAGEMENT **Chairman** Flemming Steen, **CEO** Alistair Eagles.

ADDRESSES ***Heysham (HQ)*** North Quay, Heysham Port, Heysham, Morecambe, Lancs LA3 2UH, ***Warrenpoint*** Seatruck House, The Ferry Terminal, Warrenpoint, County Down BT34 3JR, ***Liverpool:*** Seatruck Ferry Terminal, Brocklebank Dock, Port of Liverpool, L20 1DB, ***Dublin:*** Seatruck Dublin, Terminal 5, Alexandra Road, Dublin 1 Irish Republic.

TELEPHONE **Administration** +44 (0)1524 855377, **Reservations *Heysham*** +44 (0)1524 853512. ***Warrenpoint*** +44 (0)28 754400, ***Liverpool*** + (0)151 9333660, ***Dublin*** + (0) 353 18230492.

FAX **Administration** +44 (0)28 4175 4545, **Reservations *Warrenpoint*** +44 (0)28 4177 3737, ***Heysham*** +44 (0)1524 853549.

INTERNET **Email** aje@seatruckgroup.co.uk **Websites** www.seatruckferries.com *(English)*

ROUTES OPERATED Heysham - Warrenpoint (9 hrs; *CLIPPER PENNANT, SEATRUCK PANORAMA*; 2 per day), Heysham - Dublin (9 hrs; *CLIPPER POINT*; 1 per day), Liverpool - Dublin (9 hrs; *CLIPPER RANGER, SEATRUCK PACE, SEATRUCK POWER, SEATRUCK PROGRESS*; up to 4 per day).

1	**CLIPPER PENNANT**	**14759t**	**09**	**22.0k**	**142.0m**	**12P**	**-**	**120T**	**A**	**CY**	**9372688**
2	**CLIPPER POINT**	**14759t**	**08**	**22.0k**	**142.0m**	**12P**	**-**	**120T**	**A**	**CY**	**9350666**
3	**CLIPPER RANGER**	**7606t**	**98**	**17.0k**	**122.3m**	**12P**	**-**	**84T**	**A**	**IM**	**9119402**
4	**SEATRUCK PACE**	**14759t**	**09**	**22.0k**	**142.0m**	**12P**	**-**	**120T**	**A**	**CY**	**9350678**
5	**SEATRUCK PANORAMA**	**14759t**	**09**	**22.0k**	**142.0m**	**12P**	**-**	**120T**	**A**	**CY**	**9372676**
6	**SEATRUCK POWER**	**19722t**	**11**	**21.0k**	**142.0m**	**12P**	**-**	**151T**	**A**	**IM**	**9506215**
7	**SEATRUCK PROGRESS**	**19722t**	**11**	**21.0k**	**142.0m**	**12P**	**-**	**151T**	**A**	**IM**	**9506203**

CLIPPER PENNANT Built by Astilleros Sevilla SA, Seville, Spain for *Seatruck Ferries*. In January 2013 chartered to *Stena RoRo*.

CLIPPER POINT Built by Astilleros de Huelva SA, Huelva, Spain for *Seatruck Ferries*. In May 2012 chartered to *DFDS Seaways* and placed on the Immingham-Cuxhaven route. In April 2013 chartered to the organisers of the 'SATA Rally Azores 2013' car rally to take cars from Portugal to the Azores. In May began operating for *DFDS Seaways* in the Baltic. In October transferred to the Immingham - Cuxhaven route. In June 2015 the charter ended. In July she was chartered to *InterShipping*, of Morocco to operate between Algeciras and Tangiers. In September 2016 the charter ended and she was placed on the Heysham - Dublin service.

CLIPPER RANGER Built as the LEMBITU by Astilleros de Huelva SA, Huelva, Spain for the *Estonian Shipping Company*. On completion chartered to *P&O European Ferries (Irish Sea)* and placed on their Liverpool - Dublin route. In Autumn 1998 she was chartered to *Dart Line* and placed on the Dartford - Vlissingen route. In 1999 she was renamed the DART 7. In Autumn 1999 the charter was ended and she was chartered to *Cetam* of France, resumed the name LEMBITU and was used on services between Marseilles and Tunis. In 2000 she was chartered to *P&O European Ferries (Irish Sea)* and renamed the CELTIC SUN; she operated between Liverpool and Dublin. In 2001 the charter ended; she then reverted to the name LEMBITU and was chartered to *NorseMerchant Ferries* and placed on the Heysham - Dublin service. In late 2001 the charter ended and she returned to *ESCO* service in the Baltic. In 2003 chartered to *Scandlines AG* and placed on their Rostock - Helsinki - Muuga service. This service finished in December 2004 and she was chartered to *Channel Freight Ferries* in January 2005. In March 2005 chartered to *NorseMerchant Ferries* again and operated between Heysham and Belfast. Later purchased by *Elmira Shipping* of Greece and renamed the RR CHALLENGE. In June 2005 chartered to *Seatruck Ferries*. In October 2007 sold to *Attica Group* of Greece and renamed the CHALLENGE. She continued to be chartered to *Seatruck Ferries*. In January 2008 she was transferred to the Liverpool - Dublin route and in April sold to *Seatruck Ferries*. In July renamed the CLIPPER RANGER. In June 2009 replaced the SHIELD (now the HILDASAY) until the new CLIPPER PENNANT took over in October. In May 2010 inaugurated a new Heysham - Larne service. In October 2013 chartered to *Caledonian MacBrayne* to replace the MUIRNEAG. The charter ended in May 2015. In November 2015 placed on the Liverpool - Dublin route as third ship. In March 2016 transferred to the Heysham - Dublin service. In September 2016 moved to the Liverpool - Dublin routes as fourth vessel.

SEATRUCK PACE Built as the CLIPPER PACE by Astilleros Sevilla SA, Seville, Spain for *Seatruck Ferries*. In March 2012 renamed the SEATRUCK PACE. In January 2013 chartered to *Blue Water Shipping* of Denmark to carry wind turbine parts between Mostyn (Wales) and Esbjerg. Now operates on the Liverpool - Dublin route.

SEATRUCK PANORAMA Built by Astilleros de Huelva SA, Huelva Spain for *Seatruck Ferries*. Launched as the CLIPPER PENNANT and renamed the CLIPPER PANORAMA before delivery. In December 2011 renamed the SEATRUCK PANORAMA.

SEATRUCK POWER, SEATRUCK PROGRESS Built by Flensburger Schiffbau-Gesellschaft, Flensburg, Germany for *Seatruck Ferries*.

Seatruck Ferries also own the ARROW currently on charter to *Isle of Man Steam Packet Company* and the STENA PERFORMER and STENA PRECISION, currently on charter to *Stena Line*.

SOL CONTINENT LINE

THE COMPANY *SOL Continent Line* is a division of *Swedish Orient Line*, a Swedish private sector company.

MANAGEMENT **Managing Director** Ragnar Johansson, **General Manager** Jonas Wåhlin, **Commercial Area Manager, North Sea** Pär Ekelöf

ADDRESSES Svenska Orient Linien AB, Klippan 1A, SE-414 51 Gothenburg, Sweden.

TELEPHONE +46 (0)31-354 40 00. **FAX** +46 (0)31-354 40 01.

INTERNET **Email** info@sollines.se **Website** www.sollines.se/en/content/sol-continent-line *(English)*

ROUTES OPERATED Gothenburg - Zeebrugge (34 hrs; ***ELISABETH RUSS, ML FREYJA, SCHIEBORG, SLINGEBORG***; 7 per week), Oulu - Kemi - Husum - Lübeck - Gothenburg - Zeebrugge - Tilbury - Zeebrugge - Oxelosund * - Oulu (***THULELAND, TRANSTIMBER***; 1 per week), Kemi - Oulu - Antwerp - Zeebrugge - Gothenburg - Kemi (***BALTICA, VASALAND***; 1 per week).

1	**BALTICA**	21224t	90	19.0k	157.7m	0P	-	163T	A	FI	8813154
2	**ELISABETH RUSS**	10471t	99	21.0k	153.5m	12P	-	120T	A2	PT	9186429
3	**ML FREYJA**	23000t	17	19.0k	190.8m	12P	-	180T	A	IT	9799977
4	**SCHIEBORG**	21005t	00	18.0k	183.4m	12P	-	180T	A	NL	9188233
5	**SLINGEBORG**	21005t	00	18.0k	183.4m	12P	-	180T	A	NL	9188245
6	**THULELAND**	23128t	06	16.0k	190.7m	12P	-	200T	A	SE	9343261
7	**TRANSTIMBER**	23128t	07	16.0k	190.7m	12P	-	200T	A	SE	9343273
8	**VASALAND**	20203t	84	19.5k	155.0m	12P	-	150T	A	UK	8222111

BALTICA Built by Hyundai Heavy Industries, Ulsan, South Korea as the AHLERS BALTIC for *Ahlers Line* and chartered to *Finncarriers*. In 1995 acquired by *Poseidon Schiffahrt AG* of Germany and renamed the TRANSBALTICA. She continued to be chartered to *Finncarriers* and was acquired by them when they purchased *Poseidon Schiffahrt AG* (now *Finnlines Deutschland AG*) in 1997. In 2003 sold to Norwegian interests and chartered back; She was renamed the BALTICA. In recent years she operated on the Helsinki - St Petersburg - Hamina - Helsinki - Zeebrugge - Tilbury – Amsterdam - Antwerp - service with the MERCHANT. During 2007 she operated Helsinki - Turku - Antwerp on a one-week cycle. In January 2008 moved to Baltic services. In April 2011 chartered to *Power Line* to operate between Helsinki and Travemünde. In January 2013 returned to *Finnlines*. In October 2015 sold to *Godby Shipping* of Finland. In November chartered to *SOL Continent Line*.

ELISABETH RUSS Built by J J Sietas KG, Hamburg, Germany for *Ernst Russ* of Germany and chartered to *Transfennica*. In 2012 the charter ended and she was chartered to a number of operators. In November 2015 chartered to *SOL Continent Line*.

ML FREYJA Built by CN Visentini, Donada, Italy and chartered to *Mann Lines*. In June 2017 sub-chartered to *SOL Continent Line* for six months.

SCHIEBORG, SLINGEBORG, Built by Flender Werft AG, Lübeck, Germany for *Wagenborg* of The Netherlands and time-chartered to *Stora-Enso* to operate on the *Stora Enso/Cobelfret Ferries* service between Zeebrugge and Gothenburg. In November 2014 the arrangement between *Stora Enso* and *Cobelfret Ferries* ended and they were chartered to *SOL Continent Line* who took over the operation of the service.

THULELAND Built as the TRANSPULP by Aker Finnyards, Rauma, Finland for *Baltic Container Shipping* of the UK and chartered to *Rederi AB Transatlantic* of Sweden. Operated on service operated for Stora Enso Paper Group, mainly in the Baltic. In early 2011 transferred to the Gothenburg - Tilbury (once weekly) and Gothenburg - Zeebrugge (*CLdN* service) (once weekly) services. In January 2013 began operating twice weekly to Tilbury, replacing the SELANDIA SEAWAYS of *DFDS Seaways*. In January 2015 chartered to *SOL Continent Line*. In December 2016 renamed the THULELAND.

TRANSTIMBER Built as the by Aker Finnyards, Rauma, Finland for *Baltic Container Shipping* of the UK and chartered to *Rederi AB Transatlantic* of Sweden. Operated on service operated for Stora Enso Paper

Cemil Bayulgen *(Nick Widdows)*

Elisabeth Russ *(John Bryant)*

Group, mainly in the Baltic. In January 2015 chartered to *SOL Continent Line*. In early 2017 it was announced she would be renamed the TUNDRALAND but this did not occur.

VASALAND Built as the OIHONNA by Rauma Repola OY, Rauma, Finland for *Effoa-Finska Ångfartygs Ab*, of Finland. In December 1986 sold to *Fincarriers Ab* of Finland. In November 2003 sold to *Stena RoRo* of Sweden and renamed the VASALAND. Over the ensuing years, chartered to a number of companies including *Finnlines* and *Transfennica*. In September 2009 chartered to *SOL Continent Line*, initially operating purely in the Baltic but since 2016 used on their North Sea service.

FLOTA SUARDIAZ

THE COMPANY *Flota Suardiaz SL* is owned by *Grupo Suardiaz*, a Spanish private sector logistics company which operates divisions in ports, bunkering, warehousing, haulage, freight forwarding and shipping.

MANAGEMENT **Presidente** Don Juan Riva, **Director General** Alfredo Menendez Garcia.

ADDRESSES **Spain** Calle Ayala, 6 28001 Madrid, Spain, **UK** Suardiaz Shipping Ltd, Suardiaz House, 193 Shirley Road, Southampton SO15 3FG.

TELEPHONE **Spain** +34 914 31 66 40, **UK** +44 (0) 2380 211 981.

FAX **Spain** + 34 914 36 46 74, **UK** +44 (0) 2380 335309.

INTERNET **Email** infoweb@suardiaz.com, **Website** www.suardiaz.com *(English, Spanish)*.

ROUTES OPERATED **Northern Europe/Spain/Canaries/Med Lines** Emden – Sheerness – Zeebrugge – Santander – Vigo - Las Palmas – Tenerife – Casablanca – Mostaganem – Barcelona (weekly with up to two sailings per week on some sections including Emden – Sheerness and Las Palmas – Tenerife – Barcelona). **Atlantic Line** Zeebrugge – St Nazaire – Vigo – Tanger Med (twice weekly with St Nazaire - Vigo four sailings per week). **Algeria Line** Barcelona – Marseille – Alger – Mostagenem (weekly).

Services listed carry unaccompanied ro-ro cargo together with large volumes of trade cars for vehicle manufacturers and distributors and interwork between routes. Occasional irregular calls are made at North Shields, Vlissingen, Le Havre and Southampton and sailings can sometimes omit scheduled ports. The Atlantic Line is operated with European Union funding from the TEN-T Programme and supported by a GEFCO car carrying contract between St Nazaire and Vigo. Vessels are regularly transferred between routes and are often chartered out for short periods to other operators and vehicle manufacturers. In view of this, the following is a list of all vessels in the *Flota Suardiaz* fleet including those not currently serving the UK.

1	BOUZAS	15224t	02	18.5k	149.4m	12P	1265C	105T	A	ES	9249996
2	GALICIA	16361t	03	15.0k	149.4m	12P	1390C	110T	A	PT	9268409
3	GRAN CANARIA CAR	9600t	01	18.0k	132.5m	0P	1150C	42T	AS	PT	9218014
4	IVAN	8191t	96	14.6k	102.5m	0P	853C	73T	A	PT	9112040
5	L'AUDACE	15222t	99	18.5k	149.4m	12P	1233C	105T	A	ES	9187318
6	LA SURPRISE	15222t	00	18.5k	149.4m	12P	1233C	105T	A	PT	9198719
7	SUAR VIGO	16361t	03	18.5k	149.4m	12P	1356C	110T	A	ES	9250000
8	TENERIFE CAR	13122t	02	20.0k	149.4m	12P	1354C	54T	AS	PT	9249984
9	VERONA	37237t	00	20.5k	176.7m	0P	3,919C	400T	QRS	NO	9190858
10	VIKING CONSTANZA	20216t	09	18.0k	139.9m	0P	2000C	65T	AQR	SG	9407689

BOUZAS, GALICIA, L'AUDACE, LA SURPRISE, SUAR VIGO Built by Hijos de J. Barreras SA, Vigo, Portugal for *Flota Suardiaz* of Spain for use on services in the Mediterranean and to the Canaries, U.K. and Benelux. The vessels are highly flexible with a 12-driver capacity and three full height freight decks, each fitted with a mezzanine deck for cars, together with a further dedicated car deck. In addition to operating for *Flota Suardiaz* a number of vessels have spent periods on charter to *UECC*. The L'AUDACE was chartered to *P&O Ferries* to operate between Hull and Zeebrugge in early 2015. Since early 2017 she has been on charter to *Priority Ro-Ro Services* in the Caribbean sailing between Santo Domingo, Dominican Republic and San Juan, Puerto Rico.

GRAN CANARIA CAR Built as HARALD FLICK by Hijos de J. Barreras SA, Vigo, Portugal for *Naviera del Odiel*, one of the shareholders in Barreras and placed on 10 year charter to *Flota Suardiaz* of Spain for use on services in the Mediterranean and to the Canaries, U.K. and Benelux. Renamed GRAN CANARIA CAR before entering service. In 2008 ownership passed to *Navicar SA* a subsidiary of *Flota Suardiaz*. In addition to operating for *Flota Suardiaz* has been chartered to *UECC* on several occasions.

IVAN Built by Astilleros De Murueta, Vizcaya, Spain for *Adamastor - Sociedade de Navegação, Lda* a subsidiary of *Flota Suardiaz* for use on short sea services. For many years she operated a now ceased service from Sheerness and Grimsby to Calais.

TENERIFE CAR Built by Hijos de J. Barreras SA, Vigo, Portugal for *Navicar SA* a subsidiary of *Flota Suardiaz* for use on services in the Mediterranean and to the Canaries, UK and Benelux.

VERONA Built by Uljanik Shipbuilding Industries, Pula, Croatia for Montagu Bay Shipping, Monrovia, Liberia for charter to *Wallenius Wilhelmsen*. In 2002 sold to *Siem Car Carriers* of Panama. Of deep-sea ocean-going ro-ro design with a quarter ramp, she was chartered by *Suardiaz* from early 2016 onwards.

VIKING CONSTANZA Built by Kyokuyo Shipyard Corporation, Japan for *Gram Car Carriers*, Norway for operation on the charter market as part of a series of four vessels. Of short sea PTCC design the vessels have both stern and quarter ramps. In 2015 chartered by *UECC*. In 2017 chartered by *Suardiaz*.

TRANSFENNICA

THE COMPANY *Transfennica Ltd* is a Finnish private sector company wholly owned by *Spliethoff Bevrachtingskantoor* of The Netherlands.

MANAGEMENT **Managing Director** Dirk P. Witteveen, **Sales Director (UK)** Andrew Clarke.

ADDRESSES ***Finland*** Eteläranta 12, 00130 Helsinki, Finland, ***UK*** Finland House, 47 Berth, Tilbury Port, Tilbury, Essex RM18 7EH.

TELEPHONE **Administration & Reservations *Finland*** +358 (0)9 13262, ***UK*** +44 (0)1375 363 900.

FAX **Administration & Reservations *Finland*** +358 (0)9 652377, ***UK*** +44 (0)1375 840 888.

INTERNET **Email *Finland*** info@transfennica.com ***UK*** info.uk@transfennica.com

Website www.transfennica.com *(English, Finnish, Russian)*

ROUTES OPERATED Tilbury (twice weekly) to various destinations in Finland and Russia. Please see the website. All *Transfennica* ships are listed below as ships are sometimes moved between routes.

1	BORE BANK	19107t	96	20.0k	138.8m	12P	-	105T	A2	FI	9160774
2	GENCA	28301t	07	22.0k	205.0m	12P	-	200T	A2	NL	9307372
3	KRAFTCA	28301t	06	22.0k	205.0m	12P	-	200T	A2	NL	9307360
4	MIRANDA	10471t	98	22.0k	153.5m	12P	-	112T	A	FI	9183790
5	MISANA	14100t	07	20.0k	163.9m	12P	-	150T	A	FI	9348936
6	MISIDA	14100t	07	20.0k	163.9m	12P	-	150T	A	FI	9348948
7	PLYCA	28301t	09	22.0k	205.0m	12P	-	200T	A2	NL	9345398
8	PULPCA	28301t	08	22.0k	205.0m	12P	-	200T	A2	NL	9345386
9	SEAGARD	10488t	99	21.0k	153.5m	12P	-	134T	A2	FI	9198977
10	STENA FORERUNNER	24688t	02	22.0k	195.3m	12P	-	210T	A2	SE	9227259
11	TIMCA	28301t	06	22.0k	205.0m	12P	-	200T	A2	NL	9307358
12	TRICA	28301t	07	22.0k	205.0m	12P	-	200T	A2	NL	9307384

BORE BANK Built as the SERENADEN by Umoe Sterkoder AS, Kristiansund, Norway for *Rederi AB Engship* of Finland and chartered to *Transfennica*. In 2006 *Rederi AB Engship* was taken over by *Rettig Group Bore*. In 2007 converted at COSCO Shipyard, Nantong, China to add a garage on top of the weather deck, renamed AUTO BANK and placed on long-term charter to *UECC*. Generally used on the Baltic or Iberian services. In December 2016 converted back to a conventional ro-ro freighter by Öresundwerft, Landskrona, Sweden and renamed the BORE BANK. Chartered to *Transfennica*.

GENCA, KRAFTCA, PLYCA, PULPCA, TIMCA, TRICA Built by New Szczecin Shipyard (SSN), Szczecin, Poland for *Spliethoff Bevrachtingskantoor*, owners of *Transfennica*.

MIRANDA Built by J J Sietas KG, Hamburg, Germany for *Godby Shipping AB* of Finland. Initially chartered to *Transfennica*. In 2000 she was chartered to *Finnlines*. Until the end of 2007 used on a Helsinki - Hamina - Zeebrugge service only available northbound for general traffic. From January 2008 operated on *UPM-Kymmene Seaways'* service from Hamina to Lübeck, Amsterdam and Tilbury. In January 2013 chartered to *Acciona Trasmediterranea* for service in the Mediterranean. In January 2016 long-term chartered to *Stena RoRo*, who sub-chartered her to *Transfennica*.

MISANA, MISIDA Built by J J Sietas, Hamburg, Germany for *Godby Shipping AB* of Finland and time-chartered to *UPM-Kymmene* of Finland to operate between Finland, Spain and Portugal. In July 2013 charter taken over by *Finnlines*. In January 2016 long-term chartered to *Stena RoRo*, who then sub-chartered them to *Transfennica*.

SEAGARD Built by J J Sietas KG, Hamburg, Germany for *Bror Husell Chartering* of Finland (later acquired by *Bore Shipowning* of Finland) and chartered to *Transfennica*.

STENA FORERUNNER Built by Dalian Shipyard Co Ltd, Dalian, China for *Stena RoRo* and chartered to *Transfennica*.

UECC

THE COMPANY *United European Car Carriers AS* is a Norwegian private sector company jointly owned in equal shares by *Nippon Yusen Kabushiki Kaisha (NYK)* of Japan and *Wallenius Lines* of Sweden. *UECC* consists of companies in Norway, Germany, Spain, France, Portugal and the UK. The fleet technical and ship management department is based in Grimsby (UK).

MANAGEMENT **Chief Executive Officer** Glenn Edvardsen **Sales Manager UK** Nick Clark.

ADDRESSES **Norway** Karenlyst Allè 57, 0277 Oslo, **UK** 17 St. Helen's Place, London EC3A 6DG and Units 5B & 5C Appian Way, Europa Park, Grimsby, DN31 2UT.

TELEPHONE **Norway** +47 21 00 98 00, **UK** +44 (0)207 628 2855 and +44 (0)1472 269429.

FAX **Norway** +47 21 00 98 01, **UK** +44 (0)207 628 2858.

INTERNET **Email** companymail@uecc.com, **Website** www.uecc.com *(English)*.

ROUTES OPERATED **Atlantic Service** Vigo – Le Havre – Zeebrugge – Sheerness – Vigo (***BALTIC BREEZE, ARABIAN BREEZE***; weekly), Vigo – Zeebrugge – Bremerhaven – Drammen – Wallhamn – Cuxhaven – Southampton – Vigo (***ASIAN BREEZE***; weekly), **Baltic Service** Southampton – Zeebrugge – Bremerhaven – Malmo – Hanko – St Petersburg – Gdynia – Southampton (***AUTO ECO, AUTO ENERGY***; weekly), **Bristol Service** Portbury - Pasajes (***AUTOSUN***; weekly), **Biscay Services** Santander – Pasajes – Zeebrugge – Southampton – Santander (***AUTOSTAR***; weekly), Santander – Pasajes – Rotterdam - Zeebrugge – Santander (***AUTOSKY***, weekly), Pasajes – Zeebrugge – Southampton – Le Havre – Pasajes (***AUTOPRESTIGE***; weekly), **Norway Service** Bremerhaven – Oslo – Drammen – Walhamn – Oslo – Drammen – Bremerhaven (***AUTOPRIDE***; weekly), **North Sea Service** Cuxhaven – Immingham (***AUTOPRESTIGE***, twice weekly), **North – South Service** Bremerhaven – Vlissingen – Portbury – Vigo – Sagunto – Tarragona – Livorno – Pireaus – Autoport – Yenikoy – Borusan – Vigo – Southampton – Bremerhaven (***CORAL LEADER, EMERALD LEADER, OPAL LEADER, VEGA LEADER, VIKING LEADER***; weekly).

Services listed carry unaccompanied ro-ro cargo together with large volumes of trade cars and often call at additional ports for an inducement and these have included Cork, Dublin, Immingham, Liverpool, Tilbury, and Newcastle. In addition, ad-hoc short-sea contract sailings for vehicle manufacturers and distributors are also operated throughout Northern Europe. Vessels are regularly transferred between routes and contracts and the following is a list of all owned and long term chartered vessels currently in the *UECC* fleet including those not presently serving the UK. The fleet is regularly supplemented by occasional voyages made by vessels of *Flota Suardiaz* and *LDA Seaplane* (the *Louis Dreyfus Armateurs* Airbus ro-ro operation) and by deep sea ocean-going ro-ro vessels long term chartered from parent companies *NYK Line* and *Wallenius Lines* and Eukor (which is 40% owned by Wallenius). Long term chartered vessels at the time of preparation and considered out of the scope of this book were the CORAL LEADER, EMERALD LEADER, OPAL LEADER, VEGA LEADER AND VICTORY LEADER all of which belong to NYK Line.

1	AEGEAN BREEZE	27876t	83	18.0k	164.0m	0P	3242C	260T	QRS	SG	8202367
2	ARABIAN BREEZE	27876t	83	18.0k	164.0m	0P	3242C	260T	QRS	SG	8202355
3	ASIAN BREEZE	27876t	83	18.0k	164.0m	0P	3242C	260T	QRS	SG	8202381
4	AUTO BAY	19094t	96	20.0k	138.8m	12P	1610C	105T	A2	FI	9122007
5	AUTO ECO	43424t	16	18.6k	181.0m	0P	3800C	-	QRS	PT	9736365
6	AUTO ENERGY	43424t	16	18.6k	181.0m	0P	3800C	-	QRS	PT	9736377
7	AUTOPREMIER	11591t	97	20.0k	128.8m	0P	1220C	-	AS	PT	9131943
8	AUTOPRESTIGE	11596t	99	20.0k	128.8m	0P	1220C	-	AS	PT	9190157
9	AUTOPRIDE	11591t	97	20.0k	128.8m	0P	1220C	-	AS	PT	9131955
10	AUTOPROGRESS	11591t	98	20.0k	128.8m	0P	1220C	-	AS	PT	9131967
11	AUTOSKY	21010t	00	20.9k	140.0m	0P	2080C	-	AS	PT	9206774
12	AUTOSTAR	21010t	00	20.9k	140.0m	0P	2080C	-	AS	PT	9206786
13	AUTOSUN	21094t	00	20.9k	140.0m	0P	1220C	-	AS	PT	9227053
14	BALTIC BREEZE	29979t	83	17.5K	164.0m	0P	3242C	260T	QRS	SG	8312590
15	VIKING ODESSA	20216t	09	18.0k	139.9m	0P	2000C	65T	AQR	SG	9398876

AEGEAN BREEZE, ARABIAN BREEZE, ASIAN BREEZE Built by Kurushima Dockyard, Onishi, Japan for *Fuji Shipping* of Tokyo. Sold in 1988 to *Amon Shipping*. In 1990 sold to *Wallenius Lines*, Singapore and later chartered to *UECC*. Designated Breeze Class and of deep-sea ocean-going ro-ro design with quarter ramps, each was re-engined and heavily rebuilt in 2008 at COSCO Dalian Shipyard, China to extend lifespan and improve suitability for short sea service.

AUTO BAY Built as the HERALDEN by Umoe Sterkoder AS, Kristiansund, Norway for *Rederi AB Engship* of Finland and chartered to *Transfennica*. In 2006 *Rederi AB Engship* was taken over by *Rettig Group Bore*. Converted along with two sister vessels at COSCO Shipyard, Nantong, China in 2007 to add a garage on top of the weather deck, renamed AUTO BAY and placed on long-term charter to *UECC* and designated B-Class. She has generally been used on Iberian services. In July 2017 charter ended and during summer converted back to conventional ro-ro layout.

AUTO ECO, AUTO ENERGY Designated as E-Class both are Dual fuel LNG Ice Class 1A pure car and truck carriers with side and quarter ramps built by Kawasaki Heavy Industries at NACKS shipyard, Nantong, China for *UECC*. Used on Baltic services, the vessels are refuelled by a specialist barge in Zeebrugge. Both vessels are used on the Baltic service.

AUTOPREMIER, AUTOPRESTIGE, AUTOPROGRESS, AUTOPRIDE Built by Frisian Shipyard, Harlingen, the Netherlands for *UECC*. Designated P-class, they are an enlarged version of the now scrapped R-class and built to a 'Grimsby-Max' specification with greater capacity for ro-ro cargo. Generally used on scheduled sailings between Iberia or Germany and Norway, the Benelux and UK.

AUTOSKY, AUTOSTAR, AUTOSUN Built by Tsuneishi Zosen, Tadotsu, Japan for *UECC* Designated S-class, they are a further enlargement of the P-class and R-class designs and are normally used on Biscay routes.

BALTIC BREEZE Built by Kurushima Dockyard, Onishi, Japan for *Fuji Shipping Co* of Tokyo. Sold in 1988 to *Amon Shipping*. Sold to *Wallenius Lines*, Singapore in 1990. Chartered to *Eukor* then to *UECC*. Of deep-sea ocean-going ro-ro design with quarter ramps, she was re-engined and heavily rebuilt in 2008 at COSCO Dalian Shipyard, China along with her sister Breeze Class vessels.

VIKING ODESSA Built by Kyokuyo Shipyard Corporation, Japan for Gram Car Carriers, Norway for operation on the charter market as part of a series of four vessels. Of short sea PTCC design the vessels have both stern and quarter ramps. In 2015 chartered by UECC.

Clipper Point and Seatruck Power *(George Holland)*

Auto Bay as Transgard *(Matthew Davies)*

SECTION 4 - RO-RO OPERATORS CONVEYING PRIVATE TRAFFIC

The following operators employ ro-ro freight ships for the conveyance of their own traffic or traffic for a limited number of customers and do not normally solicit general traffic from hauliers or shippers.

FORELAND SHIPPING

THE COMPANY *Foreland Shipping Limited* (formerly *AWSR Shipping Limited*) is a UK private sector company. The principal shareholder in *Foreland Shipping* is *Hadley Shipping Group*.

MANAGEMENT **Chairman** Peter Morton, **Managing Director** Paul Trudgeon, **Operations Director** Stuart Williams.

ADDRESS 117-119 Houndsditch, London EC3A 7BT.

TELEPHONE +44 (0)20 7480 4140.

FAX +44 (0)20 7280 8790.

INTERNET **Website** www.foreland-shipping.co.uk *(English)*

ROUTES OPERATED No routes are operated. Ships are for charter to the *UK Ministry of Defence* for their 'Strategic Sealift Capability'.

1	ANVIL POINT	23235t	03	17.1k	193.0m	12P	-	180T	A	UK	9248540
2	EDDYSTONE	23235t	02	17.1k	193.0m	12P	-	180T	A	UK	9234070
3	HARTLAND POINT	23235t	03	17.1k	193.0m	12P	-	180T	A	UK	9248538
4	HURST POINT	23235t	02	17.1k	193.0m	12P	-	180T	A	UK	9234068

ANVIL POINT, HARTLAND POINT Built by Harland & Wolff, Belfast, UK for *AWSR Shipping*.

EDDYSTONE, HURST POINT Built by Flensburger Schiffbau-Gesellschaft, Flensburg, Germany for *AWSR Shipping*.

HOLMEN CARRIER

THE COMPANY *Holmen Carrier* is the branding of ships operated for *Holmen Paper AB*, an international company based in Sweden.

MANAGEMENT **President and CEO** Henrik Sjölund.

ADDRESS Holmen AB, P.O. Box 5407, SE-114 84 Stockholm, Sweden.

TELEPHONE +46 8 666 21 00

INTERNET **Website** www.holmen.com/en **Email** info@holmen.com *(English, Swedish)*

ROUTES OPERATED Norrköping (Sweden) - Travemünde - Sheerness - Hull - Norrköping (2 weeks; *EXPORTER, SHIPPER*, 1 per week).

1	EXPORTER	6620t	91	16.5k	122.0m	0P	-	90T	A	FI	8820860
2	SHIPPER	6620t	91	16.5k	122.0m	0P	-	90T	A	FI	8911748

EXPORTER Built as the GRANÖ by Brodogradiliste "Sava", Macvanska Mitrovica, Yugoslavia (fitted out by Fosen Mekaniske Verksteder of Rissa, Norway) for *Rederi AB Gustav Erikson* of Finland and chartered to *Transfennica* for service between Finland and Germany. In 1995 the owning company became *United Shipping* and in 2002 *Birka Cargo AB*. In 2000 she was chartered to the *Korsnäs Paper Group* to carry their traffic from Gävle (Sweden) to Chatham and Terneuzen (The Netherlands). In 2002 she was renamed the BIRKA EXPORTER. In 2005 the charter and operation of the services were taken over by *DFDS Tor Line*. The northbound Terneuzen - Gävle section became a ferry route marketed as part of the *DFDS Tor Line* network. This arrangement ceased in 2006. In 2008 chartered to *Finnlines*. In January 2010 chartered to *Holmen Paper AB*. In June 2013 renamed the EXPORTER.

SHIPPER Built as the STYRSÖ and renamed the BIRKA SHIPPER in 2002 and the SHIPPER in June 2013. Otherwise all details as the EXPORTER.

LD SEAPLANE

THE COMPANY *LD Seaplane* (formerly *Fret-CETAM*) is a French private sector company, 100% owned by *Louis Dreyfus Armateurs SAS*.

MANAGEMENT **General Manager** Jean-Louis Cadoret.

ADDRESS LD Seaplane, 21 Quai Gallieni - 92158, Suresnes Cedex, France.

TELEPHONE +33 (0)1 7038 6000.

INTERNET **Website** www.lda.fr/ld-seaplane-145 *(English)*

ROUTES OPERATED Mostyn (Wales) - Bordeaux (France) ***CIUDAD DE CADIZ***, Tunis – Tangiers Med – Cadiz (Spain) – Bordeaux ***VILLE DE BORDEAUX***, Hamburg - St Nazaire – Bordeaux ***CITY OF HAMBURG***. Vessels are used for conveying Airbus materials under contract. Spare capacity and light ship sailings are regularly used for conveying trailers, heavy rolling cargo and trade cars and calls are often made at other ports for such cargos and regularly include Pasajes, Santander, Portbury, Sheerness and Zeebrugge. In addition vessels are regularly chartered out for short periods when idle.

1	CITY OF HAMBURG	15643t	08	180k	126.5m	4P	853C	31T	A	FR	9383558
2	CIUDAD DE CADIZ	15643t	09	180k	126.5m	4P	853C	31T	A	FR	9383560
3	VILLE DE BORDEAUX	21528t	04	210k	154.3m	12P	658C	123T	A	FR	9270842

CITY OF HAMBURG, CIUDAD DE CADIZ Built by Singapore Technologies Marine Ltd, Singapore for *Louis Dreyfus Armateurs* of France. Able to operate as a conventional ro-ro or as a car carrier using portable mezzanine decks and a dedicated car deck.

VILLE DE BORDEAUX Built by JinLing Shipyard, Nanjing, China for *Louis Dreyfus Armateurs* of France. Able to operate as a conventional ro-ro or as a car carrier using portable mezzanine decks. Short periods have been previously been spent on charter to *Trasmediterranea, UECC, Cobelfret, LD Lines* and *P&O North Sea Ferries*. In 2009 laid up for a year in St Nazaire when Airbus production was temporarily reduced.

SCA TRANSFOREST

THE COMPANY *SCA Transforest* is a Swedish company.

MANAGEMENT **Managing Director (UK)** Hugo Heij.

ADDRESS ***Sweden*** Box 805, 851 23, Sundsvall, Sweden, ***UK*** Interforest Terminal London Ltd, 44 Berth, Tilbury Dock, Essex RM18 7HP.

TELEPHONE **Administration & Reservations *Sweden*** +46 (0)60 19 35 00, ***UK*** +44 (0)1375 488500.

FAX **Administration & Reservations *Sweden*** +46 (0)60-19 35 65, ***UK*** +44 (0)1375 488503.

INTERNET **Email *Sweden*** info@transforest.sca.com ***UK*** interforest.london@sca.com

Website www.sca.com/transforest *(English)*

ROUTE OPERATED Umeå - Sundsvall - Sheerness - Rotterdam (Eemhaven) - Helsingborg - Oxelösund - Umeå (8/9 day round trip; ***SCA OBBOLA, SCA ORTVIKEN, SCA ÖSTRAND***; 1 per week).

1	SCA OBBOLA	20168t	96	16.0k	170.6m	0P	-	-	A	SE	9087350
2	SCA ORTVIKEN	20154t	97	16.0k	170.4m	0P	-	-	A	SE	9087374
3	SCA ÖSTRAND	20171t	96	16.0k	170.6m	0P	-	-	A	SE	9087362

SCA OBBOLA, SCA ORTVIKEN, SCA ÖSTRAND Built as the OBBOLA, ORTVIKEN and ÖSTRAND by Astilleros Españoles, Seville, Spain for *Gorthon Lines* and chartered to *SCA Transforest*. They are designed for the handling of forest products in non-wheeled 'cassettes' but can also accommodate trailers. The ORTVIKEN was lengthened during Autumn 2000 and the others during 2001. In June

2001 purchased by *SCA Transforest*. In spring 2016 renamed the SCA OBBOLA, SCA ORTVIKEN and SCA ÖSTRAND.

SMURFIT KAPPA GROUP

THE COMPANY *Smurfit Kappa Group* is an international company registered in the Irish Republic.

MANAGEMENT Group CEO Tony Smurfit.

ADDRESS Beech Hill, Clonskeagh, Dublin 4, Irish Republic.

TELEPHONE +353 (0)1 202 7000.

INTERNET Website www.smurfitkappa.com *(English)*

ROUTE OPERATED Södertälje (Sweden) - Harraholmen (Sweden) - Bremen (Germany)- Sheerness - Terneuzen (Netherlands) - Cuxhaven (Germany) - - Sodertalje (12 days; *BALTICBORG, BOTHNIABORG*; 1 per week).

1	BALTICBORG	12460t	04	16.5 k	153.1m	OP	-	104T	A	NL	9267716
2	BOTHNIABORG	12460t	04	16.5 k	153.1m	OP	-	104T	A	NL	9267728

BALTICBORG, BOTHNIABORG Built by Bodewes Volharding, Volharding, The Netherlands (hull built by Daewoo Mangalia Heavy Industries SA, Mangalia, Romania) for *Wagenborg Shipping* of The Netherlands. Time-chartered to *Kappa Packaging* (now *Smurfit Kappa Group*). Placed on service between Piteå and Northern Europe. Northbound journeys (Terneuzen - Piteå) marketed as *RORO2 Stockholm*, with a call at Södertälje (Sweden (near Stockholm)) and, from 2005, the section Bremen - Sheerness - Terneuzen marketed as *RORO2London*. In 2007 these arrangements ceased and *Mann Lines* took over the marketing of northbound traffic, a northbound call at Harwich (Navyard) being introduced and the Södertälje call being replaced by a call at Paldiski in Estonia. This arrangement ceased in 2013 and they reverted to their previous schedules.

SECTION 5 - GB & IRELAND - CHAIN, CABLE ETC FERRIES

CUMBRIA COUNTY COUNCIL

Address Resources Directorate, Highways Transportation and Fleet, County Offices, Kendal, Cumbria

LA9 4RQ **Tel** +44 (0)1539 713040, **Fax** +44 (0)1539 713035.

Internet Email peter.hosking@cumbria.gov.uk *(English)*

Website www.cumbria.gov.uk/roads-transport/highways-pavements/windermereferry.asp *(English)*

Route Bowness-on-Windermere - Far Sawrey.

1	**MALLARD**	-	90	-	25.9m	140P	18C	-	BA	

MALLARD Chain ferry built by F L Steelcraft, Borth, Dyfed for *Cumbria County Council*.

DARTMOUTH – KINGSWEAR FLOATING BRIDGE CO LTD

Address Dart Marina, Sandquay Road, Dartmouth, Devon TQ6 9PH. **Tel** +44 (0)7866 531687.

Internet Website www.dartmouthhigherferry.com *(English)*

Route Dartmouth - Kingswear (Devon) across River Dart (higher route) (forms part of A379).

1	**HIGHER FERRY**	540t	09	-	52.7m	240P	32C	-	BA	

HIGHER FERRY Built by Ravestein BV, Deest, The Netherlands under contract to Pendennis Shipyard, Falmouth, who fitted the vessel out between January and June 2009.

ISLE OF WIGHT COUNCIL (COWES FLOATING BRIDGE)

Address Ferry Office, Medina Road, Cowes, Isle of Wight PO31 7BX. **Tel** +44 (0)1983 293041.

Route Cowes - East Cowes.

1	**FLOATING BRIDGE NO 6**	-	17	-	38.0m	-	20C	-	BA	
2Ÿ	**NO 5**	-	76	-	33.5m	-	15C	-	BA	

FLOATING BRIDGE NO 6 Chain ferry built by Mainstay Marine Solutions Ltd, Pembroke Dock, UK. Entered service in May but withdrawn after a few days. Re-entered service in June.

NO 5 Chain ferry built by Fairey Marine, East Cowes, UK for *Isle of Wight County Council*, now *Isle of Wight Council*. In January 2017 withdrawn for sale.

KING HARRY FERRY AND CORNWALL FERRIES

Address 2 Ferry Cottages, Feock, Truro, Cornwall TR3 6QJ. **Tel** +44 (0)1326 741194.

Internet Email beverley@kingharry.net **Website** www.falriver.co.uk *(English)*

Route Philliegh - Feock (Cornwall) (across River Fal)

1	**KING HARRY FERRY**	500t	06	-	55.2m	150P	34C	-	BA	UK 9364370

KING HARRY FERRY Chain ferry built by Pendennis Shipyard, Falmouth (hull constructed at Ravestein Shipyard, Deest, The Netherlands) to replace the previous ferry.

REEDHAM FERRY

Address Reedham Ferry, Ferry Inn, Reedham, Norwich NR13 3HA. **Tel** +44 (0)1493 700429.

Internet Email info@reedhamferry.co.uk **Website** www.reedhamferry.co.uk *(English)*

Route Acle - Reedham - Norton (across River Yare, Norfolk).

1	REEDHAM FERRY	-	84	-	11.3m	20P	3C	-	BA		

REEDHAM FERRY Chain ferry built by Newsons, Oulton Broad, Lowestoft, UK for *Reedham Ferry*. Maximum vehicle weight: 12 tons.

SANDBANKS FERRY

Address ***Company*** Bournemouth-Swanage Motor Road and Ferry Company, Shell Bay, Studland, Swanage, Dorset BH19 3BA. **Tel** +44 (0)1929 450203, ***Ferry*** Floating Bridge, Ferry Way, Sandbanks, Poole, Dorset BH13 7QN. **Tel** +44 (0)1929 450203.

Internet Email email@sandbanksferry.co.uk **Website** www.sandbanksferry.co.uk *(English)*

Route Sandbanks - Shell Bay (Dorset).

1	BRAMBLE BUSH BAY	625t	93	-	74.4m	400P	48C	-	BA	UK	9072070

BRAMBLE BUSH BAY Chain ferry, built by Richard Dunston (Hessle) Ltd, Hessle, UK for the *Bournemouth-Swanage Motor Road and Ferry Company*.

SOUTH HAMS DISTRICT COUNCIL

Address Lower Ferry Office, The Square, Kingswear, Dartmouth, Devon TQ6 0AA. **Tel** +44 (0)1803 861234.

Internet Website www.southhams.gov.uk/DartmouthLowerFerry *(English)*

Route Dartmouth - Kingswear (Devon) across River Dart (lower route).

1	THE TOM AVIS	-	94	-	33.5m	50P	8C	-	BA		
2	THE TOM CASEY	-	89	-	33.5m	50P	8C	-	BA		

THE TOM AVIS Float (propelled by tugs) built by c Toms & Sons, Fowey, UK for *South Hams District Council*.

THE TOM CASEY Float (propelled by tugs) built by Cosens, Portland, UK for *South Hams District Council*.

TORPOINT FERRY

Address 2 Ferry Street, Torpoint, Cornwall PL11 2AX. **Tel** +44 (0)1752 812233.

Internet Website www.tamarcrossings.org.uk *(English)*

Route Devonport (Plymouth) - Torpoint (Cornwall) across the Tamar. The three ferries operate in parallel, each on her own 'track'. Pre-booking is not possible and the above number cannot be used for that purpose.

1	LYNHER II	748t	06	-	73.0m	350P	73C	-	BA	UK	9310941
2	PLYM II	748t	04	-	73.0m	350P	73C	-	BA	UK	9310927
3	TAMAR II	748t	05	-	73.0m	350P	73C	-	BA	UK	9310939

LYNHER II, PLYM II, TAMAR II Chain ferries built by Ferguson Shipbuilders Ltd, Port Glasgow, UK to replace 1960s-built ships. Unlike previous ferries, they are registered as 'Passenger/Ro-Ro Cargo' ships and thus have gross tonnage, nation of registry and, being over 100t, an IMO number.

WATERFORD CASTLE HOTEL

Address The Island, Waterford, Irish Republic. **Tel** +353 (0)51 878203, Fax: + 353 (0)51 879 316.

Internet Email info@waterfordcastleresort.com **Website** www.waterfordcastleresort.com *(English)*

Route Grantstown - Little Island (in River Suir, County Waterford).

1•	LORELEY	110t	59	-	32.0m	57P	12C	-	BA		
2	MARY FITZGERALD	122t	72	10.0k	35.0m	100P	14C	-	BA	IR	8985531

LORELEY Chain ferry built as the LORELEY V by Ruthof, Mainz, Germany to operate between St Goarshausen and St Goar on the River Rhine. In 2004 replaced by a new vessel (the LORELEY VI) and became a reserve vessel In 2007, sold to the *Waterford Castle Hotel* and renamed the LORELEY and, in 2008 replaced the previous ferry. Self propelled and guided by cable. In August 2014 replaced by the MARY FITZGERALD and laid up.

MARY FITZGERALD Built as the STEDINGEN by Abeking & Rasmussen, Lemwerder, Germany for *Schnellastfähre Berne-Farge GmbH* (from 1993 *Fähren Bremen-Stedingen GmbH*) to operate across the River Weser (Vegesack - Lemwerder and Berne - Farge). In 2004 sold to the *Lough Foyle Ferry Company Ltd* and renamed the FOYLE RAMBLER. Generally used on the Buncrana - Rathmullan (Lough Swilly) service, which did not resume in summer 2014. In 2014 sold to *Waterford Castle Hotel* and renamed the MARY FITZGERALD. Modified to be cable guided.

SECTION 6 - GB & IRELAND - MAJOR PASSENGER-ONLY FERRIES

There are a surprisingly large number of passenger-only ferries operating in the British Isles, mainly operated by launches and small motor boats. There are, however, a few 'major' operators who operate only passenger vessels (of rather larger dimensions) and have not therefore been mentioned previously.

Aran Island Ferries BANRÍON NA FARRAIGE (117t, 27.4m, 1984, 188 passengers, IMO 8407709) (ex ARAN EXPRESS 2007), CEOL NA FARRAIGE (234t, 2001, 37.4m, 294 passengers, IMO 9246750), DRAÍOCHT NA FARRAIGE (318t, 1999, 35.4m, 294 passengers, IMO 9200897), GLÓR NA FARRAIGE (170t, 1985, 33.5m, 244 passenger, IMO 8522391) (ex ARAN FLYER 2007), SEA SPRINTER (16t, 11.6m, 35 passengers). **Routes operated** Rossaveal (Co Galway) – Inishmor, Rossaveal - Inis Meáin, Rossaveal - Inisheer. **Tel** +353 (0)91 568903 (572050 after 19.00), **Fax** +353 (0)91 568538, **Email** info@aranislandferries.com **Website** www.aranislandferries.com *(English)*

Blue Funnel Cruises HYTHE SCENE (66t, 1992, 21.3m, 162 passengers - catamaran) (ex GREAT EXPECTATIONS 2017), JENNY ANN (1979, 11.6m, 50 passengers) ex JENNY ANN 1998, ex FALDORE III 2015, ex PUFFIN BELLE 2017) JENNY R (12t, 1984, 13.7m, 75 passengers), OCEAN SCENE (279t, 1994, 29.0m, 350 passengers - catamaran, IMO 8633865), OLIVER B (21t, 1988, 12.2m, 62 passengers - catamaran), OSSIAN OF STAFFA (1993, 13.7m, 70 passengers - to be renamed). Note: The HYTHE SCENE is the regular ferry. Other vessels in the fleet (which are used for charters and excursions) can cover as necessary. **Route Operated** Southampton - Hythe, **Tel** +44 (0)2380 239800 **Email** office@bluefunnel.co.uk **Website** www.bluefunnel.co.uk *(English)*

Brixham Express BRIXHAM EXPRESS (2015, 31t, 15.0m, 98 passengers - catamaran) **Route operated** Brixham - Torquay. **Tel** +44 (0)7553 359596, **Email** info@brixhamexpress.com **Website** www.brixhamexpress.com *(English)*

Bumblebee Boat Cruises BUMBLEBEE (2012, 9.6m, 12 passengers). **Route operated** St Peter Port (Guernsey) - Braye Harbour (Alderney). **Tel** +44 (0)1481 720200, **Email** skipper@bumblebee.gg **Website** www.bumblebee.gg *(English)*

Clyde Cruises (Clyde Marine Services Ltd) CHIEFTAIN (54t, 2007, 19.5m, 100 passengers) (ex SEABUS, 2014), CLYDE CLIPPER (125t, 2009, 27m, 250 passengers), CRUISER (119t, 1974, 24.4m, 245 passengers) (ex POOLE SCENE, 2001, HYTHE HOTSPUR, 1995, SOUTHSEA QUEEN, 1978), FENCER (18t, 1976, 11.0m, 33 passengers), ROVER (48t, 1964, 19.8m, 120 passengers), THE

SECOND SNARK (45t, 1938, 22.9m, 120 passengers). **Routes operated** Glasgow city cruise, Caledonian Canal sailings, Oban from Dunstaffnage Marina, Aberdeen Harbour tours and cruises and private charters around the Clyde area. **Tel** +44 (0)1475 721281, **Email** info@clydecruises.com **Website** www.clydecruises.com www.clyde-marine.co.uk *(English).*

Clydelink ISLAND PRINCESS (1996, 13.7m, 96 passengers), RIVER VIKING (1966, 10.7m, 73 passengers) (ex TORQUAY BELLE 2016) **Route operated** Gourock - Kilcreggan (operated on behalf of *Strathclyde Partnership for Transport*), ISLAND TRADER (12 passengers), SILVER SWAN (12 passengers) **Route operated** Renfrew - Yoker (operated on behalf of *Strathclyde Partnership for Transport*). **Tel** 0871 705 0888, **Websites** www.clydelink.co.uk www.spt.co.uk/kilcreggan-ferry *(English).*

Dartmouth Steam Railway & Riverboat Company DARTMOUTH PRINCESS (ex DEVON BELLE II 2000) (22t, 1990, 18.3m, 156 passengers), KINGSWEAR PRINCESS (27t, 1978, 19.1m, 150 passengers) (ex TWIN STAR II 2010) **Route operated** Dartmouth - Kingswear. **Note:** River craft owned by this operator are also used for the ferry service on some occasions. **Tel** +44 (0)1803 555872, **Email** bookings@dsrrb.co.uk **Website** www.dartmouthrailriver.co.uk *(English)*

Doolin2Aran Ferries DOOLIN DISCOVERY (2009, 15.2m, 72 passengers), HAPPY HOOKER (77t, 1989, 19.8m, 96 passengers), JACK B (2005, 15.2m, 67 passengers), ROSE OF ARAN (113t, 1976, 20.1m, 96 passengers. IMO 7527916). **Routes operated** Doolin - Inisheer, Doolin - Inishmore, Doolin - Inishmaan. Also Cliffs of Moher Cruise **Tel** +353 (0)65 707 5949, **Email** info@doolin2aranferries.ie **Website** www.doolin2aranferries.com *(English)*

Doolin Ferry (O'Brien Line) CAILIN OIR (1999, 15.2m, 72 passengers), DOOLIN EXPRESS , (2010, 24.5m, 250 passengers), (ex BLANCHE HERMINE 2016, ex SAINT VINCENT DE PAUL 2014), QUEEN OF ARAN (113t, 1976, 20.1m, 96 passengers, IMO 7527928), TRANQUILITY (62t, 1988, 15.8m, 100 passengers). **Routes operated** Doolin - Inisheer, Doolin - Inishmaan, Doolin - Inishmore. Also cruises to Cliffs of Mohr. **Tel** +353 (0)65 707 5555, +353 (0)65 707 5618, **Email** info@doolinferry.com **Website** www.doolinferry.com *(English)*

Exe2Sea Cruises MY QUEEN (1929, 37t, 18m, 127 passengers) (ex GONDOLIER QUEEN) (laid up), ORCOMBE (1954, 14.3m, 90 passengers), PRINCESS MARINA (1936, 15.8m, 60 passengers). **Route operated** Exmouth - Starcross. **Tel** +44 (0)7974 022536 / +44 (0)7779 157280. **Email** info@exe2sea.co.uk **Website** www.exe2sea.co.uk (diverts to Facebook page) *(English)*

Fleetwood - Knott End Ferry (operated by *Wyre Marine Services Ltd*) WYRE ROSE (2005, 32 passengers). **Route operated** Fleetwood - Knott End. **Route operated** Fleetwood - Knott End. **Tel** +44 (0)1253 871113, **Ferry mobile** +44 (0) 7793 270934, **Email** info@wyremarine.co.uk **Website** www.wyre.gov.uk (search for ferry) *(English)*

Gosport Ferry HARBOUR SPIRIT (293t, 2015, 32.8m, 297 passengers, IMO 9741669), SPIRIT OF GOSPORT (300t, 2001, 32.6m, 300 passengers, IMO 8972089), SPIRIT OF PORTSMOUTH (377t, 2005, 32.6m, 300 passengers, IMO 9319894) **Route operated** Gosport - Portsmouth. **Tel** +44 (0)23 9252 4551, **Fax:** +44(0)23 9252 4802, **Email** admin@gosportferry.co.uk **Website** www.gosportferry.co.uk *(English)*

Gravesend - Tilbury Ferry (operated by the *JetStream Tours*) THAMES SWIFT (25.6t, 1995, 50 passengers (tri-maran)), (ex MARTIN CHUZZLEWIT 2001), JACOB MARLEY (29t, 1985, 15.5m, 98 passengers) (ex SOUTHERN BAY ROSE 2016, ex SEAWAYS EXPRESS 2006, ex CONDOR KESTREL). **Note** the THAMES SWIFT is the regular ferry; the JACOB MARLEY may substitute on occasions. **Route operated** Gravesend (Kent) - Tilbury (Essex), **Tel** +44 (0)1634 525202, **Email** bookings@jetstreamtours.com **Website** www.jetstreamtours.com *(English)*

Hamble - Warsash Ferry CLAIRE (2.1t, 1985, 7.3m, 12 passengers), EMILY (3.7t, 1990, 8.5m, 12 passengers), **Route operated** Hamble - Warsash (across Hamble River). **Tel** +44 (0)23 8045 4512, **Mobile** +44 (0) 7720 438402 Duty Ferryman +44 (0) 07827 157154. **Email** mike@hambleferry.co.uk, **Website** www.hambleferry.co.uk *(English)*

Harwich Harbour Foot & Bicycle Ferry HARBOUR FERRY (8t, 2016, 11.4m, 58 passengers). **Routes operated** Harwich (Ha'penny Pier) - Shotley (Marina), Harwich - Felixstowe (Landguard Point) (Easter to end of September). **Tel** +44 (0) 7919 911440, **Email** chris@harwichharbourferry.com

Bramble Bush Bay *(Kevin Mitchel)*

King Harry Ferry *(Brian Maxted)*

Website www.harwichharbourferry.com *(English)*

Hayling Ferry (operated by **Baker Trayte Marine Ltd**). PRIDE OF HAYLING (1989, 11.9m, 63 passengers), **Route operated** Eastney – Hayling Island. **Tel/Fax:** +44(0)23 9229 4800, +44(0)23 9266 2942, **Mobile** +44(0)7500 194854, **Website** www.haylingferry.net *(English)*

Hovertravel ISLAND FLYER (161t, 2016, 22.4m, 80 passengers, IMO 9737797, Griffon Hovercraft 12000TD/AP), SOLENT FLYER (161t, 2016, 40.0k, 22.4m, 80 passengers, IMO 9737785, Griffon Hovercraft 12000TD/AP), FREEDOM 90 (1990, 25.4m, 95 passengers, BHC AP1-88/100S hovercraft, converted from AP1-88/100 in 1999), ISLAND EXPRESS (1985, 25.4m, 95 passengers, BHC AP1-88/100S hovercraft, converted from BHC AP1-88/100 in 2001) (ex FREJA VIKING, 2002), **Route operated** Southsea - Ryde. **Tel** +44 1983 717700, **Email** info@hovertravel.com **Website** www.hovertravel.com *(English)*

Isle of Sark Shipping Company BON MARIN DE SERK (118t, 1983, 20.7m, 131 passengers, IMO 8303056), SARK BELLE (50t, 1979, 26.2m, 180 passengers) (ex BOURNEMOUTH BELLE 2011), SARK VENTURE (133t, 1986, 21.3m, 122 passengers, IMO 8891986), SARK VIKING (Cargo Vessel) (104t, 2007, 21.2m, 12 passengers, IMO 8648858). **Route operated** St Peter Port (Guernsey) - Sark. **Tel** +44 (0) 1481 724059, **Fax** +44 (0) 1481 713999, **Email** info@sarkshipping.gg **Website** www.sarkshippingcompany.com *(English)*

John O'Groats Ferries PENTLAND VENTURE (186t, 1987, 29.6m, 250 passengers, IMO 8834122). **Route operated** John O'Groats – Burwick (Orkney). **Tel** +44 (0)1955 611353, **Email** Office@jogferry.co.uk **Website** www.jogferry.co.uk *(English)*

Kintyre Express KINTYRE EXPRESS V (2012, 12.5m, 12 passengers), **Routes operated** Campbeltown - Ballycastle, Port Ellen (Islay) - Ballycastle,. **Tel** +44 (0) 1586 555895, **Email** info@kintyreexpress.com **Website** www.kintyreexpress.com *(English)*

Lundy Company OLDENBURG (294t, 1958, 43.6m, 267 passengers, IMO 5262146). **Routes operated** Bideford - Lundy Island, Ilfracombe - Lundy Island. Also North Devon coastal cruises and River Torridge cruises. **Tel** +44 (0)1237 470074, **Fax** +44 (0)1237 477779, **Email** info@lundyisland.co.uk **Website** www.lundyisland.co.uk *(English)*

Manche Iles Express (trading name of Société Morbihannaise de Navigation) GRANVILLE (325t, 2006, 41.0m, 245 passengers, IMO 9356476 - catamaran) (ex BORNHOLM EXPRESS 2014), VICTOR HUGO (387t, 1997, 35.0m, 195 passengers, IMO 9157806 - catamaran) (ex SALTEN 2003). **Route operated** Granville – Jersey - Sark - Guernsey, Portbail or Carteret – Jersey, Guernsey and Sark, Diélette - Alderney - Guernsey. **Tel** ***Jersey*** +44 (0)1534 880756, ***France*** +33 0825 131 050, **Fax** +33 02 33 90 03 49, **Website** www.manche-iles-express.com *(French, English)*

MBNA Thames Clippers (trading name of Collins River Enterprises Ltd) AURORA CLIPPER (181t, 2007, 37.8m, 27.5k, 220 passengers, IMO 9451824), CYCLONE CLIPPER (181t, 2007, 37.8m, 27.5k, 220 passengers, IMO 9451880), GALAXY CLIPPER (155t, 2015, 34.0m, 155 passengers, IMO 9783784), HURRICANE CLIPPER (181t, 2002, 37.8m, 27.5k, 220 passengers, IMO 9249702), JUPITER CLIPPER (155t, 2017, 35.0 m, 28.0k, 170 passengers, IMO 9223796), MERCURY CLIPPER (155t, 2017, 35.0 m, 28.0k, 170 passengers, IMO 9223801), METEOR CLIPPER (181t, 2007, 37.8m, 27.5k, 220 passengers, IMO 9451812), MONSOON CLIPPER (181t, 2007, 37.8m, 27.5k, 220 passengers, IMO 9451795), MOON CLIPPER (98t, 2001, 32.0m, 25.0k, 138 passengers, IMO 9245586) (ex DOWN RUNNER 2005), NEPTUNE CLIPPER (155t, 2015, 34.0m, 155 passengers, IMO 9783796), SKY CLIPPER (60t, 1992, 25.0m, 62 passengers) (ex VERITATUM 1995, SD10 2000), STAR CLIPPER (60t, 1992, 25.0m, 62 passengers) (ex CONRAD CHELSEA HARBOUR 1995, SD9 2000), STORM CLIPPER (60t, 1992, 25.0m, 62 passengers) (ex DHL WORLDWIDE EXPRESS 1995, SD11 2000), SUN CLIPPER (98t, 2001, 32.0m, 25.0k, 138 passengers, IMO 9232292) (ex ANTRIM RUNNER 2005), TORNADO CLIPPER (181t, 2007, 37.8m, 27.5k, 220 passengers, IMO 9451783), TWIN STAR (45t, 1974, 19.2m, 120 passengers), TYPHOON CLIPPER (181t, 2007, 37.8m, 27.5k, 220 passengers, IMO 9451771, (2015, 34.0m, 154 seats) The 'Typhoon', 'Tornado', 'Cyclone' and 'Monsoon', 'Aurora' and 'Meteor' Clippers were designed by AIMTEK and built by Brisbane Ship Constructions in Australia in 2007. 'Galaxy' and 'Neptune' were designed by One2three Naval Architects and built by Incat Tasmania, Hobart, Australia. **Routes operated** Embankment - Waterloo - Blackfriars – Bankside - London Bridge - Tower - Canary Wharf – Greenland - Masthouse Terrace - Greenwich - North Greenwich –

Pride of the Tyne *(Andrew Cooke)*

Woolwich, Bankside – Millbank - St George (Tate to Tate Service), Putney - Wandsworth - Chelsea Harbour - Cardogan - Embankment - Blackfriars, Canary Wharf - Rotherhithe Hilton Docklands Hotel (TWIN STAR). +44 (0)870 781 5049, **Fax** +44 (0)20 7001 2222, **Email** web@thamesclippers.com **Website** www.thamesclippers.com (English).

Mersey Ferries ROYAL DAFFODIL (751t, 1962, 46.6m, 860 passengers, IMO 4900868) (ex OVERCHURCH 1999) (laid up), ROYAL IRIS OF THE MERSEY (464t, 1960, 46.3m, 750 passengers, IMO 8633712) (ex MOUNTWOOD 2002), SNOWDROP (670t, 1960, 46.6m, 750 passengers, IMO 8633724) (ex WOODCHURCH 2004). **Routes operated** Liverpool (Pier Head) - Birkenhead (Woodside), Liverpool - Wallasey (Seacombe) with regular cruises from Liverpool and Seacombe to Salford along the Manchester Ship Canal. **Tel** ***Admin*** +44 (0)151 639 0609, ***Reservations*** +44 (0)151 330 1444, **Fax** +44 (0)151 639 0578, **Email** info@merseyferries.co.uk **Website** www.merseyferries.co.uk *(English)*

Mudeford Ferry (Derham Marine) FERRY DAME (4t, 1989, 9.1m, 48 passengers), JOSEPHINE (10.5t, 1997, 10.7m, 70 passengers - catamaran), JOSEPHINE II (10.5t, 2013, 11.0m, 86 passengers - catamaran). **Route operated** Mudeford Quay - Mudeford Sandbank. **Tel** +44 (0)7968 334441 **Email** information@mudefordferry.co.uk **Website** www.mudefordferry.co.uk *(English)*

Nexus (trading name of Tyne & Wear Integrated Transport Authority) PRIDE OF THE TYNE (222t, 1993, 24.0m, 240 passengers, IMO 9062166), SPIRIT OF THE TYNE (174t, 2006, 25.0m, 200 passengers). **Route operated** North Shields - South Shields. Also cruises South Shields - Newcastle. **Tel** +44 (0)191 2020747, **Email** customerservices@nexus.org **Website** www.nexus.org.uk/ferry *(English)*

Travel Trident HERM TRIDENT V (79t, 1989, 25.9m, 250 passengers), TRIDENT VI (79t, 1992, 22.3m, 250 passengers). **Route operated** St Peter Port (Guernsey) - Herm. **Tel** +44 (0)1481 721379, **Fax** +44 (0)1481 700226, **Email** peterwilcox@cwgsy.net **Website** www.traveltrident.com *(English)*

Waverley Excursions WAVERLEY (693t, 1946, 73.13m, 860 passengers, IMO 5386954).. **Routes operated** Excursions all round British Isles. However, regular cruises in the Clyde, Bristol Channel, South Coast and Thames provide a service which can be used for transport purposes and therefore she is in a sense a ferry. She is the only seagoing paddle steamer in the world. **Tel** +44 (0)845 130 4647, **Fax** +44 (0)141 248 2150, **Email** info@waverleyexcursions.co.uk **Website** www.waverleyexcursions.co.uk *(English)*

Western Isles Cruises Ltd LARVEN (14.0m, 2017, 40 passengers (catamaran)), WESTERN ISLES (45t, 1960, 18.0m, 84 passengers). **Route Operated** Mallaig - Inverie (Knoydart) - Tarbet. **Tel** +44 (0)1687 462233, **Email** info@westernislescruises.co.uk, **Website** www.westernislescruises.co.uk *(English)*

Western Lady Ferry Service WESTERN LADY VI (ex TORBAY PRINCESS ex DEVON PRINCESS II) (50t, 1981, 19.2m, 173 passengers), WESTERN LADY VII (ex TORBAY PRINCESS II, ex BRIXHAM BELLE II, ex DEVON PRINCESS III) (46t, 1984, 19.8m, 177 passengers). **Route Operated** Torquay - Brixham. **Tel** +44 (0)1803 293797, **Website** www.westernladyferry.com *(English)* Note: The service is now part of *Dartmouth Steam Railway & Riverboat Company* but is marketed separately.

White Funnel BALMORAL (735t, 1949, 62.2m, 800 passengers, IMO 5034927) Excursions in Bristol Channel, North West, South Coast, Thames and Clyde. The programme can be linked together with single fares to provide transport around the Bristol Channel'. **Tel** +44 (0)117 325 6200 **Email** balmoral@whitefunnel.co.uk **Website** www.whitefunnel.co.uk *(English)*

Oldenburg *(Brian Maxted)*

Galaxy Clipper *(Nick Widdows)*

VIKING XPRS

Viking XPRS *(Matthew Punter)*

SCANDINAVIAN & NORTHERN EUROPE REVIEW 2016-17

The following geographical review again takes the form of a voyage along the coast of the Netherlands and Germany, round the southern tip of Norway, down the Kattegat, through the Great Belt and into the Baltic, then up to the Gulf of Finland and Gulf of Bothnia.

FRISIAN ISLANDS & ELBE

TESO's new *Texelstroom* finally entered service between Den Helder and the island of Texel in September 2016, having spent most of the summer undergoing trials or being laid up. Her first few months in service were blighted by technical difficulties and she was also initially refused permission to operate using Compressed Natural Gas (CNG). The problems with *Texelstroom* necessitated the retention of the *Schulpengat* throughout 2017.

FRS have placed an order with Austal Ships of Henderson, Australia for a new 56 metre catamaran that will operate between Hamburg, Cuxhaven and Helgoland. The new craft will enter service in 2018, replacing the *Halunder Jet* which will be redeployed in Canada.

The Elb-Link service between Cuxhaven and Brunsbüttel had suffered from poor loadings ever since its inauguration in August 2015 and by autumn 2016 was in financial difficulties. Despite a refinancing by German banks which saw Saaremaa Laevakompanii (SLK) withdraw from the operation, instead chartering their two vessels to Elb-Link, the company went into administration on 1 March 2017. However, a 'new' Elb-Link started operation in late May 2017 with their former operations director Bernd Baessman having reformed the company. The service is now a one-ship operation, retaining the *Muhumaa* which has formally been renamed *Grete*. The *Saaremaa* was returned to her owners when the company went bankrupt.

NORWEGIAN DOMESTIC

Hurtigruten placed an order in early 2016 for two new expedition cruise vessels. The first ship – which has been given the name *Roald Amundsen* – will enter service in late 2018 and her sister, to be named *Fridtjof Nansen*, will arrive the following year. The company has options for two further vessels. They will be deployed in on cruises to Antarctica, Greenland and Spitsbergen.

The *Bastø VI*, Bastø-Fosen first new ship arrived from her Turkish builder in mid December, entering service in the New Year. The other two vessels in the class, the *Bastø VII* and *Bastø VIII*, arrived in Norway in March, entering service the following month.

SKAGERRAK & KATTEGAT

Fjord Line has been awarded lucrative new berthing slots at Sandefjord for their operation to Strömstad, at the expense of Color Line. The new timetable comes into effect in 2020 and Fjord Line will need to procure an additional vessel for the service. However, Color Line have announced an order for a new hybrid ferry that will enter service on the route in 2019, replacing the *Bohus*. The following year, once the new roster comes into effect, the new ship will be the sole Color Line vessel on the route with the withdrawal of *Color Viking*, whilst Fjord Line will operate two vessels.

The Port of Varberg has announced redevelopment plans which will require Stena to find a new port for their operation to Grenå from Autumn 2019. It is possible that the service will switch to Halmstad, approximately 70 kilometres south of Varberg.

HH Ferries have converted two of their Helsingør – Helsingborg double-enders to battery power. The *Tycho Brahe* and *Aurora af Helsingborg* were refitted in early 2017 in a €26 million project, part funded by the European Union.

DANISH DOMESTIC

In preparation for their new contract for the Bornholm services from September 2018, Mols-Linien adopted a new branding for their operation: Molslinjen. The *KatExpress 1* and *KatExpress 2* were

Express *(Miles Cowsill)*

Schleswig-Holstein *(Matthew Punter)*

Color Hybrid *(Color Line)*

renamed simply as *Express 1* and *Express 2* and the brand new *Express 3* (ordered as *KatExpress 3*) entered service between Sjællands Odde and Århus on 1st June 2017. The new catamaran, *Express 4*, under construction at Henderson is expected to enter service on the Kattegat route with *Express 1* and *Max Mols* being deployed to the new Bornholm contract. In addition to the new ro-pax under construction at Rauma, the company has also purchased the *Povl Anker* from Færgen to act as a support vessel. Meanwhile, Færgen has sold the *Leonora Cristina* to Lineas Fred. Olsen for delivery in September 2018, once their contract for the Bornholm services comes to an end.

SOUTH BALTIC

Scandlines' *Copenhagen* finally entered service just before Christmas, allowing the company to operate a matched service at last. She replaced the *Kronprins Frederik* which was refitted and transferred to the Puttgarden – Rødby route in freight-only configuration.

Polferries have invested in additional tonnage for the Świnoujście–Ystad route, purchasing the *Drujba* from Bulgaria. She was brought to Szczecin in June for refitting and was anticipated to enter service as the *Cracovia* in September 2017, taking the roster of the *Baltivia*, although the latter is expected to remain in service on a reduced timetable.

Polferries have also signed a letter of intent with the Morska Stocznia Remontowa Grufia shipyard at Szczecin for a new PLN 450 million ro-pax, with an option for a sister. The new vessel will be 228 metres long and powered by Liquified Natural Gas (LNG).

TT-Line started operations between Świnoujście and Bornholm in June 2017 using the *Nils Dacke* as will Polferries once the *Cracovia* enters service.

The Gotlandsbåten service folded after one season, being unable to compete with the larger and better resourced Destination Gotland. The company's catamaran, the *Express*, was chartered to Viking Line for the 2017 season.

Stena has expanded their Baltic operations, with the *Gute* joining the Karlskrona – Gdynia route as from Autumn 2017 whilst services to Latvia have been consolidated on the Nynashamn – Ventspils service. The *Stena Nordica*, back from her charter to GNV is partnering *Urd* on the Travemünde – Liepaja service.

Berlin *(Matthew Punter))*

Express 3 *(Molslinjen)*

NORTH BALTIC

Tallink's new LNG-powered *Megastar* entered service on 29 January 2017, making an immediate impression on the Tallinn – Helsinki 'Shuttle' with her array of onboard facilities and cutting edge design. Of particular note is her 'Travel Superstore' offering two levels of shopping complete with car parking spaces for passengers to load up during the crossing. The *Megastar* has replaced the *Superstar* which was sold to Corsica Ferries, refitted and entered service as the *Pascal Lota* in June 2017. Meanwhile the *Star*, Tallink's other vessel on the service, was converted to double-deck loading during her refit in March 2017.

The company has also redeployed certain units in its fleet during the early part of the year, with *Baltic Queen* being withdrawn from the Tallinn – Helsinki cruise circuit, leaving a comprehensively refitted *Silja Europa* to operate the service alone. The *Baltic Queen* was switched to the Stockholm – Tallinn service, replacing the *Romantika* which was sent to partner the *Isabelle* on the Stockholm – Riga route.

Viking Line announced in November the construction of a second new cruise ferry for the Stockholm – Turku service. The new ship will be built at Xiamen Shipbuilding in China. She will measure 218 metres in length, 63,000 gross tons and will be powered by LNG. The new ship will cost €190 million and is anticipated to enter service in Spring 2020, partnering the *Viking Grace*. The new ship will feature two Flettner rotors which will provide additional power and it has also been decided to fit a single rotor to *Viking Grace* during its annual refit next year.

Viking Line has also charted Gotlandsbåten's *Express* to provide additional capacity between Tallinn and Helsinki during the summer season of 2017. Marketed as "Viking FSTR", she partners *Viking XPRS*. The *Mariella* and *Gabriella* are again providing summer-only daytime round trips to Tallinn from Helsinki.

St Peter Line and Moby Line announced a new strategic partnership for 2017 with the Italian company refinancing the operation. The *Princess Anastasia* was placed on a new five-day circuit incorporating St Petersburg – Helsinki – Tallinn – Stockholm – Helsinki – St Petersburg. The ship was re-liveried, with Moby funnel colours to starboard and St Peter Line to port. The other vessel on the service, the *Princess Maria*, was transferred to Moby Line as part of the deal and renamed *Moby Dada* for further service to Corsica.

The Navirail service between Paldiski and Hanko and their vessel *Sailor* was purchased by DFDS in September and integrated into their route network shortly afterwards.

Praamid's new contract between the Estonian mainland and the islands of Saaremaa and Hiiumaa got off to a shaky start on its start in September with only two of their new ferries having been delivered. The *Leiger* arrived from their builders in Turkey in October 2016 and entered service shortly before Christmas. The company then chartered several of the SLK fleet to fill the gaps until the remaining three vessels, the *Tõll*, the *Piret* and the *Tiiu* arrived in service by mid-April. Praamid has continued to charter the *Hiiumaa* and *Regula* to act as a back-up vessel to their new operation. SLK's *St Ola* was meanwhile sold to Medmar of Italy and renamed *Giulia d'Abundo*.

Wasaline remain hopeful of being able to secure sufficient finance to enable them to order a new ship for their route, replacing the *Wasa Express*, with an order possible later this year.

Matthew Punter

Deutschland *(Matthew Punter)*

SECTION 7- NORTHERN EUROPE

ÆRØFÆRGERNE

THE COMPANY *Ærøfærgerne* is a Danish company, owned by the municipality of Ærø.

MANAGEMENT **Managing Director** Kelda Møller, **Marketing Coordinator** Jeanette Erikson.

ADDRESS Vestergade 1, 5970 Ærøskøbing, Denmark.

TELEPHONE **Administration & Reservations** +45 62 52 40 00.

FAX **Administration & Reservations** +45 62 52 20 88.

INTERNET **Email** info@aeroe-ferry.dk **Website** www.aeroe-ferry.dk *(Danish, English, German)*

ROUTE OPERATED Ærøskøbing (Ærø) - Svendborg (Fyn) (1hr 15mins; ***ÆRØSKØBING, MARSTAL***; every 1/2 hours), Søby (Ærø) - Faaborg (Fyn) (1hr; ***SKJOLDNÆS***; 3 per day), Søby (Ærø) - Fynshav (Als) (1hr 10mins; ***SKJOLDNÆS***; 3 per day).

1	ÆRØSKØBING	1617t	99	12.0k	49.0m	395P	42C	-	BA	DK	9199086
2	MARSTAL	1617t	99	12.0k	49.0m	395P	42C	-	BA	DK	9199074
3	SKJOLDNÆS	986t	79	11.0k	47.1m	245P	31C	-	BA	DK	7925649

ÆRØSKØBING, MARSTAL Built by EOS, Esbjerg, Denmark for *Ærøfærgerne*.

SKJOLDNÆS Built as the SAM-SINE by Søren Larsen & Sønner Skibsværft A/S, Nykøbing Mors, Denmark for *Hou-Sælvig Ruten Aps* of Denmark. Operated between Hou (Jutland) and Sælvig (Samsø). In 1995 she was taken over by *Samsø Linien*. In 2001 she was lengthened by Ørskov Christensen's Staalskibsværft, Frederikshavn, Denmark. In 2009 sold to *Ærøfærgerne* and renamed the SKJOLDNÆS.

BASTØ FOSEN

THE COMPANY *Bastø Fosen* is a Norwegian private sector company, a subsidiary of *Torghatten ASA - Brønnøysund*.

MANAGEMENT **Managing Director** May Kristin Salberg.

ADDRESS PO Box 94, 3191 Horten, Norway.

TELEPHONE **Administration** +47 33 03 17 40, **Reservations** +47 33 03 17 40 (buses only).

FAX **Administration** +47 33 03 17 49, **Reservations** +47 33 03 17 49 (buses only).

INTERNET **Email** bastohorten@fosen.no **Website** www.basto-fosen.no *(Norwegian, English)*

ROUTE OPERATED Moss - Horten (across Oslofjord, Norway) (30 mins; ***BASTØ I, BASTØ II, BASTØ III, BASTØ IV, BASTØ V, BASTØ VI***; up to every 15 mins).

1	BASTØ I	5505t	97	14.0k	109.0m	550P	200C	18L	BA	NO	9144081
2	BASTØ II	5505t	97	14.0k	109.0m	550P	200C	18L	BA	NO	9144093
3	BASTØ III	7310t	05	18.0k	116.2m	540P	212C	18L	BA	NO	9299408
4	BASTØ IV	7700t	16	16.0k	142.9m	600P	200C	30L	BA	NO	9771420
5	BASTØ V	7700t	17	16.0k	142.9m	600P	200C	30L	BA	NO	9771432
6	BASTØ VI	7870t	16	16.0k	142.9m	600P	200C	30L	BA	NO	9769219

BASTØ I, BASTØ II Built by Fosen Mekaniske Verksteder, Frengen, Norway.

BASTØ III Built by Stocznia Remontowa, Gdansk, Poland.

BASTØ IV, BASTØ V Built by Sefine Shipyard, Yalova, Turkey.

BASTØ VI Built by Cemre Shipyard, Yalova, Turkey.

COLOR LINE

THE COMPANY *Color Line ASA* is a Norwegian private sector stock-listed limited company. The company merged with *Larvik Scandi Line* of Norway (which owned *Larvik Line* and *Scandi Line*) in 1996. In 1997 the operations of *Larvik Line* were incorporated into *Color Line*; *Scandi Line* continued as a separate subsidiary until 1999, when it was also incorporated into *Color Line*. The marketing name *Color Scandi Line* was dropped at the end of 2000.

MANAGEMENT **Managing Director** Trond Kleivdal.

ADDRESS ***Commercial*** Postboks 1422 Vika, 0115 Oslo, Norway, ***Technical Management*** Color Line Marine AS, PO Box 2090, 3210 Sandefjord, Norway.

TELEPHONE **Administration** +47 22 94 44 00, **Reservations *Germany*** +49 04 31/73 00 - 100, ***Denmark*** +45 99 56 10 00, **Norway** 810 00 811.

INTERNET **Email** kundeservice@colorline.no **Website** www.colorline.com *(English, Danish, German, Norwegian, Swedish)*

ROUTES OPERATED **Conventional Ferries** Oslo (Norway) - Kiel (Germany) (19 hrs 30 mins; ***COLOR FANTASY, COLOR MAGIC***; 1 per day), Kristiansand (Norway) - Hirtshals (3 hrs 15 mins; ***SUPERSPEED 1***; 2 per day), Larvik (Norway) - Hirtshals (Denmark) (3 hrs 45 mins; ***SUPERSPEED 2***; up to 2 per day), Sandefjord (Norway) - Strömstad (Sweden) (2 hrs 30 mins; ***BOHUS, COLOR VIKING***; up to 4 per day).

1	BOHUS	9149t	71	20.5k	123.4m	1165P	240C	34T	BA	NO	7037806
2	COLOR FANTASY	75027t	04	22.3k	224.0m	2750P	750C	90T	BA	NO	9278234
3	COLOR MAGIC	75100t	07	22.3k	223.7m	2750P	550C	90T	BA	NO	9349863
4	COLOR VIKING	19763t	85	16.4k	134.0m	2000P	320C	40T	BA2	NO	8317942
5	SUPERSPEED 1	36822t	08	27.0k	211.3m	2250P	525C	121T	BA2	NO	9374519
6	SUPERSPEED 2	34231t	08	27.0k	211.3m	1800P	525C	121T	BA2	NO	9378682

BOHUS Built as the PRINSESSAN DESIREE by Aalborg Værft A/S, Aalborg, Denmark for *Rederi AB Göteborg-Frederikshavn Linjen* of Sweden (trading as *Sessan Linjen*) for their service between Gothenburg and Frederikshavn. In 1981 the company was taken over by *Stena Line* and she became surplus to requirements. During 1981 she had a number of charters including *B&I Line* of Ireland and *Sealink UK*. In 1982 she was chartered to *Sally Line* to operate as second vessel on the Ramsgate - Dunkerque service between June and September. She bore the name 'VIKING 2' in large letters on her hull although she was never officially renamed. In September 1982 she returned to *Stena Line* and in 1983 she was transferred to subsidiary company *Varberg-Grenaa Line* for their service between Varberg (Sweden) and Grenaa (Denmark), renamed the EUROPAFÄRJAN. In 1985 she was renamed the EUROPAFÄRJAN II. In 1986, following a reorganisation within *Stena Line*, ownership was transferred to subsidiary company *Lion Ferry AB* and she was named the LION PRINCESS. In 1993 she was sold to *Scandi Line* and renamed the BOHUS. In 1999 *Scandi Line* operations were integrated into *Color Line*.

COLOR FANTASY Built by Kværner Masa-Yards, Turku, Finland for *Color Line* to replace the PRINSESSE RAGNHILD on the Oslo – Kiel service.

COLOR MAGIC Built by Aker Yards, Turku, Finland (hull construction) and Rauma, Finland (fitting out), for the Oslo - Kiel route.

COLOR VIKING Built as the PEDER PAARS by Nakskov Skibsværft A/S, Nakskov, Denmark for *DSB (Danish State Railways)* for their service between Kalundborg (Sealand) and Århus (Jutland). In 1990 purchased by *Stena Line* of Sweden for delivery in 1991. In that year renamed the STENA INVICTA and entered service on the *Sealink Stena Line* Dover - Calais service. She was withdrawn from the route in February 1998, before the formation of *P&O Stena Line*, but ownership was transferred to that company. In Summer 1998, she was chartered to *Silja Line* to operate between Vaasa and Umeå under the marketing name 'WASA JUBILEE'. In Autumn 1998 she was laid up at Zeebrugge. She remained there until Autumn 1999 when she was chartered to *Stena Line* to operate between

Bohus *(John Bryant)*

Colour Magic *(Miles Cowsill)*

Holyhead and Dublin. In 2000 she was chartered to *Color Line*, renamed the COLOR VIKING and in April entered service on the Sandefjord - Strömstad service. In 2002 purchased by *Color Line*.

SUPERSPEED 1, SUPERSPEED 2 Built by Aker Yards, Rauma, Finland for the Kristiansand - Hirtshals and Larvik - Hirtshals routes. In January 2011, the SUPERSPEED 1 was modified to provide additional facilities and increase passenger capacity.

Under construction

7	NEWBUILDING	18000t	19	-	160.0m	2000P	500C	-	BA	NO

NEWBUILDING Under construction by Ulstein Verft A/S, Ulsteinvik, Norway, to replace the BOHUS on the Sandefjord - Strömstad route. She will be a hybrid vessel, operating in both battery and diesel-electric mode.

DESTINATION GOTLAND

THE COMPANY *Destination Gotland AB* is a Swedish private sector company owned by *Rederi AB Gotland*.

MANAGEMENT **Managing Director** Christer Bruzelius, **Marketing Manager** Per-Erling Evensen.

ADDRESS PO Box 1234, 621 23 Visby, Gotland, Sweden.

TELEPHONE **Administration** +46 (0)498-20 18 00, **Reservations** +46 (0)771-22 33 00.

FAX **Administration** +46 498 20 18 90 **Reservations** +46 (0)498-20 13 90.

INTERNET **Email** info@destinationgotland.se **Website** www.destinationgotland.se *(Swedish, English, German)*

ROUTES OPERATED **Fast Conventional Ferries** Visby (Gotland) - Nynäshamn (Swedish mainland) (3 hrs 15 mins; *GOTLAND, VISBY*; 1/2 per day), Visby - Oskarshamn (Swedish mainland) (2 hrs 55 mins; *GOTLAND, VISBY*; 1/4 per day). **Fast Ferries (Summer only)** Visby - Nynäshamn (2 hrs 55 mins; *GOTLANDIA II*; up to 3 per day), Visby - Oskarshamn (Swedish mainland) (2 hrs 55 mins; *GOTLANDIA*; 1 per day), Visby - Vastervik (2 hrs 10 mins; *GOTLANDIA*; 1 per day)

1	GOTLAND	29746t	03	28.5k	195.8m	1500P	500C	118T	BAS2	SE	9223796
2»	GOTLANDIA	5632t	99	35.0k	112.5m	700P	140C	-	A	SE	9171163
3»	GOTLANDIA II	6554t	06	36.0k	122.0m	780P	160C	-	A	SE	9328015
4	VISBY	29746t	03	28.5k	195.8m	1500P	500C	118T	BAS2	SE	9223784

GOTLAND, VISBY Built by Guangzhou Shipyard International, Guangzhou, China for *Rederi AB Gotland* for use on *Destination Gotland* services.

GOTLANDIA Alstom Leroux Corsair 11500 monohull vessel built as the GOTLAND at Lorient, France for *Rederi AB Gotland* and chartered to *Destination Gotland*. In 2003 renamed the GOTLANDIA. In 2006 laid up. In 2007 inaugurated a new route between Visby and Grankullavik (Öland).

GOTLANDIA II Fincantieri SF700 monohull fast ferry built at Riva Trigoso, Italy for *Rederi AB Gotland* for use by *Destination Gotland*.

Under Construction

5	THJELVAR	32000t	18	-	200.0m	1650P	-	110L	BAS2	SE	-
6	VISBORG	32000t	17	-	200.0m	1650P	-	110L	BAS2	SE	9763655

THJELVAR, VISBORG Under construction by Guangzhou Shipyard International, Guangzhou, China for Rederi AB Gotland for use on Destination Gotland services. To be LNG powered.

DFDS SEAWAYS

THE COMPANY *DFDS Seaways* is a division of *DFDS A/S*, a Danish private sector company.

MANAGEMENT CEO DFDS A/S Niels Smedegaard, **Executive Vice-President Shipping Division** Peder Gellert Pedersen, **Head of Baltic Sea Business Area** Anders Refsgaard.

ADDRESS ***Copenhagen*** Sundkrogsgade 11, 2100 Copenhagen Ø, Denmark.

TELEPHONE **Administration** +45 33 42 33 42, **Reservations *Denmark*** +45 78 79 55 36, ***Germany*** +49 (0)40-389030, ***Lithuania*** +370 46 393616, ***Sweden*** +46 454 33680

FAX **Administration** +45 33 42 33 41. INTERNET **Administration** incoming@dfdsseaways.dk, **Reservations *Denmark*** incoming@dfdsseaways.dk ***Germany*** service.de@dfds.com ***Lithuania*** booking.lt@dfds.com, ***Sweden*** pax@dfds.com

Website www.dfdsseaways.com *(English, Danish, Dutch, German, Italian, Japanese, Norwegian, Polish, Swedish)*

ROUTES OPERATED ***Passenger services*** Copenhagen - Oslo (Norway) (16 hrs 30 mins; *CROWN SEAWAYS, PEARL SEAWAYS*; 1 per day), Klaipėda (Lithuania) - Kiel (Germany) (21 hrs; *ATHENA SEAWAYS, REGINA SEAWAYS*; 7 per week), Klaipėda - Karlshamn (Sweden) (14 hrs; *OPTIMA SEAWAYS, PATRIA SEAWAYS, VICTORIA SEAWAYS*; 10 per week), Paldiski (Estonia) - Kapellskär (Sweden) (10 hrs; *LIVERPOOL SEAWAYS*; 6 per week), Paldiski - Hanko (Finland) (3 hrs; *SAILOR*; 2 per day). ***Freight only service*** Fredericia - Copenhagen - Klaipėda (*BOTNIA SEAWAYS*; 2 per week).

See Section 1 for services operating to Britain.

1	ATHENA SEAWAYS	24950t	07	23.0k	199.1m	500P	-	190T	A	LT	9350680
2F	BOTNIA SEAWAYS	11530t	00	20.0k	162.2m	12P	-	140T	A	LT	9192129
3	CROWN SEAWAYS	35498t	94	22.0k	169.4m	1940P	450C	50T	BA	DK	8917613
4	KAUNAS SEAWAYS	25606t	89	16.3k	190.9m	262P	460C	93Tr	A2	LT	8311924
5	LIVERPOOL SEAWAYS	21856t	97	20.0k	186.0m	320P	100C	135T	A	LT	9136034
6	OPTIMA SEAWAYS	25206t	99	21.5k	186.3m	327P	164C	150T	A	LT	9188427
7	PATRIA SEAWAYS	18332t	92	17.0k	154.0m	242P	-	114T	BA2	LT	8917390
8	PEARL SEAWAYS	40039t	89	21.0k	178.4m	2090P	350C	70T	BA	DK	8701674
9	REGINA SEAWAYS	25518t	10	24.0k	199.1m	600P	-	190T	A	LT	9458535
10	SAILOR	20921t	87	19.0k	157.6m	119P	50C	82L	A2	EE	8401444
11	VICTORIA SEAWAYS	24950t	09	23.0k	199.1m	600P	-	190T	A	LT	9350721
12	VILNIUS SEAWAYS	22341t	87	16.3k	190.9m	132P	460C	112Tr	A2	LT	8311900

ATHENA SEAWAYS Built as the CORAGGIO by Nuovi Cantieri Apuani, Marina di Carrara, Italy. First of an order of eight vessels for *Grimaldi Holdings* of Italy. Used on *Grimaldi Lines* Mediterranean services. In September 2010, bare-boat chartered to *Stena Line* to operate between Hook of Holland and Killingholme. In November 2011 replaced by the new STENA TRANSIT and returned to Mediterranean service. In December 2013 renamed the ATHENA SEAWAYS, chartered to *DFDS* and replaced the LIVERPOOL SEAWAYS on the Klaipėda - Kiel service. In May 2016 purchased by *DFDS*.

BOTNIA SEAWAYS Built as the FINNMASTER by Jinling Shipyard, Nanjing, China for the *Macoma Shipping Group* and chartered to *Finncarriers*. In 2008 sold to *DFDS Lisco* and in January 2009 delivered, chartered to *DFDS Tor Line* and renamed the TOR BOTNIA. Operated on the Immingham - Rotterdam route until December 2010. In January 2011 moved to the Kiel - St Petersburg route. In January 2013 renamed the BOTNIA SEAWAYS.

CROWN SEAWAYS Launched as the THOMAS MANN by Brodogradevna Industrija, Split, Croatia for *Euroway AB* for their Lübeck - Travemünde - Malmö service. However, political problems led to serious delays and, before delivery, the service had ceased. She was purchased by *DFDS*, renamed the CROWN OF SCANDINAVIA and introduced onto the Copenhagen - Oslo service. In January 2013 renamed the CROWN SEAWAYS.

Patria Seaways *(Rob de Visser)*

Gotland *(Miles Cowsill)*

KAUNAS SEAWAYS Train ferry built as the KAUNAS by VEB Mathias-Thesen-Werft, Wismar, Germany (DDR) for *Lisco* of the former Soviet Union and operated between Klaipėda and Mukran in Germany (DDR). She was part of a series of vessels built to link the USSR and Germany (DDR), avoiding Poland. In 1994/95 she was modified to offer passenger facilities and placed on the Klaipėda - Kiel service. In 2003 transferred to the Klaipėda - Karlshamn route. Early in 2004 chartered to *DFDS Tor Line* to operate between Lübeck and Riga. In 2005 returned to the Klaipėda - Karlshamn route. In May 2009 replaced by the LISCO OPTIMA and laid up. In October 2009 placed on the Travemünde - Riga route; this route ceased in January 2010 and she was laid up again. In May 2010 chartered to *Scandlines* and placed on a new Travemünde - Liepaja (Latvia) service. In December 2010 returned to *DFDS Seaways*. In March 2011 chartered to *Baltic Scandinavian Line* to operate between Paldiski (Estonia) and Kapellskär. In May returned to *DFDS Seaways* and inaugurated a new service between Kiel and Ust Luga (Russia). In May 2012 she was renamed the KAUNAS SEAWAYS and in June transferred to the Klaipėda - Sassnitz route. At the end of September 2013 this route closed and in October she was transferred to the Paldiski - Kapellskär service. After a period of lay up, in August 2015 she was chartered to *UKR Ferry* of The Ukraine to operate between Ilyichevsk, Batumi, Poti and Constanta.

LIVERPOOL SEAWAYS Built as the LAGAN VIKING by CN Visentini, Donada, Italy for *Levantina Trasporti* of Italy and chartered to *Norse Irish Ferries*, operating between Liverpool and Belfast. In 1999 the charter was taken over by *Merchant Ferries*. Purchased by *NorseMerchant Ferries* in 2001. In 2002 the service transferred to Twelve Quays River Terminal, Birkenhead. In January 2005 renamed the LIVERPOOL VIKING and in December moved to the Birkenhead - Dublin route. In August 2010 renamed the LIVERPOOL SEAWAYS. In February 2011 moved to the Klaipėda - Karlshamn service. In January 2014 chartered to *NaviRail*. In January 2015 returned to *DFDS* and placed on the Paldiski - Kapellskär service.

OPTIMA SEAWAYS Ro-pax vessel built as the ALYSSA by C N Visentini di Visentini Francesco & C Donada, Italy for *Levantina Trasporti* of Italy for charter. Initially chartered to *CoTuNav* of Tunisia for service between Marseilles, Genoa and Tunis and in 2000 to *Trasmediterranea* of Spain for service between Barcelona and Palma de Mallorca. In 2001 chartered to *Stena Line Scandinavia AB*, renamed the SVEALAND and placed as second vessel on the *Scandlines AB* freight-only Trelleborg - Travemünde service. In 2003 sub-chartered to *Scandlines AG* and placed on the Kiel - Klaipėda route, replacing the ASK and PETERSBURG. In 2004 sold to *Rederia AB Hornet*, a *Stena* company. In late 2005 the *Scandlines* Kiel -Klaipėda service ended. In early 2006 she was chartered to *TT-Line* to cover for the rebuilding of the engines of their four newest vessels. Later sold to *DFDS*, renamed the LISCO OPTIMA. In April 2012 renamed the OPTIMA SEAWAYS. Currently operates on the Karlshamn - Klaipėda route.

PATRIA SEAWAYS Ro-pax vessel built as the STENA TRAVELLER by Fosen Mekaniske Verksteder, Trondheim, Norway for *Stena RoRo*. After a short period with *Stena Line* on the Hook of Holland - Harwich service, she was chartered to *Sealink Stena Line* for their Southampton - Cherbourg route, initially for 28 weeks. At the end of the 1992 summer season she was chartered to *TT-Line* to operate between Travemünde and Trelleborg and was renamed the TT-TRAVELLER. In late 1995, she returned to *Stena Line*, resumed the name STENA TRAVELLER and inaugurated a new service between Holyhead and Dublin. In Autumn 1996 she was replaced by the STENA CHALLENGER (18523t, 1991). In early 1997 she was again chartered to *TT-Line* and renamed the TT-TRAVELLER. She operated on the Rostock - Trelleborg route. During Winter 1999/2000 her passenger capacity was increased to 250 and passenger facilities renovated. In early 2002 the charter ended and she was renamed the STENA TRAVELLER, chartered to *Stena Line* and placed on their Karlskrona - Gdynia service. This charter ended in May 2003 and she was sold to *Lisco Baltic Service* and renamed the LISCO PATRIA. Placed on the Klaipėda - Karlshamn service. In January 2006 transferred to the Klaipėda - Kiel service to replace the *Scandlines* vessel SVEALAND following that company's withdrawal from the joint route. In Spring 2006 returned to the Klaipėda - Karlshamn route. In May 2011 chartered to *Baltic Scandinavia Lines* and placed on their Paldiski - Kapellskär service. In September 2011 a controlling interest in this service was acquired by *DFDS Seaways*. In January 2012 renamed the PATRIA SEAWAYS. In September 2014 replaced by the *Sirena Seaways* and became a relief vessel. In April 2015 chartered as a windfarm accommodation vessel off Esbjerg. In January 2016 chartered to *P&O Ferries* to cover for refits on the Hull routes. In April 2016 became third vessel on the Klaipėda - Karlshamn route.

PEARL SEAWAYS Built as the ATHENA by Wärtsilä Marine, Turku, Finland for *Rederi AB Slite* of Sweden (part of *Viking Line*) and used on 24-hour cruises from Stockholm to Mariehamn (Åland). In 1993 the company went into liquidation and she was sold to *Star Cruises* of Malaysia for cruises in the Far East. She was renamed the STAR AQUARIUS. Later that year she was renamed the LANGKAPURI STAR AQUARIUS. In February 2001 sold to *DFDS* and renamed the AQUARIUS. After rebuilding, she was renamed the PEARL OF SCANDINAVIA and introduced onto the Copenhagen - Oslo service. In January 2011 renamed the PEARL SEAWAYS.

REGINA SEAWAYS Built as the ENERGIA by Nuovi Cantieri Apuani, Marina di Carrara, Italy for *Grimaldi Holdings* of Italy. In August 2011 chartered to DFDS Seaways and moved to Klaipėda for modifications. In September 2011 renamed the REGINA SEAWAYS and placed on the Klaipėda - Kiel service.

SAILOR Built as the FINNSAILOR by Gdansk Shipyard, Gdansk, Poland for *Finnlines* of Finland for freight service between Finland and Germany. In 1996 converted to ro-pax format to inaugurate a new passenger/freight service between Helsinki and Norrköping (Sweden) for subsidiary *FinnLink*. In 1997 this service was transferred to the Kapellskär - Naantali route and passengers (other than lorry drivers) ceased to be conveyed. In 2000 she was chartered to *Nordö-Link* to operate between Travemünde and Malmö. In 2002 she returned to *FinnLink*. In 2004 transferred to *Nordö-Link*. In 2007 returned to *FinnLink* as fourth ship. In early 2009 transferred to *Finnlines'* freight service operating between Helsinki, Turku and Travemünde but in April transferred back. In March 2011 moved back to *Finnlines Nordö-Link*. In November 2013 chartered to *Navirail* of Estonia to operate between Paldiski and Hanko. In January 2014 returned to *Finnlines* and placed on the Naantali - Kapellskär route. In January 2015 time chartered again to *Navirail*. In February 2015 demise chartered to *Navirail* and renamed the SAILOR. In October 2016 time chartered to *DFDS Seaways*, following their take over of the route.

VICTORIA SEAWAYS Built by Nuovi Cantieri Apuani, Marina di Carrara, Italy. Launched as the FORZA. Fifth of an order of eight vessels for *Grimaldi Holdings* of Italy. Whilst under construction, sold to *DFDS Tor Line*. On delivery renamed the LISCO MAXIMA. In March/April 2012 renamed the VICTORIA SEAWAYS. Operates between Karlshamn and Klaipėda.

VILNIUS SEAWAYS Train ferry as KAUNAS SEAWAYS. Built as the VILNIUS. In 1993 rebuilt in Liverpool to convert from a 12 passenger freight vessel to a 120 passenger ro-pax vessel. Operated on the Klaipėda – Kiel service until June 2003. Later chartered to *DFDS Tor Line* to operate between Lübeck and Riga. In Summer 2006 transferred to the *DFDS Lisco* Klaipėda - Sassnitz route. In January 2011 renamed the VILNIUS SEAWAYS. In June 2012 she was transferred to the Kiel - Ust Luga service. In June 2013 she was chartered to *Ukrferry* of the Ukraine for service in the Black Sea.

REDERIJ DOEKSEN

THE COMPANY *BV Rederij G. Doeksen en Zn BV* is a Dutch private sector company. Ferries are operated by subsidiary *Terschellinger Stoomboot Maatschappij*, trading as *Rederij Doeksen*.

MANAGEMENT Managing Director P J M Melles, **Manager Operations** R. de Vries, **Controller** R. Herrema, **Manager Hospitality, FO & CC** D Spoor, **Manager Personnel & Organization** A. Idzinga, **Manager Marketing & Communications** A. van Brummelen.

ADDRESS Waddenpromenade 5, 8861 NT Harlingen, The Netherlands.

TELEPHONE ***In The Netherlands*** 088 – 9000 888, ***From abroad*** +31 562 442 002.

FAX +31 (0)517 413303.

INTERNET **Email** info@rederij-doeksen.nl **Website** www.rederij-doeksen.nl *(Dutch, English, German))* **Facebook** www.facebook.com/rederijdoeksen **Twitter** www.twitter.com/rederijdoeksen

ROUTES OPERATED **Conventional Ferries** Harlingen (The Netherlands) - Terschelling (Frisian Islands) (2 hrs; ***FRIESLAND, MIDSLAND)*** (up to 6 per day), Harlingen - Vlieland (Frisian Islands) (1 hr 45 mins; ***VLIELAND***; 3 per day). **Fast Passenger Ferries** Harlingen - Terschelling (45 mins; ***KOEGELWIECK, TIGER***; 3 to 6 per day), Harlingen - Vlieland (45 mins; ***KOEGELWIECK, TIGER***; 2 per day), Vlieland - Terschelling (30 mins; ***KOEGELWIECK, TIGER***; 2 per day). **Freight Ferry** Harlingen

- Terschelling (2 hrs; *NOORD-NEDERLAND*), Harlingen - Vlieland (1hr 45 mins; *NOORD-NEDERLAND*).

1	FRIESLAND	3583t	89	14.0k	69.0m	1100P	122C	12L	BA	NL	8801058
2»p	KOEGELWIECK	439t	92	33.0k	35.5m	315P	0C	0L	-	NL	9035527
3	MIDSLAND	1812t	74	15.5k	77.9m	700P	55C	6L	BA	NL	7393066
4F	NOORD-NEDERLAND	361t	02	14.0k	68.0m	12P	-	_L	BA	NL	9269611
5»p	TIGER	660t	02	37.0k	52.0m	414P	0C	0L	BA	NL	9179191
6	VLIELAND	2726t	05	15.0k	64.1m	1950P	58C	4L	BA	NL	9303716

FRIESLAND Built by Van der Giessen-de Noord, Krimpen aan den IJssel, Rotterdam, The Netherlands for *Rederij Doeksen*. Used on the Harlingen - Terschelling route.

KOEGELWIECK Harding 35m catamaran built at Rosendal, Norway for *Rederij Doeksen* to operate between Harlingen and Terschelling, Harlingen and Vlieland and Terschelling and Vlieland.

MIDSLAND Built as the RHEINLAND by Werftunion GmbH & Co, Cassens-Werft, Emden, Germany for *AG Ems* of Germany. In 1993 purchased by *Rederij Doeksen* and renamed the MIDSLAND. Used mainly on the Harlingen - Terschelling route but also used on the Harlingen - Vlieland service. She is now a reserve vessel.

NOORD-NEDERLAND Catamaran built by ASB, Harwood, New South Wales, Australia for *Rederij Doeksen*. Used on freight services from Harlingen to Terschelling and Vlieland. In spring 2017 lengthened by 20 metres.

TIGER Catamaran built as the SUPERCAT 2002 by FBMA Babcock Marine, Cebu, Philippines for *SuperCat* of the Philippines. In 2007 purchased by *Rederij Doeksen* and renamed the TIGER. Operates from Harlingen to Terschelling and Vlieland.

VLIELAND Catamaran built by FBMA Babcock Marine, Cebu, Philippines for *Rederij Doeksen* to operate between Harlingen and Vlieland.

Under Construction

7	WILLEM BARENTSZ	-	18	14.0k	70.0m	600P	64C	-	BA	NL	-
8	WILLEM DE VLAMINGH	-	18	14.0k	70.0m	600P	64C	-	BA	NL	-

WILLEM BARENTSZ, WILLEM DE VLAMINGH Under construction by Strategic Marine, Vung Tau, Vietnam. They will be aluminium catamarans and LNG powered. They will replace the MIDSLAND.

REDERI AB ECKERÖ

THE COMPANY *Rederi AB Eckerö* is an Åland Islands company. It operates two ferry companies, a cruise operation from Stockholm (*Birka Cruises*), a ro-ro time chartering company (*Eckerö Shipping*) and a bus company on Åland (*Williams*).

ADDRESS PO Box 158, AX-22101 Mariehamn, Åland, Finland.

TELEPHONE Administration +358 (0)18 28 030.

FAX Administration +358 (0)18 12 011.

INTERNET Email info@rederiabeckero.ax **Website** www.rederiabeckero.ax *(English, Swedish)*

ECKERÖ LINE

THE COMPANY *Eckerö Line Ab Oy* is a Finnish company, 100% owned by *Rederi Ab Eckerö* of Åland, Finland. Until January 1998, the company was called *Eestin-Linjat*.

MANAGEMENT Managing Director Taru Keronen, **Marketing Director** Ida Toikka-Everi.

ADDRESS PO Box 307, 00181 Helsinki, Finland.

TELEPHONE Administration & Reservations +358 9 (0) 6000 4300.

INTERNET **Email** info@eckeroline.fi **Website** www.eckeroline.fi *(Swedish, Finnish, English)*

ROUTE OPERATED **Passenger Service** Helsinki (Länsisatama) - Tallinn (Estonia) (2 hrs 30 mins; *FINLANDIA*; up to 2 per day).

1	FINLANDIA	36093t	01	27.0k	175.0m	1880P	665C	116T	BA	FI	9214379

FINLANDIA Built as the MOBY FREEDOM by Daewoo Shipbuilding & Heavy Machinery Ltd, Okpo, South Korea for *Moby SpA (Moby Line)* of Italy. Operated on their Genoa/Civitavecchia/Livorno - Olbia routes. In March 2012 sold to *Eckerö Line*, and renamed the FREEDOM. Refitted at Landskrona and, in June, renamed the FINLANDIA. She entered service on 31st December 2012.

ECKERÖ LINJEN

THE COMPANY *Eckerö Linjen* is an Åland Islands company 100% owned by *Rederi AB Eckerö*.

MANAGEMENT **Managing Director** Tomas Karlsson, **Marketing Director** Maria Hellman.

ADDRESS Torggatan 2, Box 158, AX-22100 Mariehamn, Åland.

TELEPHONE **Administration** +358 (0)18 28 000, **Reservations** +358 (0)18 28 300.

FAX **Administration** +358 (0)18 28 380. **Reservations** +358 (0)18 28 230.

INTERNET **Email** info@eckerolinjen.ax **Website** www.eckerolinjen.se *(Swedish, Finnish, English)*

ROUTE OPERATED Eckerö (Åland) - Grisslehamn (Sweden) (2 hrs; *ECKERÖ*; 3 per day).

1	ECKERÖ	12358t	79	19.5k	121.1m	1500P	265C	34T	BA	SE	7633155

ECKERÖ Built as the JENS KOFOED by Aalborg Værft A/S, Aalborg, Denmark for *Bornholmstrafikken*. Used on the Rønne - Copenhagen, Rønne - Ystad and (until December 2002) Rønne - Sassnitz services. Rønne - Copenhagen service became Rønne – Køge in September 2004. In October 2004 sold to *Eckerö Linjen* for delivery in May 2005. Renamed the ECKERÖ and substantially rebuilt before entering service in early 2006. In January 2009 transferred from the Finnish to the Swedish flag.

ELB-LINK

THE COMPANY *Elb-Link Reederei GmbH* is a German private sector company. The previous company, owned by *Saaremaa Laevakompanii* of Estonia filed for bankruptcy following financial problems of the parent company in April 2017. A new company restored the service in May 2017.

MANAGEMENT **Managing Director** Bernd Bässmann.

ADDRESS Albert Ballin Platz 3, 27472 Cuxhaven, Germany.

TELEPHONE **Administration & Reservations** +49 (0)4721-3006 300.

FAX +49 (0)4721-3006 399.

INTERNET **Email** info@elb-link.de **Website** www.elb-link.de *(German, English)*

ROUTE OPERATED Cuxhaven - Brunsbüttel (across River Elbe, Germany) (1 hr approx) *GRETE* up to 6 per day).

1	GRETE	5233t	10	15.0k	97.9m	600P	150C	12L	BA	DE	9474060

GRETE Built as the MUHUMAA by Fiskerstrand Verft A/S, Aalesund, Norway for an Estonian bank and chartered to *Saaremaa Laevakompanii* of Estonia and operated on the Kuivastu - Virtsu service. In summer 2015 transferred to the *Elb-Link* service under the marketing name 'Grete' (but not renamed). In March 2017 laid up. Re-entered service in May 2017, renamed the GRETE and re-registered in Germany with engines uprated to enable a crossing time of one hour.

AG EMS

THE COMPANY *AG Ems* is a German public sector company.

MANAGEMENT Managing Director & Chief Executive Dr Bernhard Brons, **Marine Superintendent** Knut Gerdes, **Operations Manager** Hans-Jörg Oltmanns.

ADDRESS Am Aussenhafen, Postfach 1154, 26691 Emden, Germany.

TELEPHONE Administration & Reservations +49 (0)1805-180182.

FAX Administration & Reservations +49 (0)4921-890740.

INTERNET Email info@ag-ems.de **Website** www.ag-ems.de *(German)* www.borkumlijn.nl *(Dutch)* www.helgolandlinie.de *(German)*

ROUTES OPERATED Conventional Ferries Emden (Germany) - Borkum (German Frisian Islands) (2 hrs; ***GRONINGERLAND, MÜNSTERLAND, OSTFRIESLAND, WESTFALEN***; up to 4 per day), Eemshaven (The Netherlands) - Borkum (55 mins; ***GRONINGERLAND, MÜNSTERLAND, OSTFRIESLAND, WESTFALEN***; up to 4 per day). **Fast Ferry** Emden - Borkum (1 hr; ***NORDLICHT*** up to 4 per day), Eemshaven - Borkum (30 mins; ***NORDLICHT***; 1 per week in summer).

1	GRONINGERLAND	1070t	91	12.0k	44.4m	621P	30C	-	BA	DE	9002465
2	MÜNSTERLAND	1859t	86	15.5k	78.7m	1200P	70C	10L	BA	DE	8601989
3p»	NORDLICHT	435t	89	33.0k	38.8m	272P	0C	0L	-	DE	8816015
4	OSTFRIESLAND	1859t	85	16.0k	78.7m	1200P	70C	10L	BA	DE	8324622
5p	WAPPEN VON BORKUM	287t	76	11.5k	42.8m	358P	0C	0L	-	DE	7525918
6	WESTFALEN	1812t	72	15.5k	77.9m	1200P	65C	10L	BA	DE	7217004

GRONINGERLAND Built by Husumer Schiffswerft, Husum, Germany as the HILLIGENLEI for *Wyker Dampfschiffs-Reederei Föhr-Amrum GmbH* of Germany. Operated Schlüttsiel - Halligen – Wittdün (North Frisian Islands). In 2004 laid up. In late 2005 sold to *AG Ems*. In 2006 renamed the GRONINGERLAND.

MÜNSTERLAND Built by Martin Jansen GmbH & Co KG Schiffswerft, Leer, Germany for *AG Ems*.

NORDLICHT Fjellstrand 38m passenger-only catamaran built at Mandal, Norway for *AG Ems*.

OSTFRIESLAND Built by Martin Jansen GmbH & Co KG Schiffswerft, Leer, Germany for *AG Ems*. In 2015 lengthened by 15.4 m by BVT Brenn-und Verformtechnik GmbH, Bremen, Germany.

WAPPEN VON BORKUM Built as the HANNOVER by Schiffswerft Schlömer GmbH & Co KG, Oldersum, Germany for *Friesland Fahrlinie* of Germany. In 1979 sold to *AG Ems* and renamed the STADT BORKUM. In 1988 sold to *ST-Line* of Finland, operating day trips from Rauma and renamed the PRINCESS ISABELLA. In 1994 returned to *AG Ems* and renamed the WAPPEN VON BORKUM.

WESTFALEN Built by as the WESTFALEN by C Cassens Schiffswerft, Emden, Germany for *AG Ems*. Rebuilt in 1994. In 2006 renamed the HELGOLAND and inaugurated a new Wilhelmshaven - Helgoland service for subsidiary *Helgoland Linie*. In January 2016 reverted to the name WESTFALEN and used on service from Borkum.

FÆRGEN

THE COMPANIES *Danske Færger A/S* trading as *Færgen (previously Nordic Ferry Services A/S)* is a Danish mixed public and private sector company.

MANAGEMENT CEO John Steen-Mikkelsen.

ADDRESSES Dampskibskajen 3, 3700 Rønne, Denmark.

TELEPHONE Administration & Reservations +45 70 23 15 15. (Reservations not possible on FanøFærgen).

INTERNET Website www.faergen.com *(Danish, German, English)*

Finlandia *(Miles Cowsill)*

Leonora Christina *(Miles Cowsill)*

ROUTES OPERATED

AlsFærgen Fynshav (Als) - Bøjden (Fyn) (50 mins; *FRIGG SYDFYEN, FYNSHAV*; hourly (summer) two-hourly (winter)), ***BornholmerFærgen*** **Conventional Ferries** Rønne (Bornholm, Denmark) - Køge (5 hrs 30 mins; *HAMMERODDE*; 1 per day, ***April-October only:*** Rønne – Sassnitz (Germany) (3 hrs 30 mins; *POVL ANKER*; 1 per day). **Fast Ferry** Rønne - Ystad (Sweden) (1 hr 20 mins; *LEONORA CHRISTINA, VILLUM CLAUSEN*; **Peak season**: departure every 2 hours. **Low season**: 3 trips a day), ***FanøFærgen*** Esbjerg (Jutland) - Nordby (Fanø) (12 mins; *FENJA, MENJA, SØNDERHO*; every 20-40 mins), ***LangelandsFærgen*** Spodsbjerg (Langeland) - Tårs (Lolland) (45 mins; *LANGELAND, LOLLAND*; hourly), ***SamsøFærgen*** Kalundborg - Ballen (Samsø) (1 hr 15 min; *SAMSØ*; up to 4 per day).

1	FENJA	751t	98	11.5k	49.9m	396P	34C	4L	BA	DK	9189378
2	FRIGG SYDFYEN	1676t	84	13.5k	70.1m	338P	50C	8L	BA	DK	8222824
3	FYNSHAV	3380t	98	14.5k	69.2m	450P	96C	8L	BA	DK	9183025
4	HAMMERODDE	13906t	05	18.5k	124.9m	400P	342C	106T	A	DK	9323699
5	LANGELAND	4500t	12	16.0k	99.9m	600P	122C	36L	BA	DK	9596428
6»	LEONORA CHRISTINA	8235t	11	40.0k	112.6m	1400P	359C	-	BA	DK	9557848
7	LOLLAND	4500t	12	16.0k	99.9m	600P	122C	36L	BA	DK	9594690
8	MENJA	751t	98	11.5k	49.9m	396P	34C	4L	BA	DK	9189380
9	POVL ANKER	12131t	78	19.5k	121.0m	1500P	262C	26T	BA	DK	7633143
10	SAMSØ	4250t	08	16.0k	91.4m	600P	122C	30L	BA	DK	9548562
11p	SØNDERHO	93t	62	10.0k	26.3m	163P	0C	0L	-	DK	
12»	VILLUM CLAUSEN	6402t	00	40.0k	86.6m	1055P	200C	-	BA	DK	9216250

FENJA Built by Morsø Værft A/S, Nykøbing Mors, Denmark for *Scandlines Sydfyenske A/S* for the Esbjerg - Nordby service.

FRIGG SYDFYEN Built by Svendborg Skibsværft A/S, Svendborg, Denmark for *Sydfyenske Dampskibsselskab (SFDS)* of Denmark for the service between Spodsbjerg and Tårs. In June 2012 moved to the Fynshav - Bøjden route.

FYNSHAV Built as the KYHOLM by Ørskov Staalskibsværft, Frederikshavn, Denmark for *Samsø Linien* of Denmark. In October 2008 chartered to *Nordic Ferry Services* and in July 2009 sold to them. Used on the Kalundborg - Koby Kås service. In March 2015 renamed the FYNSHAV and moved to the Fynshav - Bøjden service.

HAMMERODDE Built by Merwede Shipyard, Hardinxveld-Giessendam, The Netherlands for *Bornholmstrafikken*. In Winter 2010 an additional vehicle deck was added for freight and some additional cabins.

LANGELAND Built by Sietas Werft, Hamburg, Germany for the Spodsbjerg - Tårs route.

LEONORA CHRISTINA Austal Auto-Express 113 catamaran built at Fremantle, Australia for *Færgen*. In December 2016 sold to *Ferry Gomera*, a subsidiary of *Fred. Olsen Lines* and chartered back. Used on the Rønne - Ystad route.

LOLLAND Built by Sietas Werft, Hamburg, Germany. She was launched as the SAMSØ and it was intended that she would be operated on the Hou - Sælvig service, being owned by *Samsø Linien* and operated by *Færgen*. However, these plans were dropped and in February 2012 she was renamed the LOLLAND. After delivery in March 2012 she was, in April, placed on the Spodsbjerg - Tårs route.

MENJA Built by Morsø Værft A/S, Nykøbing Mors, Denmark for *Scandlines Sydfyenske A/S* for the Esbjerg - Nordby service.

POVL ANKER Built by Aalborg Værft A/S, Denmark for *Bornholmstrafikken*. Used on the Rønne - Copenhagen (until September 2004), Rønne - Køge (October 2004-date), Rønne - Ystad and Rønne - Sassnitz services. In recent years she has operated between Rønne and Sassnitz and Rønne and Ystad in the peak summer period.

SAMSØ Built as the KANHAVE by Frantzis Shipyard, Perama, Greece. Used on the Hou - Sælvig route. In January 2015 transferred to the Kalundborg - Koby Kås (Samsø) service. Later in January 2015 the Samsø terminal was moved to Ballen. In August 2015 renamed the SAMSØ.

SØNDERHO Passenger-only ferry built by Esbjerg Jernstøberi & Maskinfabrik A/S, Esbjerg, Denmark for *Post & Telegrafvæsenet* (Danish Post Office). In 1977 taken over by *DSB*. Used on extra peak sailings and late night and early morning sailings between Esbjerg and Nordby.

VILLUM CLAUSEN Austal Auto-Express 86 catamaran built at Fremantle, Australia for *Bornholmstrafikken*. Used on the Rønne - Ystad service. Car capacity increased in 2005.

FINNLINES

THE COMPANY *Finnlines plc* is a Finnish private sector company. The Italian company *Grimaldi Compagnia de Navigazione SpA* has a controlling interest. It operates four passenger brands: *Finnlines HansaLink, Finnlines NordöLink* and *FinnLink* and *TransRussiaExpress*.

MANAGEMENT **President and CEO** Emanuele Grimaldi, **Head of Passenger Services and Line Manager HansaLink & Hanko-Rostock** Kielo Vesikko, **Line Manager NordöLink, Finnlink and Russia** Antonio Raimo.

ADDRESS PO Box 197, 00181 Helsinki, Finland.

TELEPHONE **Administration** +358 (0)10 343 50, **Passenger Reservations** +358 (0)9 231 43 100.

INTERNET ***Finnlines*** **Email** info.fi@finnlines.com **Website** ***Finnlines*** www.finnlines.com *(English, Finnish, German, Polish, Swedish)*

ROUTES OPERATED ***Finnlines Hansalink branded routes*** Helsinki (Vuosaari) - Travemünde (27 hrs; *FINNLADY, FINNMAID, FINNSTAR*; 7 per week).

Finnlines NordöLink branded route Malmö - Travemünde (9 hrs; *FINNPARTNER, FINNTRADER, NORDLINK*; up to 3 per day).

FinnLink branded route Naantali (Finland) - Långnäs - Kapellskär (Sweden) (6 hrs; *FINNCLIPPER, FINNFELLOW*, 2 per day).

1	FINNCLIPPER	29841t	99	22.0k	188.3m	440P	-	210T	BA2	SE	9137997
2	FINNEAGLE	29841t	99	22.0k	188.3m	800P	-	185T	BA2	FI	9138006
3	FINNFELLOW	33769t	00	22.0k	188.3m	452P	-	220T	BA	FI	9145164
4	FINNLADY	45923t	07	25.0k	216.0m	500P	-	300T	BA2	FI	9336268
5	FINNMAID	45923t	06	25.0k	216.0m	500P	-	300T	BA2	FI	9319466
6	FINNPARTNER	32534t	94	21.3k	183.0m	270P	-	236T	A2	SE	9010163
7	FINNSTAR	45923t	06	25.0k	216.0m	500P	-	300T	BA2	FI	9319442
8	FINNTRADER	32534t	95	21.3k	183.0m	270P	-	220T	BA2	SE	9017769
9	NORDLINK	45923t	07	25.0k	216.0m	500P	-	300T	BA2	SE	9336256

FINNCLIPPER 'Ro-pax' ferry built by Astilleros Españoles, Cadiz, Spain. Ordered by *Stena RoRo* of Sweden and launched as the STENA SEAPACER 1. In 1998 sold, before delivery, to *Finnlines* and renamed the FINNCLIPPER. Entered service on the Helsinki - Travemünde route in 1999. During Winter 1999/2000 she was converted to double-deck loading. In 2003 transferred to *FinnLink*. In 2007 an additional freight deck was added.

FINNEAGLE 'Ro-pax' vessel built by Astilleros Españoles, Cadiz, Spain. Ordered by *Stena RoRo* of Sweden and launched as the STENA SEAPACER 2. In 1998 sold, before delivery, to *Finnlines* and renamed the FINNEAGLE. Although expected to join her sister the FINNCLIPPER on the Helsinki - Travemünde route, on delivery in November 1999 she entered service with *FinnLink*. During Winter 1999/2000 she was modified for two-deck loading. She has operated on both the *FinnLink* and *Finnlines Nordö-Link* services. In July 2016 chartered to *Grimaldi Line* to operate between Barcelona and Tangiers. In Spring 2017 an additional accommodation block was added raising her passenger capacity to 800.

FINNFELLOW 'Ro-pax' ferry built as the STENA BRITANNICA by Astilleros Españoles, Cadiz, Spain for *Stena RoRo* and chartered to *Stena Line BV* to operate between Hook of Holland and Harwich. In 2003 replaced by a new STENA BRITANNICA, sold to *Finnlines*, renamed the FINNFELLOW and placed on the Helsinki – Travemünde route. In 2004 transferred to *FinnLink*.

FINNLADY, FINNMAID Built by Fincantieri-Cantieri Navali Italiani SpA, Ancona, Italy to operate between Helsinki and Travemünde.

FINNPARTNER 'Ro-pax' vessel built by Stocznia Gdanska SA, Gdansk, Poland for *Finnlines Oy* of Finland to provide a daily service conveying both freight and a limited number of cars and passengers on the previously freight-only route between Helsinki and Travemünde. In February 2007 replaced by the FINNLADY and placed on the Turku - Travemünde freight service; in May sent to the Remontowa Shipyard in Gdansk for rebuilding to increase passenger capacity and allow for two-deck through loading. Currently operating on the Travemünde - Malmö and Lübeck - St Petersburg services.

FINNSTAR Built by Fincantieri-Cantieri Navali Italiani SpA, Castellamare, Italy to operate between Helsinki and Travemünde.

FINNTRADER 'Ro-pax' vessel built by Stocznia Gdanska SA, Gdansk, Poland for *Finnlines Oy* of Finland to provide a daily service conveying both freight and a limited number of cars and passengers on the previously freight-only route between Helsinki and Travemünde. In 2006/07 rebuilt to increase passenger capacity and allow for two-deck through loading. In 2007 transferred to the Malmö - Travemünde route.

NORDLINK Built by Fincantieri-Cantieri Navali Italiani SpA, Castellamare, Italy for *Finnlines* to operate for *Finnlines NordöLink* between Travemünde and Malmö. Currently operating on the Travemünde - Malmö service.

FJORD LINE

THE COMPANY *Fjord Line* is a Norwegian company. During 2007 most of the shares of the company were purchased by *Frode and Ole Teigen*. The company bought and merged with *Master Ferries* during December 2007 and all operations are branded as *Fjord Line*.

MANAGEMENT CEO Rickard Ternblom, **Communications Director** Eva Sørås Mellgren.

ADDRESS PO Box 513, 4379 Egersund, Norway.

TELEPHONE Administration & Reservations +47 51 46 40 99.

INTERNET Email info@fjordline.com **Website** www.fjordline.com *(English, Danish, German, Dutch, Polish, Norwegian,)*

ROUTE OPERATED Conventional Ferry Bergen (Norway) – Stavanger - Hirtshals (Denmark) (17 hrs; ***BERGENSFJORD, STAVANGERFJORD***; daily), Langesund (Norway) - Hirtshals (4 hrs 30 mins; ***BERGENSFJORD, STAVANGERFJORD***, daily), Sandefjord (Norway) - Strömstad (Sweden) (2 hrs 30 mins; ***OSLOFJORD***; 2 per day), **Fast Ferry *May-August*** Kristiansand (Norway) - Hirtshals (Denmark) (2 hrs 15 min); ***FJORD CAT***; up to 3 per day).

1	BERGENSFJORD	31678t	13	21.5k	170.0m	1500P	600C	90T	BA	DK	9586617
2»	FJORD CAT	5619t	98	43.0k	91.3m	663P	220C	-	A	DK	9176060
3	OSLOFJORD	16794t	93	19.0k	134.4m	882P	350C	44T	BA	DK	9058995
4	STAVANGERFJORD	31678t	13	21.5k	170.0m	1500P	600C	90T	BA	DK	9586605

BERGENSFJORD, STAVANGERFJORD Built by Bergen Group Fosen AS, Rissa, Norway for *Fjord Line*. They operate on LNG.

FJORD CAT Incat 91-metre catamaran, built speculatively at Hobart, Tasmania, Australia. In Spring 1998, following *Incat's* acquisition of a 50% share in *Scandlines Cat-Link A/S*, she was chartered by *Nordic Catamaran Ferries K/S* to that company, operating between Århus and Kalundborg and named the CAT-LINK V. She is the current holder of the Hales Trophy for fastest crossing of the Atlantic during her delivery voyage between the USA and Falmouth, UK (although this claim is disputed

Finnpartner *(Matthew Punter)*

Oslofjord *(John Bryant)*

because it was not a genuine commercial service). In 1999 the charter was transferred to *Mols-Linien*, she was renamed the MADS MOLS and operated between Århus and Odden. Charter ended in July 2005. Laid up and renamed the INCAT 049. In 2006 sold to *Gabriel Scott Rederi (Master Ferries)* and renamed the MASTER CAT. In December 2008 purchased by *Fjord Line* renamed the FJORD CAT. Did not operate in 2009 but service resumed in 2010.

OSLOFJORD Built by Fosen Mekaniske Verksteder, Rissa, Norway for *Rutelaget Askøy-Bergen* as the BERGEN and used on the *Fjord Line* Bergen - Egersund - Hanstholm service. In April 2003 chartered to *DFDS Seaways*, renamed the DUCHESS OF SCANDINAVIA and, after modifications, introduced onto the Harwich - Cuxhaven service. In 2004 sold to *Bergensfjord KS* of Norway and chartered to *DFDS Seaways*. In 2005 sub-chartered to *Fjord Line* for 5 months (with *DFDS* officers and deck-crew) and renamed the ATLANTIC TRAVELLER. In 2006 chartered directly to *Fjord Line*. In March 2008 purchased by *Fjord Line* and renamed the BERGENSFJORD. In January 2014 renamed the OSLOFJORD, rebuilt as a day ferry by STX Finland, Rauma, Finland and, in June 2014, inaugurated a new service between Sandefjord and Strömstad.

HURTIGRUTEN

THE COMPANY *Hurtigruten AS* is a Norwegian private sector company. The service was originally provided by a consortium of companies. By 2006, through mergers and withdrawal from the operation, there were just two companies - *Troms Fylkes D/S* and *Ofotens og Vesteraalens D/S* and in that year *Hurtigruten ASA* was formed. In September 2015 it was taken over by *Silk Bidco AS* of Norway and the company changed its name to *Hurtigruten AS*.

MANAGEMENT **Chairman** Trygve Hegnar, **Chief Executive Officer** Daniel Skjeldam.

ADDRESS Hurtigruten ASA, Fredrik Lamges gate 14, Postboks 6144, 9291 Tromsø, Norway.

TELEPHONE **Administration** +47 970 57 030, **Reservations *Norway*** +47 810 03 030,

UK +44 (0)203 603711, ***Ireland*** +353 (0)1607 4420

INTERNET **Email** firmapost@hurtigruten.com uk.sales@hurtigruten.com

Websites www.hurtigruten.co.uk *(English)* www.hurtigruten.no *(Norwegian)* www.hurtigruten.de *(German)* www.hurtigruten.fr *(French)* www.hurtigruten.us *(US English)*

ROUTE OPERATED 'Hurtigruten' sail every day throughout the year from Bergen and calls at 34 ports up to Kirkenes and takes you along one of the world's most exciting coast lines, where you will find yourself close to nature, people and traditions. Daily departures throughout the year. The round trip takes just under 11 days.

1	FINNMARKEN	15539t	02	18.0k	138.5m	1000P	47C	OL	S	NO	9231951
2p	FRAM	11647t	07	18.0k	110.0m	500P	0C	OL	-	NO	9370018
3	KONG HARALD	11204t	93	18.0k	121.8m	691P	45C	OL	S	NO	9039119
4	LOFOTEN	2621t	64	16.0k	87.4m	410P	0C	OL	C	NO	5424562
5	MIDNATSOL	16151t	03	18.0k	135.7m	1000P	45C	OL	S	NO	9247728
6	NORDKAPP	11386t	96	18.0k	123.3m	691P	45C	OL	S	NO	9107772
7	NORDLYS	11204t	94	18.0k	121.8m	691P	45C	OL	S	NO	9048914
8	NORDNORGE	11384t	97	18.0k	123.3m	691P	45C	OL	S	NO	9107784
9	POLARLYS	11341t	96	18.0k	123.0m	737P	35C	OL	S	NO	9107796
10	RICHARD WITH	11205t	93	18.0k	121.8m	691P	45C	OL	S	NO	9040429
11p	SPITSBERGEN	7344t	09	16.0k	100.5m	335P	0C	OL	-	NO	9434060
12	TROLLFJORD	16140t	02	18.0k	135.7m	822P	45C	OL	S	NO	9233258
13	VESTERÅLEN	6262t	83	18.0k	108.6m	560P	35C	OL	S	NO	8019368

FINNMARKEN Built by Kværner Kleven Skeppsvarv, Ulsteinvik, Norway for *Ofotens og Vesteraalens D/S*. In October 2009 chartered as a support vessel for the Gorgon Project (natural gas) in Western Australia. In November 2011 returned to *Hurtigruten* and, in February 2012, returned to service.

Kong Harald *(John Bryant)*

Lofoten *(John Bryant)*

FRAM Built by Fincantieri-Cantieri Navali Italiani SpA at Trieste for *Hurtigruten Group ASA* (ordered by *OVDS*). Since 2007 she has operated cruises around Greenland and Svalbad during the summer period and in South America during the winter and this has been the pattern since. She is named after Fridtjof Nansen's expedition ship FRAM and has ice class 1A/1B.

KONG HARALD Built by Volkswerft, Stralsund, Germany for *Troms Fylkes D/S*.

LOFOTEN Built by A/S Aker Mekaniske Verksted, Oslo, Norway for *Vesteraalens D/S*. In 1988 she was sold to *Finnmark Fylkesrederi og Ruteselskap*. In 1996 she was sold to *Ofotens og Vesteraalens D/S*. In 2002 she was replaced by the FINNMARKEN but she then operated summer cruises and in the winter months substituted for the NORDNORGE when that vessel was sailing in the Chilean Fjords and Antarctica. Since 2008 she has operated on the main Hurtigruten roster.

MIDNATSOL Built by Fosen Mekaniske Verksteder, Rissa, Norway for *Troms Fylkes D/S*. From 2016 also used as an expedition ship in the Antarctic.

NORDKAPP Built by Kværner Kleven Skeppsvarv, Ulsteinvik, Norway for *Ofotens og Vesteraalens D/S*. During the winters of 2005/06 and 2006/07 she operated cruises in South America but following the delivery of the FRAM she now remains on the Hurtigruten throughout the year.

NORDLYS Built by Volkswerft, Stralsund, Germany for *Troms Fylkes D/S*. In 2002 sold to *Kilberg Shipping KS* of Norway and leased back on 15 year bareboat charter with options to repurchase. She was laid up during winter 2008/09 until required to replace the damaged RICHARD WITH from the end of January. She now operates full-time on the Hurtigruten roster.

NORDNORGE Built by Kværner Kleven, Ulsteinvik, Norway for *Ofotens og Vesteraalens D/S*. During winters 2002/03 - 2007/08 she operated cruises in South America. During most of Winter 2008/09 she was used as an accommodation vessel for a liquefied natural gas field. Laid up at Bremerhaven during winter 2009/10.

POLARLYS Built by Ulstein Verft A/S, Ulsteinvik, Norway for *Troms Fylkes D/S*.

RICHARD WITH Built by Volkswerft, Stralsund, Norway for *Ofotens og Vesteraalens D/S*. In 2002 sold to *Kystruten KS*, of Norway and leased back on 15 year bareboat charter with options to re-purchase.

SPITSBERGEN Built as the ATLANTIDA by Estaleiros Navais de Viana do Castelo, Viana do Castelo, Portugal for *Atlanticoline* of Portugal as a ro-ro ferry to operate in the Azores. Although completed in 2009, she was never delivered because she did not meet the required specification. In June 2015 purchased by *Hurtigruten* and renamed the NORWAY EXPLORER. Taken initially to the Öresund Drydocks Shipyard, Landskrona, Sweden and then onto Fosen's Rissa Shipyard, near Trondheim, for rebuilding to make her suitable for Hurtigruten service and cruising in polar waters. In May 2016 renamed the SPITSBERGEN and entered service on the *Hurtigruten*, running along-side the LOFOTEN. Unlike other *Hurtigruten* vessels, no cars can be conveyed.

TROLLFJORD Built by Fosen Mekaniske Verksteder, Rissa, Norway for *Troms Fylkes D/S*.

VESTERÅLEN Built by Kaarbös Mekaniske Verksted A/S, Harstad, Norway for *Vesteraalens D/S*. From 1987 owned by *Ofotens og Vesteraalens D/S* and from 2006 by *Hurtigruten Group ASA*.

Under Construction

14p	**ROALD AMUNDSEN**	**20889t**	**18**	**-**	**140.0m**	**530P**	**0C**	**0L**	**S**	**NO**	**-**
15p	**FRIDTJOF NANSEN**	**20889t**	**19**	**-**	**140.0m**	**530P**	**0C**	**0L**	**S**	**NO**	**-**

ROALD AMUNDSEN, FRIDTJOF NANSEN Under construction by Kleven Verft, Ulsteinvik, Norway. They are designed to cope with both polar waters (for cursing) and service on the regular routes along the Norwegian coastline. There is an option for two more.

FÆRGESELSKABET LÆSØ

THE COMPANY *Færgeselskabet Læsø K/S* is a Danish public sector company, 50% owned by the county of North Jutland and 50% by the municipality of Læsø.

MANAGEMENT **Managing Director** Lars Ricks, **Marketing Manager** Bente Faurholt.

ADDRESS Havnepladsen 1, Vesterø Havn, 9940 Læsø, Denmark.

TELEPHONE **Administration & Reservations** +45 98 49 90 22

INTERNET **Email** info@laesoe-line.dk **Website** www.laesoe-line.dk *(Danish, German)*

ROUTE OPERATED Læsø - Frederikshavn (Jutland) (1 hr 30 mins; *ANE LÆSØ, MARGRETE LÆSØ*; up 7 per day).

1	ANE LÆSØ	2208t	95	12.0k	53.8m	440P	72C	-	BA	DK	9107370
2	MARGRETE LÆSØ	3668t	97	13.5k	68.5m	586P	76C	12L	BA	DK	9139438t

ANE LÆSØ Built as the VESBORG by Ørskov Stålskibsværft, Ørskov, Denmark for *Samsø Linien*. In March2012 sold to *Læsø Færgen*. Rebuilt by Soby Yard, Aerø, Denmark and renamed the ANE LÆSØ. Between September 2014 and February 2015 she operated on the Hou - Sælvig (Samsø) service which had been taken over by *Samsø Rederi* before their new SAMSØ (now PRINSESSE ISABELLA) was delivered. She will continue to act as reserve vessel on this route.

MARGRETE LÆSØ Built as the LÆSØ FÆRGEN by A/S Norsdsøværftet, Ringkøbing, Denmark for *Andelsfærgeselskabet Læsø* of Denmark. In June 1997 renamed the MARGRETE LÆSØ. In July 1999 transferred to *Færgeselskabet Læsø*.

LINDA LINE

Lindaliini AS (trading as *Linda Line*) is an Estonian Company owned by three Estonian investors - Enn Rohula (26.8%), Urmas Sardis & Janek Veeber (73.2%).

MANAGEMENT **CEO** Enn Rohula.

ADDRESS Ädala 4A, Tallinn 10614, Estonia.

TELEPHONE **Administration (Estonia)** +372 6999 340 **Reservations (Finland)** +358 (0)600 0668 970.

INTERNET **Email** info@lindaline.ee **Website** www.lindaline.ee *(Estonian, Finnish, English Russian)*

ROUTE OPERATED Tallinn (Estonia) – Helsinki (Finland) (1hr 40 mins, ***KAROLIN***; up 3 to per day (April – December) depending on winter ice conditions).

1p	KAROLIN	636t	00	40.0k	42.0m	402P	0C	0L	EE	9124433

KAROLIN Construction began 1995 at Austal Ships Pty Ltd (Hendersons) initially as the OCEANFAST FERRIES NO 16 and later the CARAIBE-JET but not completed until 2000. In 2000 sold to *AG Ems of Germany* as the POLARSTERN for services between from Emden and Frisian Island of Borkum and Helgoland (summer only). In 2009 sold to *Lindaliini AS* and renamed the KAROLIN.

MOBY SPL

THE COMPANY *Moby SPL* is a joint venture between *Moby Lines* of Italy and *St. Peter Line*, a Russian owned, EU registered private sector company.

MANAGEMENT **CEO** Sergei Kotenev.

ADDRESS Ostrovskogo sq. 7, St. Petersburg, 191025 Russia.

TELEPHONE ***Russia*** +7 (812) 337-20-60, ***Finland*** +358 (0)9 6187 2000 ***Germany*** +49 (0)611 140 22 02.

INTERNET **Email** sales@stpeterline.com **Website** www.stpeterline.com

(Russian, English, Estonian, Finnish, Swedish)

ROUTES OPERATED St Petersburg - Helsinki - Tallinn - Stockholm - Helsinki - St Petersburg ***SPL PRINCESS ANASTASIA***; 1 per week), St Petersburg - Helsinki - St Petersburg. ***SPL PRINCESS ANASTASIA***; 1 per week).

Spitsbergen *(John Bryant)*

Express 2 *(Peter Therkildsen)*

1	**SPL PRINCESS ANASTASIA**	37583t	86	22.0k	177.0m	2500P	380C	42L	BA	IT	8414582

SPL PRINCESS ANASTASIA Built as the OLYMPIA by Oy Wärtsilä Ab, Turku, Finland for *Rederi AB Slite* of Sweden for *Viking Line* service between Stockholm and Helsinki. In 1993 she was chartered to *P&O European Ferries* to inaugurate a new service between Portsmouth and Bilbao. Renamed the PRIDE OF BILBAO. During the summer period she also operated, at weekends, a round trip between Portsmouth and Cherbourg. In 1994 she was purchased by the *Irish Continental Group* and re-registered in the Bahamas. In 2002 her charter was extended for a further five years and again for a further three years from October 2007. The Cherbourg service ended at the end of 2004. In September 2010 redelivered to *Irish Continental Group*. In October 2010 renamed the BILBAO. In November 2010 chartered to *St. Peter Line*, in February 2011 renamed the SPL PRINCESS ANASTASIA and in April 2011 inaugurated a new Stockholm - St Petersburg service. In February 2011 purchased by an associated company of *St. Peter Line*. During January and February 2014 she served as a floating hotel at the Winter Olympics in Sochi, Russia. In November 2016 sold to *Moby Lines* of Italy and chartered to *Moby SPL*.

MOLSLINJEN

THE COMPANY *Mols-Linien A/S* (from March 2017 trading as *Molslinjen*) is a Danish private sector company; previously a subsidiary of *J Lauritzen A/S*, it was sold in 1988 to *DIFKO No LXII (Dansk Investeringsfond)*. Since 1994 shares in the company have been traded on the Stock Exchange. In January 1999 a 40% share in the company was acquired by *Scandlines Danmark A/S*. Their *Scandlines Cat-Link* Århus - Kalundborg service became part of *Mols-Linien* in February 1999 and the service was switched from Kalundborg to Odden in April 1999. The *Scandlines* share in the company was acquired by the *Clipper Group* in 2007.

MANAGEMENT **CEO** Søren Jespersen, **Marketing Manager** Mikkel Hybel.

ADDRESS Hveensgade 4, 8000 Aarhus C, Denmark.

TELEPHONE **Administration** +45 89 52 52 00, **Reservations** +45 70 10 14 18 (press 1).

FAX **Administration** +45 89 52 53 93.

INTERNET **Email** molslinjen@molslinjen.dk **Website** www.molslinjen.dk *(Danish)*

ROUTES OPERATED ***All year*** Århus (Jutland) - Odden (Sealand) (1 hr 5 mins; *EXPRESS 1, EXPRESS 2, EXPRESS 3*; up to 12 per day), ***April - October- weekends only*** Ebeltoft (Jutland) - Odden (45 mins; *MAX MOLS*; up to 3 per day).

1»	**EXPRESS 1**	10504t	09	40.0k	112.6m	1200P	417C	34L	A	DK	9501590
2»	**EXPRESS 2**	10500t	13	40.0k	112.6m	1000P	417C	34L	A	DK	9561356
3»	**EXPRESS 3**	10842t	17	40.0k	109.4m	1000P	411C	34L	A	DK	9793064
4»	**MAX MOLS**	5617t	98	43.0k	91.3m	800P	220C	-	A	DK	9176058

EXPRESS 1 Incat 112m catamaran built by Incat Tasmania Pty Ltd for *MGC Chartering* of the Irish Republic. Launched as the INCAT 066. On completion, sold to for *MGC Chartering* of the Irish Republic and renamed the MGC 66. In April 2009 chartered to *LD Lines*, renamed the NORMAN ARROW and, in June, placed on the Dover - Boulogne route. In November 2009 withdrawn and laid up for the winter. In April 2010 began operating on the Portsmouth Le Havre - route. In March 2012 chartered to *Mols-Linien* and renamed the KATEXPRESS 1 (Note: in upper and lower case spelt 'KatExpress 1'). Entered service in May 2012. In January 2017 renamed the EXPRESS 1.

EXPRESS 2 Incat 112m catamaran built by Incat Tasmania Pty Ltd. Launched as INCAT 067. In March 2013 chartered to *Mols-Linien* and renamed the KATEXPRESS 2 for ten years with a purchase option. (Note: in upper and lower case spelt 'KatExpress 2'). Entered service in May 2013. In March 2017 renamed the EXPRESS 2.

EXPRESS 3 Incat 109m catamaran built by Incat Tasmania Pty Ltd, Hobart, Australia.

MAX MOLS Incat 91-metre catamaran, built speculatively at Hobart, Tasmania, Australia. In Spring 1998, following *Incat's* acquisition of a 50% share in *Scandlines Cat-Link A/S*, she was sold to that company and named the CAT-LINK IV. In 1999 purchased by *Mols-Linien* and renamed the MAX MOLS. In 2000 chartered to *Marine Atlantic* of Canada to operate between Port aux Basques (Newfoundland) and North Sydney (Nova Scotia). Returned to *Mols-Linien* in Autumn 2000. In Summer 2002 chartered to *Riga Sea Lines* to operate between Riga and Nynäshamn. Returned to *Mols-Linien* in Autumn 2002. In 2004 chartered to *P&O Ferries* to operate between Portsmouth and Caen. Operated under the marketing name 'Caen Express'. In November 2004 returned to *Mols-Linien* and placed on the Århus - Odden route to enhance the service. In June 2017 transferred to the Ebeltoft - Odden route.

Under construction

5»	**EXPRESS 4**	-	19	40.0k	109.0m	1006P	425C	36L	A	DK	-
6	**NEWBUILDING**	-	18	-	158.0m	400P	-	90L	BA	DK	-

EXPRESS 4 Austal 109m catamaran under construction by from Austal Ships, Fremantle, Australia. Likely to operate on the Århus - Odden route. Another vessel or vessels will be redeployed to the Ystad (Sweden) and Rønne (Bornholm) when *Molslinjen* takes over the Bornholm contract from *Danske Færger A/S* in September 2018.

NEWBUILDING 2 Under construction by Rauma Marine Constructions Oy, Rauma, Finland. She will operate between Køge and Rønne (Bornholm) when *Molslinjen* takes over the Bornholm contract from *Danske Færger A/S* in September 2018.

REEDEREI NORDEN-FRISIA

THE COMPANY *Aktiengesellschaft Reederei Norden-Frisia* is a German public sector company.

MANAGEMENT **President/CEO** C U Stegmann, **Managing Director/CFO** Prok. Graw, **Technical Manager** Prok. H Stolle.

ADDRESS Postfach 1262, 26534 Norderney, Germany.

TELEPHONE ***Administration*** +49 (0)4931 987 0.

FAX ***Administration*** +49 (0)4931 987 1131.

INTERNET ***Email*** info@reederei-frisia.de ***Website*** www.reederei-frisia.de *(German)*

ROUTES OPERATED **Car Ferries & Passenger Ferries** Norddeich (Germany) - Norderney (German Frisian Islands) (1 hr; *FRISIA I, FRISIA III, FRISIA IV, FRISIA VI*; up to 15 per day), Norddeich - Juist (German Frisian Islands) (1 hr 20 mins; *FRISIA II, FRISIA VII*; up to 15 per day). **Excursion Vessels** *(FRISIA IX, FRISIA X, RÜM HART, WAPPEN VON NORDENEY*; varies).

1	**FRISIA I**	1020t	70	12.3k	63.7m	1500P	53C	-	BA	DE	7018604
2	**FRISIA II**	1125t	78	12.0k	63.3m	1340P	53C	-	BA	DE	7723974
3	**FRISIA III**	1786t	15	12.0k	74.3m	1342P	60C	-	BA	DE	9732450
4	**FRISIA IV**	1574t	02	12.0k	71.7m	1342P	60C	-	BA	DE	9246839
5	**FRISIA VI**	768t	68	12.0k	54.9m	1096P	35C	-	BA	DE	8827179
6F	**FRISIA VII**	363t	84	12.0k	53.0m	12P	30C	-	BA	DE	8891807
7p	**FRISIA IX**	571t	80	11.0k	57.0m	785P	0C	-	-	DE	7924310
8p	**FRISIA X**	187t	72	12.0k	36.3m	290P	0C	-	-	DE	7222308
9p	**FRISIA XI**	105t	69	12.0k	35.4m	940P	0C		-	DE	8137237
10p	**WAPPEN VON NORDENEY**	154t	67	14.0k	31.1m	200P	0C		-	DE	7935395

FRISIA I, FRISIA II, FRISIA VI Built by Jos L Meyer Werft, Papenburg, Germany for *Reederei Norden-Frisia*. Passenger capacities relate to the summer season. Capacity is reduced during the winter.

FRISIA III Built by Cassen-Werft, Emden, Germany.

FRISIA IV Built by Schiffswerft und Maschinenfabrik Cassens GmbH, Emden, Germany for *Reederei Norden-Frisia* to replace the FRISIA VIII.

FRISIA VII Built by Schlömer Werft, Oldersum, Germany for *Reederei Norden-Frisia*. Conveys ro-ro freight to Norderney and Juist.

FRISIA IX, FRISIA X Built by Schiffswerft Julius Diedrich GmbH & Co. KG, Oldersum, Germany for *Reederei Norden-Frisia*. The FRISIA IX was built to convey 9 cars at the bow end but is now used in passenger-only mode. These ships are generally used for excursions.

FRISIA XI Built by Julius Diedrich Schiffswerft, Odersum, Germany as the BALTRUM IV for *Baltrum-Linie* of Germany. In November 1982 sold to *Wyker Dampfschiffs-Reederei* and renamed the RÜM HART. In March 2014 sold to *Reederei Norden-Frisia*. In October renamed the FRISIA XI.

WAPPEN VON NORDENEY Built by Cassens-Werft, Emden, Germany for *Reederei Norden-Frisia*. Used for excursions.

POLFERRIES

THE COMPANY *Polferries* is the trading name of *Polska Zegluga Baltycka SA (Polish Baltic Shipping Company)*, a Polish state-owned company.

MANAGEMENT **President** Piotr Redmerski.

ADDRESS ul Portowa 41, 78-100 Kolobrzeg, Poland.

TELEPHONE **Administration & Reservations *Poland*** +48 94 35 52 100, ***Sweden*** +46 (0)8 520 686 60.

INTERNET **Email** info@polferries.pl **Website** www.polferries.pl *(Polish, Danish, English, German, Swedish)*

ROUTES OPERATED Świnoujście - Ystad (7 hrs; *BALTIVIA, CRACOVIA, MAZOVIA*; 2 per day), Gdansk - Nynäshamn (Sweden) (18 hrs; *WAWEL*; 3 per week.

1	BALTIVIA	17790t	81	19.0k	146.9m	250P	30C	80L	BA	BS	7931997
2	CRACOVIA	25028t	02	22.8k	180.0m	550P	-	150T	BA	BS	9237242
3	MAZOVIA	25996t	96	21.0k	168.0m	200P	-	154T	BA2	BS	9010814
4	WAWEL	25318t	80	19.0k	163.9m	900P	550C	75L	A2	BS	7814462

CRACOVIA Built as the MURILLO by Astilleros Españoles SA, Seville, Spain for *Trasmediterranea* of Spain. Used mainly on the service between Cadiz and Canary Islands. In June 2014 sold to *Bulgaria West Port* of Bulgaria and renamed the DRUJBA. She operated between Bourgas, Bulgaria, Batumi (Georgia) and Novorossiysk (Russia). In March 2017 sold to *Polferries* and, in June 2017, renamed the CRACOVIA. In September 2017 introduced onto the Świnoujście - Ystad route.

BALTIVIA Built as the SAGA STAR by Fartygsentreprenader AB, Kalmar, Sweden for *TT-Saga-Line* and, from 1982, used on freight services between Travemünde and Trelleborg/Malmö. (Originally ordered by *Rederi AB Svea* as the SAGALAND). In 1989 sold to *Cie Meridionale* of France, renamed the GIROLATA and used on *SNCM* (later *CMR*) services in the Mediterranean. In 1993 she was chartered back to *TT-Line*, resumed her original name and was used on the Travemünde - Trelleborg service. Following delivery of the ROBIN HOOD and the NILS DACKE in 1995, she was transferred to the Rostock - Trelleborg route. In July 1997 she was purchased by *TT-Line* and in 1998 passenger facilities were completely renovated to full ro-pax format; following the delivery of the TOM SAWYER she was transferred back to the Travemünde - Trelleborg route, operating additional freight sailings. Briefly transferred back to Rostock - Trelleborg when the charter of the TT-TRAVELLER ended. Withdrawn in 2002, sold to *Transmanche Ferries* and renamed the DIEPPE. In 2006 replaced by the SEVEN SISTERS, sold to *Polferries*, renamed the BALTIVIA and, in 2007, placed on the Gdansk - Nynäshamn route. In February 2013 transferred to the Świnoujście – Ystad service.

MAZOVIA Built as the GOTLAND by Pt Dok Kodja Bahri, Kodja, Indonesia for *Rederi AB Gotland* for charter. In 1997 briefly chartered to *Tor Line* and then to *Nordic Trucker Line*, to operate between Oxelösund and St Petersburg (a ro-ro freight service). In June 1997 she was chartered to *SeaWind*

Mazovia *(Miles Cowsill)*

Huckleberry Finn *(Miles Cowsill)*

Line, enabling a twice-daily passenger service to be operated. In late 1997 she was sold to *Finnlines* and renamed the FINNARROW. She started operating twice weekly between Helsinki and Travemünde. During Summer 1998 she was transferred to *FinnLink*; a bow door was fitted and she was modified to allow for two-level loading. In 2003 transferred to *Nordö Link*. In 2005 returned to *FinnLink*. In 2006 transferred to *Finnlines Nordö Link* again. In 2007 chartered to *Stena Line* to operate between Karlskrona and Gdynia. In December 2011 transferred to the Hook of Holland - Killingholme route. In March 2011 returned to *Finnlines* and placed on the Travemünde - Malmö service. In October 2011 transferred to *FinnLink*. Between January and March 2013 chartered to *Stena Line* to cover Irish Sea routes during the refit period but withdrawn from service prematurely following an accident. In April 2013 chartered to *Grimaldi Line* of Italy for five years and renamed the EUROFERRY BRINDISI. In October 2014 sold to the *Grimaldi Group* of Italy. In November sold to *Polferries* and renamed the MAZOVIA. Entered service in June 2015 on the Świnoujście- Ystad service.

WAWEL Built as the SCANDINAVIA by Kockums Varvet AB, Malmö, Sweden for *Rederi AB Nordö* of Sweden. After service in the Mediterranean for *UMEF*, she was, in 1981, sold to *SOMAT* of Bulgaria, renamed the TZAREVETZ and used on *Medlink* services between Bulgaria and the Middle East, later on other routes. In 1986 she was chartered to *Callitzis* of Greece for a service between Italy and Greece. In 1988 she was sold to *Sealink*, re-registered in The Bahamas and renamed the FIESTA. She was then chartered to *OT Africa Line*. During Autumn 1989 she was rebuilt at Bremerhaven to convert her for passenger use and in March 1990 she was renamed the FANTASIA and placed on the Dover - Calais service. Later in 1990 she was renamed the STENA FANTASIA. In 1998 transferred to *P&O Stena Line*. In 1999 she was renamed the P&OSL CANTERBURY. In 2002 renamed the PO CANTERBURY. In Spring 2003 replaced by the PRIDE OF CANTERBURY and laid up at Dunkerque. Later in the year sold to *GA Ferries* and renamed the ALKMINI A. In 2004 moved to Greece and, after a partial rebuild (including the welding up of the bow door) placed on the Igoumenitsa – Brindisi route. Later in 2004 sold to *Polferries* and renamed the WAWEL; rebuilt to increase the number of cabins. In 2005 placed on the Świnoujście – Ystad service. In May 2015 transferred to the Gdansk - Nynäshamn route.

Under Construction

5	**NEWBUILDING**	**-**	**19**	**18.0k**	**202.4m**	**400P**	**-**	**180T**	**BA2**	**-**	**-**

NEWBUILDING Under construction by Gryfia Marine Repair Shipyard SA, Szczecin, Poland. Likely to replace the BALTIVIA on the Świnoujście - Ystad route. Dual fuel - diesel and LNG.

PRAAMID

THE COMPANY *Praamid* is the trading name of the ferry operation of the *Port of Tallinn*, a company owned by the Republic of Estonia. It takes over the operation of services to the islands of Hiiumaa and Saaremaa in October 2016.

ADDRESS Sadama 25, Tallinn 15051, Estonia.

TELEPHONE 618 1310

INTERNET **Email** info@praamid.ee **Website** www.praamid.ee *(Estonia, English)*

ROUTES OPERATED Kuivastu - Virtsu (Saaremaa) (28 mins; *HIIUMAA, PIRET, TOLL*; up to 25 per day), Rohuküla - Heltermaa (Hiiumaa) (1 hr 30 mins; *LEIGER, TIIU*; up to 11 per day).

1	**HIIUMAA**	**5233t**	**11**	**15.0k**	**97.9m**	**600P**	**150C**	**20L**	**BA2**	**EE**	**9481805**
2	**LEIGER**	**4012t**	**16**	**10.0k**	**114.0m**	**700P**	**150C**	**-**	**BA**	**EE**	**9762675**
3	**PIRET**	**4012t**	**17**	**10.0k**	**114.0m**	**700P**	**150C**	**-**	**BA**	**EE**	**9762663**
4	**REGULA**	**3774t**	**71**	**14.5k**	**71.2m**	**580P**	**105C**	**20L**	**BA2**	**EE**	**7051058**
5	**TIIU**	**4012t**	**17**	**10.0k**	**114.0m**	**700P**	**150C**	**-**	**BA**	**EE**	**9762687**
6	**TOLL**	**4012t**	**17**	**10.0k**	**114.0m**	**700P**	**150C**	**-**	**BA**	**EE**	**9762651**

HIIUMAA Built by Fiskerstrand Verft A/S, Aalesund, Norway for *Saaremaa Laevakompanii*. In October 2016 charter transferred to *Praamid*.

LEIGER, TIIU Built by Sefine Shipyard, Yalova, Turkey. LNG powered.

PIRET, TOLL Built by Remontowa Shipyard, Gdansk, Poland (The PIRET's hull was subcontracted to Irko, Gdansk, Poland). LNG powered.

REGULA Built by Jos L Meyer, Papenburg, Germany for *Stockholms Rederi AB Svea* of Sweden for the service between Helsingborg and Helsingør operated by *Linjebuss International AB* (a subsidiary company). In 1980 she was sold to *Scandinavian Ferry Lines*. During Winter 1984/85 she was rebuilt to increase vehicle and passenger capacity. In 1991 ownership was transferred to *SweFerry* and operations to *ScandLines* on the Helsingborg - Helsingør service. Ownership later transferred to *Scandlines AB*. In 1997 sold to *Saaremaa Laevakompanii*. In October 2016 chartered to *Praamid*. Following delivery of new vessels, she has been retained as spare vessel.

SAMSØ REDERI

THE COMPANY *Samsø Rederi* is a Danish public sector company owned by the Samsø Municipality.

MANAGEMENT **Managing Director** Carsten Kruse.

ADDRESS Sælvig 64, 8305 Samsø, Denmark.

TELEPHONE **Administration and Reservations** + 45 7022 5900.

INTERNET **Email** tilsamsoe@samsoe.dk **Website** www.tilsamsoe.dk (Danish, German, English).

ROUTE OPERATED Sælvig (Samsø) - Hou (Jutland) (1 hr; ***PRINSESSE ISABELLA***; up to 7 per day).

1	PRINSESSE ISABELLA	5478t	15	9.9k	100.0m	600P	160C	16T	BA	DK	9692806

PRINSESSE ISABELLA Built as the SAMSØ by Stocznia Remontowa, Gdansk, Poland. Entered service in March 2015. In June 2015 renamed the PRINSESSE ISABELLA.

SCANDLINES

THE COMPANY In 2007, the owners of *Scandlines AG*, the Danish Ministry of Transport and Energy and Deutsche Bahn AG, decided to sell their shares. The new owner was a consortium of the 3i Group (UK), Allianz Capital Partners GmbH (Germany) (40% of the shares each) and *Deutsche Seereederei GmbH* (Germany) (20% of the shares). The company was subsequently transformed into a private limited company and now trades under the name Scandlines GmbH, uniting the companies *Scandlines Deutschland GmbH* and *Scandlines Danmark A/S*. With *Deutsche Seereederei GmbH* selling its shares in *Scandlines GmbH* in 2010, 3i and Allianz Capital Partners held 50% of the shares each. During 2012 *Stena Line* took over the Travemünde - Ventspils, Travemünde - Liepaja and Nynäshamn - Ventspils routes, took full control of the joint routes - Rostock - Trelleborg and Sassnitz - Trelleborg services and took over the vessels used. The freight-only route between Rostock and Hanko passed to *SOL*. In November 2013 3i Group purchased Allianz Capital Partners' share and now control 100% of the company.

MANAGEMENT **CEO** Søren Poulsgaard Jensen, **Managing Director & Chief Customer Officer** Morten Haure-Petersen.

ADDRESS Am Bahnhof 3a, 18119 Rostock, Germany.

TELEPHONE **Administration & Reservations *Denmark*** +45 33 15 15 15, ***Germany*** +49 (0)381-77 88 77 66.

INTERNET **Email** info@scandlines.com **Website** www.scandlines.com *(Danish, German, English)*.

ROUTES OPERATED Rødby (Lolland, Denmark) - Puttgarden (Germany) (45 mins; ***DEUTSCHLAND, HOLGER DANSKE, KRONPRINS FREDERIK, PRINS RICHARD, PRINSESSE BENEDIKTE, SCHLESWIG-HOLSTEIN (HOLGER DANSKE*** *specially for dangerous goods)*; half-hourly train/vehicle ferry + additional road freight-only sailings), Gedser (Falster, Denmark) - Rostock (Germany) (2 hours; ***BERLIN, COPENHAGEN***; every 2 hours).

1	BERLIN	22319t	16	20.5k	169.5m	1300P	460C	96L	BA2	DE	9587855
2	COPENHAGEN	22319t	16	20.5k	169.5m	1300P	460C	96L	BA2	DK	9587867

3	DEUTSCHLAND	15187t	97	18.5k	142.0m	1200P	364C	30Lr	BA2	DE	9151541
4F	HOLGER DANSKE	2779t	76	14.9k	86.8m	12P	-	12L	BA	DK	7432202
5	KRONPRINS FREDERIK	16071t	81	20.5k	152.0m	1082P	210C	46T	BA	DE	7803205
6	PRINS RICHARD	14822t	97	18.5k	142.0m	1100P	364C	36Lr	BA2	DK	9144419
7	PRINSESSE BENEDIKTE	14822t	97	18.5k	142.0m	1100P	364C	36Lr	BA2	DK	9144421
8	SCHLESWIG-HOLSTEIN	15187t	97	18.5k	142.0m	1200P	364C	30Lr	BA2	DE	9151539

BERLIN Partly built by Volkswerft Stralsund, Stralsund, Germany for *Scandlines* to operate on the Gedser - Rostock route. The propulsion system allows for adaption to LNG. Originally due to enter service in Spring 2012, construction was seriously delayed. It was then found that she did not meet the specification and the order was cancelled. She was 90% finished and had undertaken sea trials. In March 2014, purchased by *Scandferries ApS* of Denmark (an associated company) and towed, firstly to Blohm + Voss Shipyards, Hamburg and then to Fayard Shipyard, Odense to be completed with an almost completely new superstructure. Her engines were also modified from straight diesel to diesel-electric hybrid. In May 2016 chartered to *Scandlines* and entered service on the Gedser - Rostock route,

COPENHAGEN As the BERLIN except that at the time of purchase by *Scandlines*, she had been launched but was only 50% finished. Entered service in Autumn 2016.

DEUTSCHLAND Train/vehicle ferry built by Van der Giessen-de Noord, Krimpen aan den IJssel, Rotterdam, The Netherlands for *DFO* for the Puttgarden - Rødby service. During Winter 2003/04 a new hoistable deck was added for cars by Neptun Yard Rostock, (Germany).

HOLGER DANSKE Built by Aalborg Værft A/S, Aalborg, Denmark as a train/vehicle ferry for *DSB* for the Helsingør - Helsingborg service. In 1991 transferred to the Kalundborg - Samsø route (no rail facilities). In 1997 transferred to subsidiary *SFDS A/S*. Withdrawn at the end of November 1998 when the service passed to *Samsø Linien*. In 1999 began operating between Rødby and Puttgarden as a road-freight-only vessel, carrying, among others, loads which cannot be conveyed on passenger vessels.

KRONPRINS FREDERIK Train/vehicle ferry built by Nakskov Skibsværft A/S, Nakskov, Denmark for *DSB* for the Nyborg - Korsør service. Withdrawn in 1997. After conversion to a car/lorry ferry, she was transferred to the Gedser - Rostock route (no rail facilities). In March 2017, following modifications, transferred to the Rødby - Puttgarden route to provide extra capacity for lorry traffic. Also serves as reserve vessel on Gedser - Rostock service.

PRINS RICHARD, PRINSESSE BENEDIKTE Train/vehicle ferries, built by Ørskov Christensen Staalskibsværft A/S, Frederikshavn, Denmark for *Scandlines A/S* for the Rødby - Puttgarden service. During Winter 2003/04 a new hoistable deck was added for cars by Neptun Yard Rostock, (Germany).

SCHLESWIG-HOLSTEIN Train/vehicle ferry built by Van der Giessen-de Noord, Krimpen aan den IJssel, Rotterdam, The Netherlands for *DFO* for the Puttgarden - Rødby service. During Winter 2003/04 a new hoistable deck was added for cars by Neptun Yard Rostock, (Germany).

SCANDLINES HELSINGØR - HELSINGBORG

THE COMPANY *Scandlines Helsingør - Helsingborg* is the trading name of *HH Ferries Group*, a Swedish private sector company owned by First State Investments, a subsidiary of Commonwealth Bank of Australia. Previously a joint venture between *Scandlines* and *Stena Line*, it was acquired by First State Investments in January 2015. Although now a separate company, it currently operates as part of the *Scandlines* network.

ADDRESS Knutpunkten 43, S-252 78, Helsingborg, Sweden.

TELEPHONE **Administration** +46 (0)42 18 60 00 **Reservations** +45 33 15 15 15.

FAX **Administration** +46 (0)42 18 60 49.

INTERNET **Email** info@hhferriesgroup.com **Website** hhferriesgroup.com *(Danish, English, Swedish)* www.scandlines.com *(Danish, German, English)*

ROUTES OPERATED Helsingør (Sealand, Denmark) - Helsingborg (Sweden) (20 mins; *AURORA AF HELSINGBORG, MERCANDIA IV, MERCANDIA VIII, HAMLET, TYCHO BRAHE*; up to every 15 mins)

1	**AURORA AF HELSINGBORG**	10918t	92	14.0k	111.2m	1250P	225C	25Lr	BA	SE	9007128
2	**HAMLET**	10067t	97	13.5k	111.2m	1000P	244C	34L	BA	DK	9150030
3	**MERCANDIA IV**	4296t	89	13.0k	95.0m	420P	170C	18L	BA	DK	8611685
4	**MERCANDIA VIII**	4296t	87	13.0k	95.0m	420P	170C	18L	BA	DK	8611623
5	**TYCHO BRAHE**	11148t	91	14.5k	111.2m	1250P	240C	35Lr	BA	DK	9007116

AURORA AF HELSINGBORG Train/vehicle ferry built by Langsten Verft A/S, Tomrefjord, Norway for *SweFerry* for *ScandLines* joint *DSB/SweFerry* service between Helsingør and Helsingborg.

HAMLET Road vehicle ferry built by Finnyards, Rauma, Finland for *Scandlines* (50% owned by *Scandlines AG* and 50% owned by *Scandlines AB* of Sweden) for the Helsingør - Helsingborg service. Sister vessel of the TYCHO BRAHE but without rail tracks.

MERCANDIA IV Built as the SUPERFLEX NOVEMBER by North East Shipbuilders Ltd, Sunderland, UK for *Vognmandsruten* of Denmark. In 1989 sold to *Mercandia* and renamed the MERCANDIA IV. In 1990 she began operating on their *Kattegatbroen* Juelsminde - Kalundborg service. In 1996 she was transferred to their *Sundbroen* Helsingør - Helsingborg service. In 1997 the service and vessel were leased to *HH-Ferries*. In 1999 she was purchased by *HH-Ferries*. She has been equipped to carry dangerous cargo. Now owned by *Scandlines Helsingør - Helsingborg*.

MERCANDIA VIII Built as the SUPERFLEX BRAVO by North East Shipbuilders Ltd, Sunderland, UK for *Vognmandsruten* of Denmark and used on their services between Nyborg and Korsør and Copenhagen (Tuborg Havn) and Landskrona (Sweden). In 1991 she was chartered to *Scarlett Line* to operate on the Copenhagen and Landskrona route. In 1993 she was renamed the SVEA SCARLETT but later in the year the service ceased and she was laid up. In 1996 she was purchased by *Mercandia*, renamed the MERCANDIA VIII and placed on their *Sundbroen* Helsingør - Helsingborg service. In 1997 the service and vessel were leased to *HH-Ferries*. In 1999 she was purchased by *HH-Ferries*. Now owned by *Scandlines Helsingør - Helsingborg*. Now reserve vessel. Between April and July 2015 she operated between Puttgarden and Rødby for *Scandlines*, following damage sustained by the PRINSESSE BENEDIKTE at Gdansk during a refit.

TYCHO BRAHE Train/vehicle ferry, built by Tangen Verft A/S, Tomrefjord, Norway for *DSB* for the *ScandLines* joint *DSB/SweFerry* service between Helsingør and Helsingborg.

SMYRIL LINE

THE COMPANY *Smyril Line* is a Faroe Islands company.

MANAGEMENT **Adm. Director** Rúni Vang Poulsen, **Accounting and Department Manager** Nina Djurhuus.

ADDRESS Yviri við Strond 1, PO Box 370, 110 Tórshavn, Faroe Islands.

TELEPHONE **Administration & Reservations** +298-34 59 00.

FAX +298-345901.

INTERNET **Email** office@smyrilline.com **Website** www.smyrilline.com *(English, French, Dutch German)* www.smyrilline.fo *(Danish, Faroese, Icelandic, Norwegian, Swedish)*

ROUTES OPERATED ***Winter/Early Spring*** Tórshavn (Faroes) - Hirtshals (Denmark) (36 hrs; *NORRÖNA*; 1 per week), ***Spring/Early Summer/Autumn*** Tórshavn - Hirtshals (36 hrs; *NORRÖNA*; 1 per week), Tórshavn - Seyðisfjördur (Iceland) (19 hrs; *NORRÖNA*; 1 per week), ***Summer*** Tórshavn - Hirtshals (Denmark) (30 hrs; *NORRÖNA*; 2 per week), Tórshavn - Seyðisfjördur (Iceland) (19 hrs; *NORRÖNA*; 2 per week). ***Freight services*** Tórshavn - Hirtshals - St Petersburg (*EYSTNES, HVITANES*), Thorlakshofn (Iceland) - Tórshavn - Rotterdam (*MYKINES*).

1F	**EYSTNES**	4610t	81	15.0k	102.2m	0P	-	24T	AS	FO	7922166

2F	**HVITANES**	4636t	80	12.0k	77.3m	0P	-	14T	AS	FO	7915541
3F	**MYKINES**	18979t	96	20.0k	138.5m	12P	1452C	105T	A2	FO	9121998
4	**NORRÖNA**	35966t	03	21.0k	164.0m	1482P	800C	134T	BA	FO	9227390

EYSTNES Con-ro vessel (only the main deck can take trailers) built as the COMETA by Fosen Mekaniske Verksteder, Rissa, Norway for *Nor-Cargo*. Until 2010 she operated for *Sea-Cargo* between Norwegian ports and Immingham; afterwards she operated on *Nor-Cargo* Norwegian domestic services. In September 2015 sold to *Smyril Line* and renamed the EYSTNES.

HVITANES Con-ro vessel (only the main deck can take trailers) built as the TANAGER by Bergen Mekaniske Verksteder, Bergen, Norway for *NorCargo* of Norway. In September 2015 sold to *Smyril Line* and renamed the EYSTNES.

MYKINES Built as the TRANSGARD by Umoe Sterkoder, Kristiansund, Norway for *Bror Husell Chartering* of Finland for long-term charter to *Transfennica* and used between Rauma and Antwerp and Hamina and Lübeck. Later chartered to *Finncarriers*. In 2005 she underwent conversion in Poland to add a garage on top of the original weather deck and was placed on long-term charter to *UECC*. She was generally used on the Baltic or Iberian services. In 2007 renamed AUTO BALTIC. In January 2016 chartered to *Flotta Suardiaz*. In April 2017 sold to *Smyril Line* to inaugurate a new service between Thorlakshofn (Iceland), Tórshavn and Rotterdam and renamed the MYKINES.

NORRÖNA Built by Flender Werft, Lübeck, Germany for *Smyril Line*, to replace the existing NORRÖNA. Originally due to enter service in Summer 2002, start of building was delayed by financing difficulties. She was to have been built at Flensburger Schiffbau-Gesellschaft, Flensburg, Germany, but delays in arranging finance led to change of shipyard.

STENA LINE

THE COMPANY *Stena Line Scandinavia AB* is a Swedish private sector company. During 2012, the operations of subsidiary *Scandlines AB* of Sweden were absorbed and some of the Baltic operations and vessels of *Scandlines GmbH* of Germany were taken over. In *2015 Stena Line Scandinavia's* share in *Scandlines AB* where sold and the route Helsingborg - Helsingør sold to new owners.

MANAGEMENT CEO Niclas Mårtensson, **Chief Operating Officer** Hans Nilsson.

ADDRESS Danmarksterminalen, 405 19 Gothenburg, Sweden.

TELEPHONE **Administration** +46 (0)31-85 80 00, **Reservations** +46 (0)31 704 00 00.

INTERNET **Email** info@stenaline.com **Website** www.stenaline.com *(Czech, Danish, Dutch, English, French, German, Latvian, Lithuanian, Norwegian, Polish, Russian, Swedish)*

ROUTES OPERATED **Conventional Ferries** Gothenburg (Sweden) - Frederikshavn (Denmark) (3 hrs 15 mins; *STENA DANICA, STENA JUTLANDICA*; up to 6 per day), Gothenburg - Kiel (Germany) (14 hrs; *STENA GERMANICA, STENA SCANDINAVICA*; 1 per day), Frederikshavn - Oslo (Norway) (8 hrs 45 mins; *STENA SAGA*; 1 per day), Varberg (Sweden) - Grenaa (Denmark) (4 hrs; *STENA NAUTICA*; 2 per day), Karlskrona (Sweden) - Gdynia (Poland) (10 hrs 30 mins; *GUTE, STENA BALTICA, STENA SPIRIT, STENA VISION*; 3/4 per day), Rostock (Germany) - Trelleborg (Sweden) (7 hrs); *MECKLENBURG-VORPOMMERN, SKÅNE*; 3 per day)), Sassnitz (Germany) - Trelleborg (4 hrs 15 mins; *SASSNITZ*; 1 per day), Travemünde (Germany) - Liepaja (Latvia) (27 hrs; *STENA NORDICA, URD*; 5 per week), Nynäshamn (Sweden) – Ventspils (Latvia) (12 hrs; *SCOTTISH VIKING, STENA FLAVIA*; 12 per week). **Freight Ferry** Gothenburg - Frederikshavn (3 hrs 45 mins; *STENA GOTHICA*; 2 per day).

1	**GUTE**	7616t	79	15.0k	138.8m	88P	-	60T	BA	SE	7802794
2	**MECKLENBURG-VORPOMMERN**	36185t	96	22.0k	199.9m	600P	445C	230Tr	A2	DE	9131797
3	**SASSNITZ**	21154t	89	18.5k	171.5m	875P	314C	50Tr	BA2	DE	8705383
4	**SCOTTISH VIKING**	26500t	09	24.0k	186.5m	800P	185C	120L	A	IT	9435454
5	**SKÅNE**	42705t	98	21.0k	200.2m	600P	520C	240Tr	AS2	SE	9133915
6	**STENA BALTICA**	22542t	07	23.0k	167.0m	160P	-	140L	BA2	UK	9364978

Mykines *(Peter Therkildsen)*

Sassnitz *(Miles Cowsill)*

7»•	STENA CARISMA	8631t	97	40.0k	88.0m	900P	210C	-	A	SE	9127760
8	STENA DANICA	28727t	83	19.5k	154.9m	2274P	555C	120T	BAS2	SE	7907245
9	STENA FLAVIA	26904t	08	24.0k	186.5m	852P	185C	120L	A	DK	9417919
10	STENA GERMANICA	51837t	01	22.0k	240.1m	900P	-	250L	BA	SE	9145176
11F	STENA GOTHICA	13144t	82	18.0k	171.0m	186P	-	104T	AS	SE	7826867
12	STENA JUTLANDICA	29691t	96	21.5k	183.7m	1500P	550C	156T	BAS2	SE	9125944
13	STENA NAUTICA	19504t	86	19.4k	134.0m	700P	330C	70T	BA2	SE	8317954
14	STENA NORDICA	24206t	01	25.7k	169.8m	405P	375C	90L	BA2	UK	9215505
15	STENA SAGA	33750t	81	22.0k	166.1m	2000P	510C	76T	BA	SE	7911545
16	STENA SCANDINAVICA	55050t	03	22.0k	240.1m	900P	-	260L	BA	SE	9235517
17	STENA SPIRIT	39169t	88	20.0k	175.4m	2400P	550C	120T	BAS2	BS	7907661
18	STENA VISION	39178t	87	20.0k	175.4m	2400P	550C	120T	BAS2	SE	7907659
19	URD	13144t	81	17.5k	171.0m	186P	-	104T	AS	DK	7826855

GUTE Built as the GUTE by Falkenbergs Varv AB, Falkenberg, Sweden for *Rederi AB Gotland* of Sweden. Used on service between Gotland and the Swedish mainland. In 1988 chartered to *Brambles Shipping* of Australia and used between Port Melbourne (Victoria) and Burnie (Tasmania). In 1992 she was renamed the SALLY SUN and chartered to *Sally Ferries*, operating between Ramsgate and Dunkerque. In 1994 she inaugurated a Ramsgate - Vlissingen service, which was later changed to Dartford - Vlissingen. In 1995 she was chartered to *SeaWind Line*, renamed the SEAWIND II and operated between Stockholm and Turku. In 1997 she was chartered to *Nordic Trucker Line* for the Oxelösund - St Petersburg service and in 1998 she returned to *SeaWind Line*. In 1998, after *Rederi AB Gotland*-owned *Destination Gotland* regained the franchise to operate to Gotland, she was renamed the GUTE and resumed her summer role of providing summer freight back-up to the passenger vessels, but with a number of short charters during the winter. In Autumn 2002 chartered to *Amber Lines* for the Karlshamn - Liepaja service. In February 2003 chartered to *NATO* for the Iraq crisis. Returned to *Destination Gotland* in Summer 2003. In Autumn 2003 chartered to *Scandlines Amber Lines* to operate between Karlshamn and Liepaja. In 2004 lengthened by 20.3m by Nauta Shiprepair, Gdynia, Poland. In Autumn 2004 chartered to *Riga Sea Line* to inaugurate a freight service between Riga and Nynäshamn. In Autumn 2005 the service ended and the vessel was laid up. In January 2006 chartered to *Lisco* and placed on the Klaipėda - Karlshamn route, also undertaking two trips from Klaipėda to Baltiysk. In May 2006 chartered to *SeaWind Line*. In March 2007 chartered to *Baltic Scandinavian Line*. Charter ended September 2007. Apart from a trip to Cameroon, conveying Swedish UN Troops for Chad, she remained laid up until October 2008 when she was chartered to *Baltic Scandinavian Line* to operate between Härnösand and Kaskinen. In 2009 this service closed and she was laid up. At the end of March 2015 she was chartered to *Færgen* to operate between Køge and Rønne covering for the HAMMERODDE. She returned to layup in May. In August 2017 chartered to *Stena Line* to operate as fourth ship on the Karlskrona - Gdynia route.

MECKLENBURG-VORPOMMERN Train/vehicle ferry built by Schichau Seebeckwerft, Bremerhaven, Germany for *DFO* for the Rostock - Trelleborg service. During Winter 2002/03 modified to increase freight capacity and reduce passenger capacity. In September 2012 sold to *Stena Line*.

SASSNITZ Train/vehicle ferry built by Danyard A/S, Frederikshavn, Denmark for *Deutsche Reichsbahn*. In 1993 ownership transferred to *DFO*. Used on the Sassnitz - Trelleborg service. In September 2012 sold to *Stena Line*.

SCOTTISH VIKING Built by CN Visentini, Porto Viro, Italy for *Epic Shipping* of the UK and chartered to *Norfolkline*. Operated between Zeebrugge and Rosyth until December 2010. In January 2010 chartered to *Scandlines* and placed on the Nynäshamn - Ventspils service. In September 2012 charter transferred to *Stena Line*.

SKÅNE Train/vehicle ferry built by Astilleros Españoles, Cadiz, Spain for an American trust and chartered to *Scandlines*. She is used on the Trelleborg - Rostock service.

STENA BALTICA Built as the COTENTIN by STX Finland, Helsinki, Finland for *Brittany Ferries*. Used on freight service from Poole to Cherbourg and Santander. In March 2013 replaced by the BARFLEUR (operating to Cherbourg only). During summer 2013 operated twice weekly from Poole to Bilbao and

Santander. In October 2013 sold to *Stena RoRo* and renamed the STENA BALTICA. In November 2013 chartered to *Stena Line* and replaced the STENA ALEGRA on the Karlskrona - Gdynia route.

STENA CARISMA Westamarin HSS 900 craft built at Kristiansand, Norway for *Stena Line* for the Gothenburg - Frederikshavn service. Work on a sister vessel, approximately 30% completed, was ceased. She has not operated since 2013.

STENA DANICA Built by Chantiers du Nord et de la Méditerranée, Dunkerque, France for *Stena Line* for the Gothenburg - Frederikshavn service.

STENA FLAVIA Built by CN Visentini, Porto Viro, Italy for *Epic Shipping* of the UK. Launched as the WATLING STREET. On delivery, chartered to *ISCOMAR* of Spain and renamed the PILAR DEL MAR. In 2009 laid up until February 2010 when she was chartered to *Acciona Trasmediterranea* of Spain and operated between Barcelona and Tangiers. Later that month, chartered to *T-Link* and resumed the name WATLING STREET. In May 2011 chartered to *Scandlines* and placed on the Travemünde - Ventspils service. In April 2012, sold to *Stena RoRo*; she continued to be chartered to *Scandlines*. In September 2012 charter transferred to *Stena Line*. In April 2013 renamed the STENA FLAVIA. Now .operates one weekly roundtrip from Nynäshamn to Liepaja, two roundtrips to Nynäshamn to Ventspils and once weekly Ventspils - Travemünde.

STENA GERMANICA Ro-pax ferry built as the STENA HOLLANDICA by Astilleros Españoles, Cadiz, Spain for *Stena RoRo* and chartered to *Stena Line BV* to operate between Hook of Holland and Harwich. In 2007 lengthened by 50m at Lloyd Werft, Bremerhaven and passenger capacity increased to 900. Between May and August 2010 refurbished at Gdansk and had an 100 additional cabins added. At the end of August entered service on the Gothenburg - Kiel route, renamed the STENA GERMANICA III. In September, after the previous STENA GERMANICA had been renamed the STENA VISION, she was renamed the STENA GERMANICA.

STENA GOTHICA Built as the LUCKY RIDER by Nuovi Cantieri Apuania S.P.A., Marina De Carrara, Italy, a ro-ro freight ferry, for *Delpa Maritime* of Greece. In 1985 she was acquired by *Stena Line* and renamed the STENA DRIVER. Later that year she was acquired by *Sealink British Ferries* and renamed the SEAFREIGHT FREEWAY to operate freight-only services between Dover and Dunkerque. In 1988 she was sold to *SOMAT* of Bulgaria for use on *Medlink* services in the Mediterranean and renamed the SERDICA. In 1990 she was sold and renamed the NORTHERN HUNTER. In 1991 she was sold to *Blæsbjerg* of Denmark, renamed the ARKA MARINE and chartered to *DSB*. She was then converted into a ro-pax vessel, renamed the ASK and introduced onto the Århus - Kalundborg service. Purchased by *Scandlines A/S* of Denmark in 1997. In 1999 she was, after some modification, transferred to *Scandlines Euroseabridge* and placed on the Travemünde - Klaipėda route. In 2000 she was transferred to the Rostock - Liepaja route. Lengthened by 20m in 2001 and, in late 2001, chartered to *Nordö Link* to operate between Travemünde and Malmö. In late 2002 replaced by the FINNARROW and returned to *Scandlines*. She was transferred to the Rostock - Trelleborg route whilst the MECKLENBURG-VORPOMMERN was being rebuilt. She was then transferred to the Kiel - Klaipėda route. In 2003 chartered to *Scandlines AB* to operate on the Trelleborg - Travemünde route. In April 2005 the charter ended and she returned to *Scandlines AG*. Initially she was due to replace the FELLOW on the Nynäshamn – Ventspils route during her annual refit. In Autumn 2005 moved to the Rostock - Ventspils route. In January 2009 moved to the Nynäshamn – Ventspils route. In January 2011 moved to the Travemünde - Liepaja route. In May 2011 laid up. In November introduced as second vessel. In September 2012 sold to *Stena Line*. In September 2015 to move to the Gothenburg - Frederikshavn freight service and renamed the STENA GOTHICA.

STENA JUTLANDICA Train/vehicle 'ro-pax' vessel built by Van der Giessen-de Noord, Krimpen aan den IJssel, Rotterdam, The Netherlands for *Stena Line* to operate between Gothenburg and Frederikshavn. She was launched as the STENA JUTLANDICA III and renamed on entry into service.

STENA NAUTICA Built as the NIELS KLIM by Nakskov Skibsværft A/S, Nakskov, Denmark for *DSB (Danish State Railways)* for their service between Århus (Jutland) and Kalundborg (Sealand). In 1990 she was purchased by *Stena Rederi* of Sweden and renamed the STENA NAUTICA. In 1992 she was chartered to *B&I Line*, renamed the ISLE OF INNISFREE and introduced onto the Rosslare - Pembroke Dock service, replacing the MUNSTER (8093t, 1970). In 1993 she was transferred to the Dublin - Holyhead service. In early 1995 she was chartered to *Lion Ferry*. She was renamed the LION KING. In

Stena Gothica *(Richard Seville)*

Stena Baltica *(Miles Cowsill)*

1996 she was replaced by a new LION KING and renamed the STENA NAUTICA. During Summer 1996 she was chartered to *Transmediterranea* of Spain but returned to *Stena RoRo* in the autumn and remained laid up during 1997. In December 1997 she was chartered to *Stena Line* and placed on the Halmstad - Grenaa route. This route ended on 31st January 1999 and she was transferred to the Varberg - Grenaa route. During Winter 2001/02 she was rebuilt to heighten the upper vehicle deck and allow separate loading of vehicle decks; passenger capacity was reduced. On 16th February 2004 she was hit by the coaster JOANNA and holed. Returned to service at the end of May 2004 after repairs at Gothenburg and Gdansk.

STENA NORDICA Built as the EUROPEAN AMBASSADOR by Mitsubishi Heavy Industries, Shimonoseki, Japan for *P&O Irish Sea* for their Liverpool - Dublin service. Service transferred to from Liverpool to Mostyn in November 2001. Also operated between Dublin and Cherbourg once a week. In 2004 the Mostyn route closed and she was sold to *Stena RoRo*. Chartered to *Stena Line* to operate between Karlskrona and Gdynia and renamed the STENA NORDICA. In 2008 transferred to the Holyhead - Dublin service. In February 2015 replaced by the STENA SUPERFAST X and chartered to *DFDS Seaways*. Renamed the MALO SEAWAYS and, in April 2015, placed on the Dover - Calais route. Withdrawn from traffic in February 2016 and laid up. In June 2016 charter ended. Renamed the STENA NORDICA and chartered to *GNV* of Italy to operate between Sicily and the Italian mainland. In January 2017 chartered to *Stena Line* and performed refit relief duties in the Irish Sea. In April placed on the Travemünde - Liep ja service.

STENA SAGA Built as the SILVIA REGINA by Oy Wärtsilä Ab, Turku, Finland for *Stockholms Rederi AB Svea* of Sweden. She was registered with subsidiary company *Svea Line* of Turku, Finland and was used on *Silja Line* services between Stockholm and Helsinki. In 1981 she was sold to *Johnson Line* and in 1984 sold to a Finnish Bank and chartered back. In 1990 she was purchased by *Stena RoRo* of Sweden for delivery in 1991. In 1991 she was renamed the STENA BRITANNICA and took up service on the Hook of Holland - Harwich service for Dutch subsidiary *Stena Line BV*, operating with a British crew. In 1994 she was transferred to the Oslo - Frederikshavn route and renamed the STENA SAGA. During Winter 2002/03 rebuilt to increase passenger capacity by 200.

STENA SCANDINAVICA Ro-pax vessel built by Hyundai Heavy Industries, Ulsan, South Korea, for *Stena RoRo*. Launched and delivered in January 2003 as the STENA BRITANNICA II. Chartered to *Stena Line* for use on the Hook of Holland - Harwich service, replacing the 2000-built STENA BRITANNICA, now the FINNFELLOW of *FinnLink*. In March 2003 renamed the STENA BRITANNICA. In 2007 lengthened at Lloyd Werft, Bremerhaven. In September 2010 renamed the BRITANNICA. Between October 2010 and April 2011 refurbished and had 100 additional cabins added at Gdansk. In April 2011 renamed the STENA SCANDINAVICA IV and entered service on the Gothenburg - Kiel route. In May, after the previous STENA SCANDINAVICA had been renamed the STENA SPIRIT, she was renamed the STENA SCANDINAVICA.

STENA SPIRIT Built as the STENA SCANDINAVICA by Stocznia i Komuni Paryski, Gdynia, Poland for *Stena Line* for the Gothenburg - Kiel service (launched as the STENA GERMANICA and names swapped with sister vessel before delivery). There were originally intended to be four vessels. Only two were delivered to *Stena Line*. The third (due to be called the STENA POLONICA) was sold by the builders as an unfinished hull to *Fred. Olsen Lines* of Norway and then resold to *ANEK* of Greece who had her completed at Perama and delivered as EL VENIZELOS for service between Greece and Italy. The fourth hull (due to be called the STENA BALTICA) was sold to *A Lelakis* of Greece and was to be rebuilt as a cruise ship to be called REGENT SKY; however, the project was never completed. The hull was broken up in 2004. During the summer period on some days, the vessel arriving in Gothenburg overnight from Kiel operates a round trip to Frederikshavn before departing for Kiel the following evening. During Winter 1998/99 she was modified to increase freight capacity and reduce the number of cabins. In April 2011 replaced by the former STENA BRITANNICA (renamed the STENA SCANDINAVICA IV) and entered CityVarvet in Gothenburg for refurbishment. In June 2011 she was renamed the STENA SPIRIT and, in July 2011, transferred to the Karlskrona - Gydnia route.

STENA VISION Built as the STENA GERMANICA by Stocznia im Lenina, Gdansk, Poland for *Stena Line* for the Gothenburg - Kiel service. During the summer period on some days, the vessel arriving in Gothenburg overnight from Kiel operates a round trip to Frederikshavn before departing for Kiel the following evening. During Winter 1998/99 modified to increase freight capacity and reduce the number of cabins. In August 2010 replaced by the former STENA HOLLANDICA (renamed the STENA

GERMANICA III initially) and entered CityVarvet in Gothenburg for refurbishment. In September she was renamed the STENA VISION and, in November, transferred to the Karlskrona - Gydnia route.

URD Built as the EASY RIDER by Nouvi Cantieri Aquania SpA, Venice, Italy, a ro-ro freight ferry, for *Delpa Maritime* of Greece and used on Mediterranean services. In 1985 she was acquired by *Sealink British Ferries* and renamed the SEAFREIGHT HIGHWAY to operate a freight-only service between Dover and Dunkerque. In 1988 she was sold to *SOMAT* of Bulgaria for use on *Medlink* services in the Mediterranean and renamed the BOYANA. In 1990 she was sold to *Blæsbjerg* of Denmark, renamed the AKTIV MARINE and chartered to *DSB*. In 1991 she was converted into a ro-pax vessel, renamed the URD and introduced onto the Århus - Kalundborg service. Purchased by *Scandlines* in 1997. Withdrawn at the end of May 1999 and, after modification, transferred to the *Balticum Seaways* (later *Scandlines Balticum Seaways*) Århus - Aabenraa - Klaipėda route. In 2001 lengthened and moved to the Rostock - Liepaja route. In Autumn 2005 this route became Rostock - Ventspils. Withdrawn from Rostock - Ventspils in November 2009. Vessel inaugurated new service Travemünde - Ventspils in January 2010. Replaced by the WATLING STREET in May 2011 and moved to the Travemünde - Liepaja route. In October 2012 sold to *Sol Dru A/S* (a subsidiary of *Swedish Orient Line*) and chartered to *Stena Line*. In August 2013 sold to *Stena Line*.

STRANDFARASKIP LANDSINS

THE COMPANY *Strandfaraskip Landsins* is owned by the Faroe Islands Government.

ADDRESS Sjógøta 5, Postboks 30, 810 Tvøroyri, Faroe Islands.

TELEPHONE **Administration & Reservations** +298 34 30 00.

FAX **Administration & Reservations** +298 34 30 01.

INTERNET **Email** fyrisitingssl.fo **Website** www.ssl.fo *(Faroese)*

ROUTES OPERATED **Passenger and Car Ferries** Tórshavn (Streymoy) - Tvøroyri (Suduroy) (1 hr 50 mins; *SMYRIL*; up to 3 per day), Klaksvík - Sydradali (20 min; *SAM*; up to 6 per day), Skopun – Gamlarætt (30 mins; *TEISTIN*; up to 9 per day). **Passenger-only Ferries** Sørvágur - Mykines (1 hr 15 mins; *JÒSUP (chartered ship)*; up to 3 per day, May to August only), Hvannasund - Svínoy (40 mins) - Kirkja (20 mins) - Hattarvik (10 mins) - Svínoy (30 mins; *RITAN*; up to 4 per day), Sandur - Skúvoy (35 mins; *SILDBERIN*; up to 5 per day), Tórshavn - Nólsoy (25 mins; *TERNAN*; up to 5 per day.

1p	RITAN	81t	71	10.5k	22.1m	125P	0C	0L	-	FO	
2	SAM	217t	75	9.7k	30.2m	115P	17C	-	A	FO	7602168
3p	SILDBERIN	34t	79	7.5k	11.2m	30P	0C	0L	-	FO	
4	SMYRIL	12670t	05	21.0k	135.0m	976P	200C	32L	A	FO	9275218
5p	SÚLAN	11t	87	-	12.0m	40P	0C	0L	-	FO	
6	TEISTIN	1260t	01	11.0k	45.0m	288P	33C	2L	BA	FO	9226102
7	TERNAN	927t	80	12.0k	39.7m	319P	0C	0L	BA	FO	7947154

RITAN Built by Monnickenda, Volendam, The Netherlands. Used on the Hvannasund – Svínoy-Kirkja- Hattarvik service.

SAM Built by Blaalid Slip & Mek Verksted, Raudeberg, Norway. Used on the Klaksvik - Syòradali route and the Leirvik - Syòradali route.

SILDBERIN Built at Tvøroyri, Faroe Islands. Used on the Sandur - Skúvoy route.

SMYRIL Built by IZAR, San Fernando, Spain for *Strandfaraskip Landsins*. Operates on the Tórshavn – Tvøroyri service.

SÚLAN Built by Faaborg Værft A/S, Faaborg, Denmark. Used on the Sørvágur - Mykines service. Now conveys freight to Skúvoy.

TEISTIN Built by P/F Skipasmidjan a Skala, Skala, Faroe Islands for *Strandfaraskip Landsins*. Used on the Skopun – Gamlarætt service.

TERNAN Built by Tórshavnar Skipasmidja P/f, Tórshavn, Faroe Islands for *Strandfaraskip Landsins*. Used on the Tórshavn - Nólsoy service.

SYLTFÄHRE

THE COMPANY *Syltfähre* (*Syltfærge* in Danish) is the trading name of *Römö-Sylt Linie GmbH & Co. KG*, a German private sector company, a subsidiary of *FRS (Förde Reederei Seetouristik)* of Flensburg.

MANAGEMENT **Managing Director RSL** Birte Dettmers, **CEO Römö-Sylt Linie** Christian Baumberger, Götz Becker, Jan Kruse.

ADDRESS ***Germany*** Am Fähranleger 3, 25992 List, Germany, ***Denmark*** Kilebryggen, 6792 Rømø, Denmark.

TELEPHONE **Administration** +49 (0)461 864 0, **Reservations *Germany*** +49 (0)461 864 601, ***Denmark*** +49 461 864 601.

INTERNET **Email** info@rsl.de **Website** www.syltfaehre.de *(Danish, English, German)*

ROUTE OPERATED List auf Sylt (Sylt, Germany) - Havneby (Rømø, Denmark) (approx. 40 mins; *SYLTEXPRESS*; variable - approx two-hourly). **Note**: The Danish island of Rømø is linked to the Danish mainland by a toll-free road causeway; the German island of Sylt is linked to the German mainland by a rail-only causeway on which cars are conveyed on shuttle wagons.

1	SYLTEXPRESS	3650t	05	16.0k	88.2m	600P	80C	10L	BA	CY	9321823

SYLTEXPRESS Built by Fiskerstrand Verft A/S, Aalesund, Norway for *Römö-Sylt Linie*.

TALLINK/SILJA LINE

THE COMPANY *AS Tallink Grupp* is an Estonian private sector company. *Tallink Silja Oy* is a Finnish subsidiary, *Tallink Silja AB* is a Swedish subsidiary.

MANAGEMENT ***AS Tallink Grupp*: Chairman of Management Board** Janek Stalmeister, ***Tallink Silja Oy* Managing Director** Margus Schults, ***Tallink Silja AB* Managing Director** Marcus Risberg.

ADDRESSES ***AS Tallink Grupp*** Sadama 5/7, Tallinn 10111, Estonia, ***Tallink Silja Oy*** P.O. Box 100, 00181 Helsinki, Finland, ***Tallink Silja AB*** Box 27295, 10253 Stockholm, Sweden.

TELEPHONE ***AS Tallink Grupp*** +372 (0)640 9800, ***Tallink Silja Oy* Administration** +358 (0)9 18041, **Reservations** +358 (0)600 15700, ***Tallink Silja AB* Administration** +46 (0)8 6663300, **Reservations** +46 (0)8 222140, **Reservations *Germany*** +49 (0)40 547 541 222.

FAX ***AS Tallink Grupp* Administration** + 372 (0)640 9810, ***Tallink Silja Oy* Administration** +358 (0)9 180 4633, ***Tallink Silja AB* Administration** +46 (0) 8 663400.

INTERNETEmail info@tallink.ee **Websites** www.tallinksilja.com *(17 languages, see the internet page)*, www.tallink.com (corporate site) *(English)*

INTERNET **Email** info@tallink.ee **Websites** www.tallinksilja.com *(English, Danish, Estonian, Finnish, German, Latvia, Norwegian, Swedish, Russian)*, www.tallink.com (corporate site)

ROUTES OPERATED **Tallink branded services *Passenger Ferries*** Helsinki - Tallinn: ***Shuttle*** (2 hrs;, *MEGASTAR, STAR*; up to 6 per day), ***Cruise Ferries*** (3 hrs 30 - 4hrs 30 mins; *SILJA EUROPA*; normally 2 per day), Stockholm - Mariehamn (Åland) - Tallinn (14 hrs; *BALTIC QUEEN, VICTORIA I*; daily), Stockholm - Riga (Latvia) (16 hrs; *ISABELLE, ROMANTIKA*; daily), ***Freight-only Ferries*** Kapellskär - Paldiski (9 hrs - 11 hrs; *REGAL STAR*, alternate days (round trip on Sunday)), Helsinki - Tallinn (3 hrs 30 mins; *SEA WIND*; 2 per day).

Silja Line branded services Helsinki (Finland) - Mariehamn (Åland) - Stockholm (Sweden) (16 hrs; *SILJA SERENADE, SILJA SYMPHONY*; 1 per day), Turku (Finland) - Mariehamn (Åland) (day)/Långnäs (Åland) (night) - Stockholm (11 hrs; *BALTIC PRINCESS, GALAXY*; 2 per day).

1	ATLANTIC VISION	30285t	02	27.9k	203.3m	728P	695C	110L	BA2	CA	9211509

Stena Scandinavica *(Miles Cowsill)*

Romantika *(Miles Cowsill)*

2	BALTIC PRINCESS	48300t	08	24.5k	212.0m	2800P	300C	82T	BA	FI	9354284
3	BALTIC QUEEN	48300t	09	24.5k	212.0m	2800P	300C	82T	BA	EE	9443255
4	GALAXY	48915t	06	22.0k	212.0m	2800P	300C	82T	BA	SE	9333694
5	ISABELLE	35154t	89	21.5k	170.9m	2420P	364C	30T	BA	LV	8700723
6	MEGASTAR	49000t	16	27.0k	212m	2800P	-	-	BA2	EE	9773064
7F	REGAL STAR	15281t	00	17.5k	156.6m	100P	-	120T	A	EE	9087116
8	ROMANTIKA	40803t	02	22.0k	193.8m	2178P	300C	82T	BA	EE	9237589
9F	SEA WIND	15879t	72	17.5k	154.4m	260P	55C	88Tr	BAS	EE	7128332
10	SILJA EUROPA	59912t	93	21.5k	201.8m	3000P	400C	68T	BA	EE	8919805
11	SILJA SERENADE	58376t	90	21.0k	203.0m	2800P	410C	70T	BA	FI	8715259
12	SILJA SYMPHONY	58377t	91	21.0k	203.0m	2800P	410C	70T	BA	SE	8803769
13	STAR	36249t	07	27.5k	185.0m	1900P	450C	120L	BA2	EE	9364722
14	VICTORIA I	40975t	04	22.0k	193.8m	2500P	300C	823T	BA	EE	9281281

ATLANTIC VISION Built as the SUPERFAST IX by Howaldtswerke Deutsche Werft AG, Kiel, Germany for *Attica Enterprises* for use by *Superfast Ferries*. She operated between Rostock and Södertälje from January until April 2002. In May 2002 she began operating between Rosyth and Zeebrugge (with the SUPERFAST X (now the STENA SUPERFAST X)). In 2004 fitted with additional cabins and conference/seating areas. In 2005 transferred to the Rostock – Hanko (later Helsinki) route. In 2006 sold to *Tallink*. In October 2008 chartered to *Marine Atlantic* of Canada to operate on the North Sydney-Port aux Basques service and renamed the ATLANTIC VISION.

BALTIC PRINCESS Built by Aker Yards, Helsinki. A large part of the hull was built at St Nazaire, France. In August 2008 replaced the GALAXY on the Tallinn - Helsinki route. In February 2013 transferred to the Stockholm - Turku service.

BALTIC QUEEN Built by STX Europe, Rauma, Finland. Currently operates between Stockholm and Tallinn.

GALAXY Built by Aker Yards, Rauma, Finland to operate as a cruise ferry on the Tallinn - Helsinki route. In July 2008 transferred to the Stockholm - Turku route and rebranded as a *Silja Line* vessel.

ISABELLE Built as the ISABELLA by Brodogradevna Industrija, Split, Yugoslavia for *SF Line*. Used on the *Viking Line* Stockholm - Naantali service until 1992 when she was switched to operating 24-hour cruises from Helsinki and in 1995 she was transferred to the Stockholm - Helsinki route. During 1996 she additionally operated day cruises to Muuga in Estonia during the 'layover' period in Helsinki. In 1997 she was transferred to the Stockholm - Turku route. in January 2013 she was replaced by the VIKING GRACE. After covering for the AMORELLA during her refit period she was laid up. In April 2013 sold to *Hansa Link Limited*, a subsidiary of *AS Tallink Grupp* and renamed the ISABELLE. In May placed on the Stockholm - Riga service, replacing the SILJA FESTIVAL.

MEGASTAR Built by Meyer Turku, Turku, Finland to operate on the Tallinn - Helsinki Shuttle. She is LNG/diesel dual powered. An option on a second vessel was allowed to lapse in March 2016.

REGAL STAR Partly built by Sudostroitelnyy Zavod Severnaya Verf, St Petersburg. Work started in 1993 (as a deep-sea ro-ro) but was never completed. In 1999 the vessel was purchased, taken to Palumba SpA, Naples and completed as a short-sea ro-ro with accommodation for 80 drivers. In 2000 she was delivered to *MCL* of Italy and placed on a route between Savona and Catania. In September of that year she was chartered to *Grimaldi Ferries* and operated on a route Salerno – Palermo – Valencia. In late 2003 she was sold to *Hansatee Shipping* of Estonia and, in 2004, placed on the Kapellskär – Paldiski route, replacing the KAPELLA. From February 2006 she was transferred to the Helsinki – Tallinn service, replacing the KAPELLA due to the hard ice conditions. She continued in this service for the summer, but the returned to the Paldiski – Kapellskär service. In June 2010 moved to the *SeaWind Line* Stockholm – Turku service for the summer seasons and returned to the Kapellskär - Paldiski route in the autumn.

ROMANTIKA Built by Aker Finnyards, Rauma, Finland for *Tallink Grupp* to operate for *Tallink* between Tallinn and Helsinki. Currently operating between Stockholm and Riga.

Silja Symphony *(Miles Cowsill)*

Baltic Queen *(Miles Cowsill)*

SEA WIND Train/vehicle ferry built as the SVEALAND by Helsingørs Skipsværft, Helsingør, Denmark for *Stockholms Rederi AB Svea* and used on the *Trave Line* Helsingborg (Sweden) - Copenhagen (Tuborg Havn) - Travemünde freight service. In 1981 she was sold to *TT-Saga Line* and operated between Travemünde and Malmö. In 1984 she was rebuilt to increase capacity and renamed the SAGA WIND. In 1989 she was acquired by *Silja Line* subsidiary *SeaWind Line*, renamed the SEA WIND and inaugurated a combined rail freight, trailer and lower-priced passenger service between Stockholm and Turku. This route later became freight-only. In January 2015 transferred to the Tallinn - Helsinki freight service.

SILJA EUROPA Built by Jos L Meyer, Papenburg, Germany. Ordered by *Rederi AB Slite* of Sweden for *Viking Line* service between Stockholm and Helsinki and due to be called EUROPA. In 1993, shortly before delivery was due, *Rederi AB Slite* went into liquidation and the order was cancelled. A charter agreement with her builders was then signed by *Silja Line* and she was introduced onto the Stockholm - Helsinki route as SILJA EUROPA. In early 1995 she was transferred to the Stockholm - Turku service. In January 2013 she was transferred to the Helsinki - Tallinn route. In August 2014 chartered to an Australian company as an accommodation vessel. In March 2016 joined the BALTIC PRINCESS as second vessel on the Helsinki - Tallinn 'Cruise' service. In December 2016 resumed the role of sole cruise vessel on the route.

SILJA SERENADE, SILJA SYMPHONY Built by Masa-Yards Oy, Turku, Finland for *Silja Line* for the Stockholm - Helsinki service. In 1993, SILJA SERENADE was transferred to the Stockholm - Turku service but in early 1995 she was transferred back to the Helsinki route.

STAR Built by Aker Yards, Helsinki, Finland for *Tallink* to operate on the Tallinn - Helsinki route. In January 2017 modified at Vene Balti Shipyard, Tallinn to allow for two deck loading.

VICTORIA I Built by Aker Finnyards, Rauma, Finland for *Tallink*. Operates between Tallinn and Stockholm.

AS Tallink Grupp also own the STENA SUPERFAST VII and STENA SUPERFAST VIII, currently on charter to *Stena Line (UK)*.

TESO

THE COMPANY *TESO (Texels Eigen Stoomboot Onderneming)* is a Dutch private company, with most shares owned by inhabitants of Texel.

MANAGEMENT Managing Director Cees de Waal.

ADDRESS Pontweg 1, 1797 SN Den Hoorn, The Netherlands.

TELEPHONE Administration +31 (0)222 36 96 00, **Reservations** Not applicable.

FAX Administration +31 (0)222 36 96 59.

INTERNET Email info@teso.nl **Website** www.teso.nl *(Dutch, English, German)*

ROUTE OPERATED Den Helder (The Netherlands) - Texel (Dutch Frisian Islands) (20 minutes; *DOKTER WAGEMAKER, TEXELSTROOM*; hourly).

1	DOKTER WAGEMAKER	13256t	05	15.6k	130.0m	1750P	320C	44L	BA2	NL	9294070
2Ÿ	SCHULPENGAT	8311t	90	13.6k	110.4m	1750P	156C	25L	BA2	NL	8802313
3	TEXELSTROOM	16400t	16	15.0k	135.4m	1750P	350C	44L	BA2	NL	9741918

DOKTER WAGEMAKER Built at Galatz, Romania (hull and superstructure) and Royal Schelde, Vlissingen (fitting out) for *TESO*.

SCHULPENGAT Built by Verolme Scheepswerf Heusden BV, Heusden, The Netherlands for *TESO*. In June 2016 laid up.

TEXELSTROOM Built by LaNaval Shipyard, Sestao, Spain to replace the SCHULPENGAT in June 2016.

TT-LINE

THE COMPANY *TT-Line GmbH & Co KG* is a German private sector company.

MANAGEMENT **Managing Directors** Hanns Heinrich Conzen & Jens Aurel Scharner, **Sales Manager** Dirk Lifke.

ADDRESS Zum Hafenplatz 1, 23570, Travemünde, Germany.

TELEPHONE +49 (0)4502 801 81.

INTERNET **Email** info@ttline.com **Website** www.ttline.com *(English, German, Polish, Swedish)*

ROUTES OPERATED ***Passenger Ferries*** Travemünde (Germany) - Trelleborg (Sweden) (8 hrs 30 mins/9 hrs 30 mins; *NILS HOLGERSSON, PETER PAN*; 2 per day). ***Ro-pax Ferries*** Travemünde (Germany) - Trelleborg (Sweden) (7 hrs 30 mins/8 hrs 15 mins; *ROBIN HOOD*; 1 per day), Rostock (Germany) - Trelleborg (Sweden) (5 hrs 30 mins/6 hrs 30 mins/7 hrs 30 mins; *HUCKLEBERRY FINN, TOM SAWYER*; 3 per day, Świnoujście (Poland) - Trelleborg (Sweden) (7 hrs; *NILS DACKE*; 1 per day), Świnoujście (Poland) - Rønne (Bornholm, Denmark) (5 hrs (day), 6 hrs 30 mins (night); *NILS DACKE*; 1 per week) (summer only).

1	HUCKLEBERRY FINN	26391t	88	18.0k	177.2m	400P	280C	121T	BAS2	SE	8618358
2	NILS DACKE	26796t	95	18.5k	179.7m	300P	-	157T	BA	CY	9087465
3	NILS HOLGERSSON	36468t	01	18.0k	190.8m	744P	-	171T	BAS2	DE	9217230
4	PETER PAN	36468t	01	18.0k	190.8m	744P	-	171T	BAS2	SE	9217242
5	ROBIN HOOD	26790t	95	18.5k	179.7m	317P	-	157T	BA	DE	9087477
6	TOM SAWYER	26478t	89	18.0k	177.2m	400P	280C	121T	BAS2	DE	8703232

HUCKLEBERRY FINN Built as the NILS DACKE by Schichau Seebeckwerft AG, Bremerhaven, Germany, as a ro-pax vessel. During Summer 1993 rebuilt to transform her into a passenger/car ferry and renamed the PETER PAN, replacing a similarly named vessel (31356t, 1986). On arrival of the new PETER PAN in Autumn 2001 she was renamed the PETER PAN IV. She was then converted back to ro-pax format, renamed the HUCKLEBERRY FINN and, in early 2002, transferred to the Rostock -Trelleborg route.

NILS DACKE, Ro-pax vessels built as the ROBIN HOOD by Finnyards, Rauma, Finland. She operated on the Travemünde - Trelleborg and Travemünde - Helsingborg routes. In December 2014 she was renamed the NILS DACKE and transferred to Cypriot registry. Moved to the Trelleborg - Świnoujście route.

NILS HOLGERSSON, PETER PAN Built by SSW Fähr und Spezialschiffbau GmbH, Bremerhaven, Germany for the Travemünde - Trelleborg route.

TOM SAWYER Built as the ROBIN HOOD by Schichau Seebeckwerft AG, Bremerhaven, Germany, as a ro-pax vessel. During Winter 1992/93 rebuilt to transform her into a passenger/car ferry and renamed the NILS HOLGERSSON, replacing a similarly named vessel (31395t, 1987) which had been sold to *Brittany Ferries* and renamed the VAL DE LOIRE. In 2001 converted back to ro-pax format and renamed the TOM SAWYER. Transferred to the Rostock - Trelleborg route.

ROBIN HOOD Ro-pax vessels built as the NILS DACKE, by Finnyards, Rauma, Finland. She operated on the Travemünde - Trelleborg and Travemünde - Helsingborg routes. In January 2014, she was transferred to a new Trelleborg - Świnoujście service and changed to Polish registry. In December 2014 she was renamed the ROBIN HOOD and transferred German Registry. Moved to the Travemünde - Trelleborg route.

UNITY LINE

THE COMPANY *Unity Line* is a Polish company owned by *Polish Steamship Company (Polsteam)*. The operator manages seven ferries on two routes: Świnoujście - Ystad and Świnoujście - Trelleborg. Three ships are owned by *Euroafrica Shipping* which was previously a partner in the company; the ships continue to be operationally managed by to *Unity Line*.

MANAGEMENT **Managing Director** Jarosław Kotarski.

ADDRESS Plac Rodla 8, 70-419 Szczecin, Poland.

TELEPHONE **Administration& Reservations** +48 (0)91 88 02 909.

FAX **Administration** +48 91 35 95 885.

INTERNET **Email** rezerwacje@unityline.pl **Website** www.unityline.pl *(Polish, Swedish)*

ROUTES OPERATED **Passenger Service** Świnoujście (Poland) - Ystad (Sweden) (6 hrs 30 mins (day), 9 hrs (night); *POLONIA, SKANIA*; 2 per day). **Freight Services** Świnoujście (Poland) - Ystad (Sweden) (8 hrs (day), 9 hrs (night); *JAN SNIADECKI, KOPERNIK*; 2 per day), Świnoujście (Poland) - Trelleborg (Sweden) (6 hrs 30 mins (day), 9 hrs (night); *GALILEUSZ, GRYF, WOLIN*; 3 per day).

1F+	GALILEUSZ	15848t	92	17.0k	150.4m	160P	-	115L	A	CY	9019078
2F+	GRYF	18653t	90	16.0k	158.0m	180P	-	125L	BA	BS	8818300
3F+	JAN SNIADECKI	14417t	88	17.0k	155.1m	57P	-	70Lr	SA2	CY	8604711
4F+	KOPERNIK	13788t	77	18.0k	160.1m	360P	-	60Lr	SA2	CY	7527887
5	POLONIA	29875t	95	17.2k	169.9m	920P	440C	145Lr	SA2	BS	9108350
6	SKANIA	23933t	95	22.5k	173.7m	1400P	430C	140L	BA	BS	9086588
7F+	WOLIN	22874t	86	17.5k	188.9m	370P	-	110Lr	SA	BS	8420842

GALILEUSZ Built as the VIA TIRRENO by Van der Giessen-de Noord, Krimpen aan den IJssel, The Netherlands for *Viamare di Navigazione SpA* of Italy. Initially operated between Voltri and Termini Imerese. In 1998 transferred to the Genoa - Termini Imerese route and in 2001 to the Genoa - Palermo route. In 2006 sold to *Euroafrica Shipping*, renamed the GALILEUSZ and in November introduced onto the *Unity Line* Świnoujście - Ystad service. In February 2007 transferred to the new Świnoujście- Trelleborg route.

GRYF Built as the KAPTAN BURHANETTIN ISIM by Fosen Mekaniske Verksteder, Fevag, Norway for *Turkish Cargo Lines* of Turkey to operate between Trieste (Italy) and Derince (Turkey). In 2002 chartered to *Latlines* to operate between Lübeck and Riga (Latvia). In 2003 chartered to *VentLines* to inaugurate a new service between Travemünde and Ventspils. In 2004 sold to *Polsteam*, managed by *Unity Line* and renamed the GRYF. Entered service in 2005. In February 2007 transferred to the new Świnoujście - Trelleborg route.

JAN SNIADECKI Built by Falkenbergs Varv AB, Falkenberg, Sweden for *Polish Ocean Lines* to operate between Świnoujście and Ystad. Now operates for *Unity Line* on this route.

KOPERNIK Train/vehicle ferry built as the ROSTOCK by Bergens Mekaniske Verksted A/S, Bergen, Norway for *Deutsche Reichsbahn* of Germany (DDR). Used on freight services between Trelleborg and Sassnitz. In 1992 modified to increase passenger capacity in order to run in passenger service. In 1993 ownership transferred to *DFO* and in 1994 she opened a new service from Rostock to Trelleborg. In 1997 she was used when winds precluded the use of the new MECKLENBURG-VORPOMMERN. Following modifications to this vessel in late 1997, the ROSTOCK continued to operate to provide additional capacity until the delivery of the SKÅNE of *Scandlines AB*, after which she was laid up. In 1999 she was sold to *SeaWind Line*, renamed the STAR WIND and operated in freight-only mode between Stockholm and Turku. Initial plans to bring her passenger accommodation up to the standards required for Baltic night service were dropped. In October 2002 replaced by the SKY WIND and transferred to the Helsinki - Tallinn route. She carried a limited number of ordinary passengers on some sailings. In May 2005 returned to the Stockholm - Turku service, no longer carrying ordinary passengers, but was laid up after a few weeks. In October sold to *Euro Shipping OÜ* of Estonia, a company linked to *Saaremaa Laevakompanii*, and renamed the VIRONIA. In 2006 inaugurated a new service between Sillamäe (Estonia) and Kotka (Finland). In 2007

Wolin *(J.J. Jagaer)*

Gryf *(J.J. Jagaer)*

sold to *Euroafrica Shipping*, renamed the KOPERNIK and, in April 2008, placed on the Świnoujście - Ystad route, replacing the MIKOLAJ KOPERNIK.

POLONIA Train/vehicle ferry built by Langsten Slip & Båtbyggeri A/S, Tomrefjord, Norway for *Polonia Line Ltd* and managed by *Unity Line*.

SKANIA Built as the SUPERFAST I by Schichau Seebeckwerft, Bremerhaven, Germany for *Superfast Ferries* of Greece. Operated between Patras and Ancona (Italy). In 1998 transferred to the Patras - Igoumenitsa (Greece) - Bari (Italy) route. In 2004 sold to a subsidiary of *Grimaldi Lines*, renamed the EUROSTAR ROMA and placed on the Civitavecchia (Italy) - Barcelona (Spain) service. In 2008 sold to *Polsteam* and renamed the SKANIA. After modifications, she was placed on the *Unity Line* Świnoujście - Ystad service as second passenger vessel. In during the peak summer period in 2010 operated a round trip between Ystad and Rønne for *Bornholmstrafikken*.

WOLIN Train/vehicle ferry built as the ÖRESUND by Moss Rosenberg Værft, Moss, Norway for *Statens Järnvägar (Swedish State Railways)* for the 'DanLink' service between Helsingborg and Copenhagen. Has 817 metres of rail track. Service ceased in July 2000 and vessel laid up. In 2001 sold to *Sea Containers Ferries* and in 2002 converted at Gdansk, Poland to a passenger ferry. She was chartered to *SeaWind Line*, renamed the SKY WIND and in Autumn 2002 replaced the STAR WIND on the Stockholm - Turku service. In 2007 sold to *Polsteam*, renamed the WOLIN and placed on the *Unity Line* Świnoujście - Trelleborg service.

VIKING LINE

THE COMPANY *Viking Line Abp* is a Finnish company Listed on the Helsinki Stock Exchange since 1995.

MANAGEMENT **President & CEO** Jan Hanses, **Executive Vice President/Deputy CEO and Chief Financial Officer at Viking Line Abp** Andreas Remmer.

ADDRESS Box 166, AX-22100 Mariehamn, Åland, Finland.

TELEPHONE **Administration** +358 (0)18 27000, **Reservations** +358 (0)600 41577.

INTERNET **Email** international.sales@vikingline.com **Websites** www.vikingline.com *(English)* www.vikingline.fi *(Finnish)* www.vikingline.se *(Swedish)* www.vikingline.ee *(Estonian)* www.vikingline.de *(German)*

ROUTES OPERATED ***Conventional Ferries - all year*** Stockholm (Sweden) - Mariehamn (Åland) - Helsinki (Finland) (14 hrs; ***GABRIELLA, MARIELLA***; 1 per day), Stockholm - Mariehamn (day)/Långnäs (Åland) (night) - Turku (Finland) (9 hrs 10 mins; ***AMORELLA, VIKING GRACE***; 2 per day), Kapellskär (Sweden) - Mariehamn (Åland) (2 hrs 15 mins; ***ROSELLA***; up to 3 per day), Helsinki - Tallinn (2 hrs 30 mins; ***VIKING XPRS,*** 2 per day), Cruises from Stockholm to Mariehamn (21 hrs - 24 hrs round trip (most 22 hrs 30 mins); ***VIKING CINDERELLA***; 1 per day), ***Fast Ferry - April-October*** Helsinki - Tallinn (1 hr 45 mins; ***EXPRESS,*** 3 per day).

1	AMORELLA	34384t	88	21.5k	169.4m	2450P	450C	53T	BA	FI	8601915
2»	EXPRESS	5902t	98	43.0k	91.3m	868P	195C	-	A	SE	9176046
3	GABRIELLA	35492t	92	21.5k	171.2m	2420P	400C	50T	BA	FI	8917601
4	MARIELLA	37799t	85	22.0k	176.9m	2500P	400C	60T	BA	FI	8320573
5	ROSELLA	16850t	80	21.3k	136.0m	1700P	340C	40T	BA	AL	7901265
6	VIKING CINDERELLA	46398t	89	21.5k	191.0m	2500P	100C	-	BA	SE	8719188
7	VIKING GRACE	57000t	13	23.0k	214.0m	2800P	556C	90L	BA	FI	9606900
8	VIKING XPRS	34000t	08	25.0k	185.0m	2500P	250C	60L	BA	EE	9375654

AMORELLA Built by Brodogradevna Industrija, Split, Yugoslavia for *SF Line* for the Stockholm - Mariehamn - Turku service.

EXPRESS Incat 91m catamaran built at Hobart, Tasmania, Australia for *Buquebus* of Argentina as the CATALONIA I and used by *Buquebus España* on their service between Barcelona (Spain) and Mallorca. In April 2000 chartered to *P&O Portsmouth* and renamed the PORTSMOUTH EXPRESS. During Winter 2000/01 she operated for *Buquebus* between Buenos Aires (Argentina) and Piriapolis (Uruguay) and

Amorella *(Miles Cowsill)*

Viking Grace *(Miles Cowsill)*

Amorella *(Miles Cowsill)*

was renamed the CATALONIA. Returned to *P&O Portsmouth* in Spring 2001 and was renamed the PORTSMOUTH EXPRESS. Returned to *Buquebus* in Autumn 2001 and then returned to *P&O Portsmouth* in Spring 2002. Laid up in Europe during Winter 2002/03 and renamed the CATALONIA. She returned to *P&O Ferries* in Spring 2003 trading under the marketing name 'Express'. In November she was renamed the EXPRESS. In 2004 she operated as the 'Cherbourg Express'. In 2005 transferred to *P&O Irish Sea* and operated on the Larne - Cairnryan/Troon service. The charter ended in October 2015 and she was chartered to *Gotlandsbåten* to operate between Västervik (Sweden) and Visby (Gotland). Entered service in April 2016 but service ceased in October. In April 2017 chartered to *Viking Line* to operate between Helsinki and Tallinn. Branded as 'VIKING FSTR' but registered name unchanged.

GABRIELLA Built as the FRANS SUELL by Brodogradiliste Industrija, Split, Croatia for *Sea-Link AB* of Sweden to operate for subsidiary company *Euroway AB*, who established a service between Lübeck, Travemünde and Malmö. In 1994 this service ceased and she was chartered to *Silja Line*, renamed the SILJA SCANDINAVIA and transferred to the Stockholm - Turku service. In 1997 she was sold to *Viking Line* to operate between Stockholm and Helsinki. She was renamed the GABRIELLA. In 2014, a daytime sailing during summer from Helsinki to Tallinn was introduced.

MARIELLA Built by Oy Wärtsilä Ab, Turku, Finland for *SF Line*. Used on the Stockholm - Helsinki service. During 1996 additionally operated short cruises to Muuga in Estonia during the 'layover' period in Helsinki. In 2014, a daytime sailing during summer from Helsinki to Tallinn was introduced.

ROSELLA Built by Oy Wärtsilä Ab, Turku, Finland for *SF Line*. Used mainly on the Stockholm - Turku and Kapellskär - Naantali services until 1997. From 1997 operated 21 to 24-hour cruises from Stockholm to Mariehamn under the marketing name 'The Dancing Queen', except in the peak summer period when she operated between Kapellskär and Turku. In Autumn 2003 transferred to a new twice-daily Helsinki - Tallinn ferry service. In May 2008 placed on the Mariehamn - Kapellskär route under the Swedish flag. In 2011 she was extensively rebuilt at Balti Laevaremondi Tehas in Tallinn, Estonia. Cabin capacity was lowered from 1184 to 418 and the restaurant and shop areas were increased. In January 2014 placed under the Finnish flag.

VIKING CINDERELLA Built as the CINDERELLA by Wärtsilä Marine Ab, Turku, Finland for *SF Line*. Until 1993 provided additional capacity between Stockholm and Helsinki and undertook weekend cruises from Helsinki. In 1993 she replaced the OLYMPIA (a sister vessel of the MARIELLA) as the main Stockholm - Helsinki vessel after the OLYMPIA had been chartered to *P&O European Ferries* and renamed the PRIDE OF BILBAO. In 1995 switched to operating 20-hour cruises from Helsinki to Estonia in the off peak and the Stockholm - Mariehamn - Turku service during the peak summer period (end of May to end of August). From 1997 she remained cruising throughout the year. In Autumn 2003 she was transferred to the Swedish flag, renamed the VIKING CINDERELLA and transferred to Stockholm - Mariehamn cruises. She operates these cruises all year round.

VIKING GRACE Built by STX Europe, Turku, Finland. She operates between Stockholm and Turku. She is powered by LNG. Entered service in January 2013.

VIKING XPRS Built by Aker Yards, Helsinki to operate between Helsinki and Tallinn. In January 2014 placed under the Estonian flag.

Under construction

9	**NEWBUILDING**	**63000t**	**20**	**23.0k**	**218.0m**	**2800P**	**556C**	**90L**	**BA**	**FI**

NEWBUILDING Under construction by Xiamen Shipbuilding Industry Co. Ltd, Xiamen, China. She will be LNG powered and will replace the AMORELLA on the Stockholm - Mariehamn - Turku service.

WAGENBORG

THE COMPANY *Wagenborg Passagiersdiensten BV* is a Dutch private sector company.

MANAGEMENT **Managing Director** Ger van Langen.

ADDRESS Reeweg 4, 9163 ZM Nes, Ameland, The Netherlands.

TELEPHONE **Administration & Reservations** ***International*** +31 88 1031000, ***Netherlands*** 0900 9238.

FAX **Administration & Reservations** +31 (0)519 542905.

INTERNET **Email** info@wpd.nl **Website** www.wpd.nl *(Dutch, English, German)*

ROUTES OPERATED ***Car Ferries*** Holwerd (The Netherlands) - Ameland (Frisian Islands) (45 minutes; ***OERD, SIER***; up to 14 per day), Lauwersoog (The Netherlands) - Schiermonnikoog (Frisian Islands) (45 minutes; ***MONNIK, ROTTUM***; up to 6 per day).

1	MONNIK	1121t	85	12.2k	58.0m	1000P	46C	9L	BA	NL	8408961
2	OERD	2286t	03	11.2k	73.2m	1200P	72C	22L	BA	NL	9269673
3	ROTTUM	1121t	85	12.2k	58.0m	1000P	46C	9L	BA	NL	8408959
4	SIER	2286t	95	11.2k	73.2m	1200P	72C	22L	BA	NL	9075761

MONNIK Built by Scheepswerf Hoogezand, Hoogezand, The Netherlands for *Wagenborg Passagiersdiensten BV* as the OERD. In 2003, on delivery of the new OERD, she was renamed the MONNIK. Used on the Lauwersoog - Schiermonnikoog route.

OERD Built by Scheepswerf Bijlsma Lemmer, Lemmer, The Netherlands for *Wagenborg Passagiersdiensten BV*. Used on the Ameland - Holwerd route.

ROTTUM Built as the SIER by Scheepswerf Hoogezand, Hoogezand, The Netherlands for *Wagenborg Passagiersdiensten BV* and used on the Holwerd - Ameland route. In 1995 renamed the ROTTUM and transferred to the Lauwersoog - Schiermonnikoog route.

SIER Built by Shipyard Bijlsma, Wartena, The Netherlands for *Wagenborg Passagiersdiensten BV*. Used on the Ameland - Holwerd route.

WASALINE

THE COMPANY *Wasaline* is the trading name of *NLC Ferry Oy Ab*, a Finnish company, jointly owned by the cities of Vaasa and Umeå.

MANAGEMENT **Managing Director** Peter Ståhlberg.

ADDRESS ***Finland*** Skeppsredaregatan 3, 65170 Vasa, Finland ***Sweden*** Blå Vägen 4, 91322 Holmsund, Sweden.

TELEPHONE **Administration & Reservations** ***Finland*** +358 (0)207 716 810, ***Sweden*** +46 (0)90 185 200.

INTERNET ***Email*** info@wasaline.com ***Website*** www.wasaline.com *(English, Finnish, Swedish)*

ROUTE OPERATED Vaasa (Finland) - Umeå (Sweden) (4 hrs; ***WASA EXPRESS***; 1/2 per day).

1	WASA EXPRESS	17053t	81	17.0k	140.8m	1100P	450C	84T	BAS2	FI	8000226

WASA EXPRESS Built by Oy Wärtsilä AB, Helsinki, Finland as the TRAVEMÜNDE for *Gedser-Travemünde Ruten* of Denmark for their service between Gedser (Denmark) and Travemünde (Germany). In 1986 the company's trading name was changed to *GT Linien* and in 1987, following the takeover by *Sea-Link AB* of Sweden, it was further changed to *GT Link*. The vessel's name was changed to the TRAVEMÜNDE LINK. In 1988 she was purchased by *Rederi AB Gotland* of Sweden, although remaining in service with *GT Link*. Later in 1988 she was chartered to *Sally Ferries* and entered service in December on the Ramsgate - Dunkerque service. She was renamed the SALLY STAR. In 1997 she was transferred to *Silja Line*, to operate between Vaasa and Umeå during the summer period, and operated under the marketing name WASA EXPRESS (although not renamed). She returned to *Rederi AB Gotland* in Autumn 1997, was renamed the THJELVAR and entered service with *Destination Gotland* in January 1998. Withdrawn and laid up in December 2003. In 2004 chartered to *Color Line* to inaugurate a new service between Larvik and Hirtshals. Renamed the COLOR TRAVELLER. Operated in reduced passenger mode on this service but in summer peak period operated between Frederikshavn and Larvik in full passenger mode. In December 2006 returned to *Rederi AB Gotland*. In 2007 renamed the THJELVAR, chartered to *Scandlines* and placed on the Gedser – Rostock route. Renamed the ROSTOCK. In Autumn 2008 withdrawn and laid up. In June 2009 sub-chartered to *Comarit* of Morocco for two months. In September she resumed the name THJELVAR. In August 2008 she was chartered to *Fred. Olsen SA* of Spain, renamed the BETANCURIA and placed on the Las Palmas - Puerto del Rosario - Arrecife service. In September 2012 laid up. In October 2012 purchased by *NLC Ferry Oy Ab* and, in November, renamed the WASA EXPRESS. Entered service in January 2013.

WYKER DAMPFSCHIFFS-REEDEREI

THE COMPANY *Wyker Dampfschiffs-Reederei* is a German company.

MANAGEMENT CEO Axel Meynköhn.

ADDRESS PO Box 1540, 25933 Wyk auf Föhr, Germany.

TELEPHONE **Administration & Reservations** +49 (0) 46 67 - 9 40 30.

INTERNET ***Email*** info@faehre.de ***Website*** www.faehre.de *(Danish, English, German)*

ROUTES OPERATED Dagebüll - Föhr (50min; *NORDFRIESLAND, RUNGHOLT; SCHLESWIG-HOLSTEIN, UTHLANDE*; up to 14 per day), Dagebüll - Amrun (90 min (120 min via Föhr); *NORDFRIESLAND, RUNGHOLT, SCHLESWIG-HOLSTEIN, UTHLANDE*; 7 per day), Föhr - Amrum (1 hr; *NORDFRIESLAND, RUNGHOLT; SCHLESWIG-HOLSTEIN, UTHLANDE*; up to 4 per day), Schlüttsiel - Hooge - Langeness (2 hrs; *HILLIGENLEI*; up to 2 per day).

1	**HILLIGENLEI**	**467t**	**85**	**19.0k**	**38.3m**	**200P**	**22C**	**-**	**BA**	**DE**	**8411217**
2	**NORDFRIESLAND**	**2287t**	**95**	**12.0k**	**67.0m**	**1200P**	**55C**	**-**	**BA**	**DE**	**9102758**
3	**RUNGHOLT**	**2268t**	**92**	**12.5k**	**67.9m**	**975P**	**55C**	**-**	**BA**	**DE**	**9038660.**
4	**SCHLESWIG-HOLSTEIN**	**3202t**	**11**	**12.0k**	**75.9m**	**1200P**	**75C**	**-**	**BA**	**DE**	**9604378**
5	**UTHLANDE**	**1960t**	**10**	**12.0k**	**75.9m**	**1200P**	**75C**	**-**	**BA**	**DE**	**9548407**

HILLIGENLEI Built as the PELLWORM by Husumer Schiffswerft, Husum, Germany for *Neue Pellwormer Dampfschiffahrtsgesellschaft* of Germany and operated between Pellworm and Strucklahnungshörn. In 1996 sold to Sven Paulsen, Altwarp, Germany and renamed the ADLER POLONIA. Operated between Altwarp and Novo Warpno (Poland). In 2002 sold to *Wyker Dampfschiffsreederei* and renamed the HILLIGENLEI I. In February 2010 renamed the HILLIGENLEI.

NORDFRIESLAND, RUNGHOLT Built by Husumer Schiffswerft, Husum, Germany for *Wyker Dampfschiffsreederei*.

SCHLESWIG-HOLSTEIN Built by Neptun Werft GmbH, Rostock, Germany for *Wyker Dampfschiffsreederei*.

UTHLANDE Built by J.J. Sietas GmbH & Co KG, Hamburg, Germany for *Wyker Dampfschiffsreederei*.

Under Construction

6	**NEWBUILDING**	**-**	**18**	**12.0k**	**75.9m**	**1200P**	**75C**	**-**	**BA**	**DE**	**-**

NEWBUILDING Under construction by Neptun Werft GmbH, Rostock, Germany for *Wyker Dampfschiffsreederei*.

SECTION 8 - OTHER VESSELS

The following passenger vessels are, at the time of going to print, not operating and are owned by companies which do not currently operate services or are used on freight -only services. They are therefore available for possible re-deployment, either in the area covered by this book or elsewhere. Passenger vessels operating freight-only services outside the scope of this book are also included here. Exceptionally we have included two freight-only vessels possibly to be chartered to an operator serving the UK. Withdrawn vessels not yet disposed of and owned by operating companies are shown under the appropriate company and marked ' '.

Caledonian Maritime Assets Ltd

1	CANNA	69t	76	8.0k	24.3m	140P	6C	1L	B	UK

CANNA Built by James Lamont & Co Ltd, Port Glasgow, UK for *Caledonian MacBrayne*. She was the regular vessel on the Lochaline - Fishnish (Mull) service. In 1986 she was replaced by the ISLE OF CUMBRAE and until 1990 she served in a relief capacity in the north, often assisting on the Iona service. In 1990 she was placed on the Kyles Scalpay (Harris) - Scalpay service (replaced by a bridge in Autumn 1997). In Spring 1997 *Caledonian MacBrayne* was contracted to operate the Ballycastle - Rathlin Island route and she was transferred to this service. In June 2008 she was chartered by *Caledonian Maritime Assets Limited* to *Rathlin Island Ferry Ltd* who took over the operation of the service. In June 2017 replaced by the SPIRIT OF RATHLIN and withdrawn.

Cromarty Ferry Company

1	CROMARTY QUEEN	68t	10	9.0k	17.3m	50P	4C	-	B	UK

CROMARTY QUEEN Built by Southampton Marine Services for *Cromarty Ferry Company*. Withdrawn at the end of the 2015 summer season and laid up.

Saaremaa Laevakompanii

1	HARILAID	1028t	85	9.9k	49.9m	120P	35C	5L	BA	EE	8727367
2	KÖRGELAID	1028t	87	9.9k	49.9m	190P	35C	5L	BA	EE	8725577
3	SAAREMAA	5900t	10	15.0k	97.9m	600P	150C	12L	BA	EE	9474072

HARILAID, KÖRGELAID Built by Riga Shiprepair Yard, Riga, Latvia (USSR) for *ESCO* of Estonia. In 1994 transferred to *Saaremaa Laevakompanii*. In October 2016 transferred to *Praamid* until new vessels were delivered. Then laid up in Tallinn.

SAAREMAA Built by Fiskerstrand Verft A/S, Ålesund, Norway for an Estonian bank and chartered to *Saaremaa Laevakompanii* of Estonia and operated on the Kuivastu - Virtsu service. In summer 2015 transferred to the *Elb-Link* service. In March 2017 laid up in Cuxhaven.

SECTION 9 - SISTERS – A LIST OF SISTER (OR NEAR SISTER) VESSELS IN THIS BOOK

The following vessels are sisters or near sisters. This refers to 'as built' condition; some ships will subsequently have been modified and become different from their sister vessels.

ÆRØSKØBING, MARSTAL *(Ærøfærgerne)*

AMORELLA, GABRIELLA *(Viking Line)*, ISABELLE *(Tallink Silja Line)*, CROWN OF SCANDINAVIA *(DFDS Seaways)*.

ARGYLE, BUTE *(Caledonian MacBrayne)*.

ATLANTIC VISION *(Tallink)*, STENA SUPERFAST VII, STENA SUPERFAST VIII, STENA SUPERFAST X *(Stena Line)*.

AURORA AF HELSINGBORG, HAMLET, TYCHO BRAHE *(Scandlines - Helsingborg - Helsingør)*.

BALTIC QUEEN, BALTIC PRINCESS, GALAXY *(Tallink Silja Line).*

BASTØ I, BASTØ II *(Bastø Fosen).*

BASTØ IV, BASTØ V, BASTØ VI *(Bastø Fosen).*

BEN-MY-CHREE *(Isle of Man Steam Packet Company),* COMMODORE CLIPPER *(Condor Ferries),* HAMMERODDE *(Bornholmstrafikken)* (Near sisters).

BERGENSFJORD, STAVANGERFJORD *(Fjord Line).*

BERLIN, COPENHAGEN *(Scandlines).*

BORE SEA *(CLdN/Cobelfret),* BORE SONG *(P&O Ferries).*

CANNA *(Rathlin Island Ferry Ltd),* CLEW BAY QUEEN *(Clare Island Ferry Company),* COLL *(Arranmore Island Ferries),* EIGG *(Caledonian MacBrayne),* MORVERN *(Arranmore Fast Ferries),* RAASAY *(Caledonian MacBrayne),* RHUM *(Arranmore Island Ferries).*

CARRIGALOE, GLENBROOK *(Cross River Ferries).*

CATRIONA, HALLAIG, LOCHINVAR *(Caledonian MacBrayne)*

COLOR FANTASY, COLOR MAGIC *(Color Line).*

COLOR VIKING *(Color Line),* STENA NAUTICA *(Stena Line).*

CÔTE D'ALBATRE, SEVEN SISTERS *(DFDS Seaways).*

CÔTE DES DUNES, CÔTE DES FLANDRES *(DFDS Seaways).*

DAGALIEN, DAGGRI *(Shetland Islands Council).*

DELFT SEAWAYS, DOVER SEAWAYS, DUNKERQUE SEAWAYS *(DFDS Seaways).*

DEUTSCHLAND, SCHLESWIG-HOLSTEIN *(Scandlines).*

EARL SIGURD, EARL THORFINN *(Orkney Ferries).*

ECKERÖ *(Eckerö Linjen),* POVL ANKER *(Bornholmstrafikken).*

ERNEST BEVIN, JAMES NEWMAN, JOHN BURNS *(Woolwich Free Ferry).*

EPSILON *(Irish Ferries),* ETRETAT *(Brittany Ferries),* SCOTTISH VIKING, STENA HORIZON, STENA LAGAN, STENA MERSEY, STENA FLAVIA *(Stena Line).*

EUROPEAN CAUSEWAY, EUROPEAN HIGHLANDER *(P&O Ferries).*

FENJA, MENJA *(Færgen).*

FINNCLIPPER, FINNEAGLE, FINNFELLOW *(Finnlines),* STENA GERMANICA *(Stena Line).*

FINNLADY, FINNMAID, FINNSTAR, NORDLINK *(Finnlines).*

FINNPARTNER, FINNTRADER *(Finnlines).*

GOTLAND, VISBY *(Destination Gotland).*

GRETE *(Elb-Link),* HIIUMAA *(Praamid),* SAAREMAA *(Saaremaa Laevakompanii).*

HJALTLAND, HROSSEY *(NorthLink Ferries).*

HUCKLEBERRY FINN, TOM SAWYER *(TT-Line).*

KAUNAS SEAWAYS *(DFDS Seaways),* VILNIUS SEAWAYS *(DFDS Seaways).*

KING SEAWAYS, PRINCESS SEAWAYS *(DFDS Seaways).*

KONG HARALD, NORDLYS, RICHARD WITH *(Hurtigruten).*

KRONPRINS FREDERIK, PRINS JOACHIM *(Scandlines).*

LANGELAND, LOLLAND *(Færgen)*.

LOCH DUNVEGAN, LOCH FYNE *(Caledonian MacBrayne)*.

LOCH LINNHE, LOCH RANZA, LOCH RIDDON, LOCH STRIVEN *(Caledonian MacBrayne)*.

LYNHER II, PLYM II, TAMAR II *(Torpoint Ferries)*.

MARIELLA *(Viking Line)*, SPL PRINCESS ANASTASIA *(Moby SPL)*.

MERCANDIA IV, MERCANDIA VIII *(Stena Line)*.

MIDNATSOL, TROLLFJORD *(Hurtigruten)*.

MIDSLAND, WESTFALEN *(Rederij Doeksen)*.

MONNIK, ROTTUM *(Wagenborg)*.

MÜNSTERLAND, OSTFRIESLAND *(AG Ems)*.

NILS DACKE, ROBIN HOOD *(TT-Line)*.

NILS HOLGERSSON, PETER PAN *(TT-Line)*.

NORBANK, NORBAY *(P&O Ferries)*.

NORDKAPP, NORDNORGE, POLARLYS *(Hurtigruten)*.

OERD, SIER *(Wagenborg)*.

OILEAN NA H-OIGE, SANCTA MARIA *(Bere Island Ferries)*.

PRIDE OF BRUGES, PRIDE OF YORK *(P&O Ferries)*.

PRIDE OF CANTERBURY, PRIDE OF KENT *(P&O Ferries)*.

PRIDE OF HULL, PRIDE OF ROTTERDAM *(P&O Ferries)*.

PRINS RICHARD, PRINSESSE BENEDIKTE *(Scandlines)*.

RED EAGLE, RED FALCON, RED OSPREY *(Red Funnel Ferries)*.

ROMANTIKA, VICTORIA I *(Tallink Silja Line)*.

SILJA SERENADE, SILJA SYMPHONY *(Tallink Silja Line)*.

SOUND OF SCARBA, SOUND OF SHUNA *(Western Ferries)*.

SOUND OF SEIL, SOUND OF SOAY *(Western Ferries)*.

SPIRIT OF BRITAIN, SPIRIT OF FRANCE *(P&O Ferries)*.

ST CECILIA, ST FAITH *(Wightlink)*.

STENA ADVENTURER, STENA SCANDINAVICA *(Stena Line)*.

STENA BRITANNICA, STENA HOLLANDICA *(Stena Line)*.

STENA GOTHICA, URD *(Stena Line)*.

STENA SPIRIT, STENA VISION *(Stena Line)*.

SUPERSPEED 1, SUPERSPEED 2 *(Color Line)*.

WIGHT LIGHT, WIGHT SKY, WIGHT SUN *(Wightlink)*.

Fast Ferries

EXPRESS 1, EXPRESS 2, EXPRESS 3 *(Mols-Linien)*.

RED JET 1, RED JET 2 *(Red Funnel Ferries)*.

WIGHT RYDER I, WIGHT RYDER II *(Wightlink)*.

Spirit of Rathlin *(Don Irvine)*

Bore Bank *(Peter Therkildsen)*

Freight Ferries

ADELINE, WILHELMINE *(CLdN/Cobelfret Ferries),*

AEGEAN BREEZE, ARABIAN BREEZE, ASIAN BREEZE, BALTIC BREEZE *(UECC).*

AMANDINE, OPALINE *(CLdN/Cobelfret Ferries).*

ANVIL POINT, EDDYSTONE *(Foreland Shipping),* FINNMERCHANT *(Finnlines),* HARTLAND POINT *Foreland Shipping),* HURST POINT*(Foreland Shipping),* MASSIMO MURA *(CLdN/Cobelfret Ferries).*

ARROW *(Isle of Man Steam Packet),* CLIPPER RANGER *(Seatruck Ferries),* HELLIAR, HILDASAY *(NorthLink Ferries).*

AUTO BAY *(UECC),* BORE BANK *(Transfennica),* MYKINES *(Smyril Line)*

AUTO ECO, AUTO ENERGY *(UECC)*

AUTOPREMIER, AUTOPRESTIGE, AUTOPRIDE, AUTOPROGRESS *(UECC).*

AUTOSKY, AUTOSTAR, AUTOSUN *(UECC).*

BALTICBORG, BOTHNIABORG *(Smurfit Kappa Group)*

BEGONIA SEAWAYS, FICARIA SEAWAYS, FREESIA SEAWAYS, PRIMULA SEAWAYS *(DFDS Seaways).*

BOTNIA SEAWAYS, FINLANDIA SEAWAYS *(DFDS Seaways),* FINNHAWK, FINNKRAFT *(Finnlines).*

BRITANNIA SEAWAYS, SELANDIA SEAWAYS, SUECIA SEAWAYS *(DFDS Seaways).*

CAPUCINE, SEVERINE *(Stena Line).*

CAROLINE RUSS *(Stena Line),* ELISABETH RUSS *(SOL Continent Line),* MIRANDA *(Transfennica),* MISTRAL *(P&O Ferries),* SEAGARD *(Transfennica).*

CELANDINE, CELESTINE, CLEMENTINE, MELUSINE, VALENTINE, VICTORINE *(CLdN/Cobelfret Ferries).*

CLIPPER PENNANT, CLIPPER POINT, SEATRUCK PACE, SEATRUCK PANORAMA *(Seatruck Ferries).*

CORONA SEAWAYS *(DFDS Seaways),* FINNBREEZE, FINNMILL, FINNPULP, FINNSEA, FINNSKY, FINNSUN, FINNTIDE, FINNWAVE *(Finnlines),* FIONIA SEAWAYS, HAFNIA SEAWAYS, JUTLANDIA SEAWAYS *(DFDS Seaways).*

CYMBELINE, UNDINE *(CLdN/Cobelfret Ferries).*

FINNCARRIER, FINNMASTER *(Finnlines),* MN PELICAN *(Brittany Ferries),* SC CONNECTOR *(Sea-Cargo).*

GARDENIA SEAWAYS, TULIPA SEAWAYS *(DFDS Seaways).*

GENCA, KRAFTCA, PLYCA, PULPCA, TIMCA, TRICA *(Transfennica).*

MAGNOLIA SEAWAYS, PETUNIA SEAWAYS *(DFDS Seaways).*

MAZARINE, PALATINE, PEREGRINE, VESPERTINE *(CLdN/Cobelfret Ferries).*

MISANA, MISIDA *(Transfennica)*

NORSKY, NORSTREAM *(P&O Ferries).*

OBBOLA, ORTVIKEN, ÖSTRAND *(SCA Transforest).*

PAULINE, YASMINE *(CLdN/Cobelfret Ferries).*

SCHIEBORG, SLINGEBORG *(SOL Continent Line),* SOMERSET *(CLdN/Cobelfret Ferries).*

SEATRUCK POWER, SEATRUCK PROGRESS *(Seatruck Ferries),* STENA PERFORMER, STENA PRECISION *(Stena Line).*

STENA FORERUNNER *(Transfennica),* STENA FORETELLER *(Mann Lines).*

STENA TRANSIT, STENA TRANSPORTER *(Stena Line).*

SECTION 10 - CHANGES SINCE FERRIES 2017 - BRITISH ISLES AND NORTHERN EUROPE

DISPOSALS

The following vessels, listed in *Ferries 2017 - British Isles and Northern Europe* have been disposed of - either to other companies listed in this book or others. Company names are as used in that publication.

AEGNA *(Saaremaa Laevakompanii)* No longer listed.

AUTO BALTIC *(Flota Suardiaz)* In May 2014 sold to *Smyril Line* and renamed the MYKINES.

AUTO BANK *(UECC)* In December 2016 converted back to a conventional freight ro-ro, renamed the BORE BANK and chartered to *Transfennica*.

BASTØ VII *(Bastø Fosen)* In January 2017 sold to *Fjord 1* of Norway and renamed the SULAFJORD. Operates between Mortavika and Arsvågen.

BASTØ VIII *(Bastø Fosen)* In April 2017 sold to *Torghatten Nord AS* of Norway and renamed the TRANOY.

CAILIN AN AISEAG *(Highland Ferries)* In April 2013 renamed the BHOY TAYLOR (not previously reported).

CANNA *(Rathlin Island Ferries)* In June 2017 charter ended.

DUCHESS M *(Gravesend - Tilbury Ferry)* Withdrawn from service in May 2017.

FRISIA V *(Reederei Norden-Frisia)* In November 2016 sold for scrapping.

GOSPORT QUEEN *(Gosport Ferry)* In January 2017 sold to *London Party Boats* and renamed the PEARL OF LONDON. After rebuilding entered service in July.

GREAT EXPECTATIONS *(Hythe Ferry)* In May 2017 sold to *Blue Funnel Cruises* and renamed the HYTHE SCENE.

GUTE *(Rederi AB Gotland)* In August 2017 chartered to *Stena Line* to operate as fourth ship on the Karlskrona - Gdynia route.

GYLEN LADY *(Kerrera Ferry)* In July 2017 chartered to *Caledonian MacBrayne* following their take-over of the service. To be replaced.

HIIUMAA *(Saaremaa Laevakompanii)* In October 2016 charter transferred to *Praamid*.

IONAS *(Saaremaa Laevakompanii)* In October 2016 charter transferred to *Praamid*. In January 2017, charter ended.

KAITAKI *(Irish Ferries)* In June 2017 sold to *KiwiRail* of New Zealand.

MERILIN *(Linda Line)* In May 2017 sold to *Daezer Shipping* of South Korea and renamed the EL DORADO.

MUHUMAA *(Saaremaa Laevakompanii)* In April 2017 chartered to *Elb-Link* and renamed the GRETE.

PAULINE RUSS *(Transfennica)* In May 2017 charter ended. Chartered to *Baleària* of Spain to operate between Algeciras and Tangiers.

PETERSBURG *(Sassnitz - Ust Luga Ferry)* This vessel has been laid up in Riga, Latvia since September 2016.

PRINCESS MARIA *(St Peter Line)* In November 2016 sold to *Moby Lines* of Italy and renamed the MOBY DADA. Operates between Genoa and Bastia (Corsica).

PRINCESS POCAHONTAS *(Gravesend - Tilbury Ferry)* Following the company's ceasing to operate the service in May 2017, this vessel no longer operates as reserve ferry.

REGULA *(Saaremaa Laevakompanii)* In October 2016 chartered to *Praamid*.

RUNÖ *(Saaremaa Laevakompanii)* In May 2017 transferred to *AS Kihnu Veeteed* of Estonia. No longer listed.

SAILOR *(Navirail)* In October 2016 transferred to *DFDS Seaways*.

ST OLA *(Saaremaa Laevakompanii)*. In May 2017 sold to *Medmar* of Italy and renamed the MEDMAR GIULIA.

STRANGFORD FERRY *(Strangford Lough Ferry Service)* In February 2017 withdrawn.

SUPER-FAST BALEARES *(DFDS Seaways)* In January 2017 charter ended.

SUPERSTAR *(Tallink/Silja Line)* In December 2015 sold to *Medinvest SpA (Corsica Ferries Group)* and chartered back. In January 2017 delivered and in March renamed the PASCAL LOTA.

TINA MARIE *(Hayling Ferry)* No longer operated.

URIAH HEEP *(Hythe Ferry)* In November 2016 withdrawn from traffic flowing an accident and sold.

VESSELS RENAMED

The following vessels have been renamed since the publication of *Ferries 2017 - British Isles and Northern Europe* without change of operator.

KATEXPRESS 1 *(Mols-Linien)* In January 2017 renamed the EXPRESS 1.

KATEXPRESS 2 *(Mols-Linien)* In January 2017 renamed the EXPRESS 2.

KATEXPRESS 3 *(Mols-Linien)* Renamed the EXPRESS 3 before delivery.

KATEXPRESS 4 *(Mols-Linien)* Under construction. To be called EXPRESS 4, not as stated.

TRANSPULP *(SOL Continent Line)* In December 2016 renamed the THULELAND.

COMPANY CHANGES

Gravesend - Tilbury Ferry In May 2017 service taken over by *JetStream Tours* with a different vessel.

Hythe Ferry In May 2017 *White Horse Ferries* ceased to operate the service. It was transferred to *Blue Funnel Cruises* along with the vessel GREAT EXPECTATIONS.

Kerrera Ferry In July 2017 service taken over by *Caledonian MacBrayne*.

Mols-Linien In March 2017 trading named changed to *Molslinjen*.

Navirail In November 2016 service taken over by *DFDS Seaways*.

Sassnitz - Ust Luga Ferry This operator appears to have cessed trading.

St. Peter Line In December 2016 joint venture formed with *Moby Lines* of Italy, trading as *Moby SPL*.

Saaremaa Laevakompanii This operator has ceased trading following the transfer of its two main routes to *Praamid*.

Starlight Ferries This operator has ceased trading.

LATE NEWS

Arranmore Island Ferry Services have purchased the LORELEY from ***Waterford Castle Hotel*** and renamed her the SPIRIT OF LOUGH SWILLY. They are operating her on the Lough Swilly service in lieu of the COLL or RHUM, which remain at Arranmore Island.

Stena Line (UK) The charter of the CAPUCINE and SEVERINE will end in December 2017. They will be replaced in January 2018 by the MISANA and MISIDA, currently on charter to ***Transfennica***.

FERRIES ILLUSTRATED

AMORELLA 207,208
AURORA AF HELSINGBORG 6
AUTO BANK 141
BALTIC QUEEN 201
BALTIC PRINCESS 20
BARFLEUR 62
BEN-MY-CHREE 54
BERLIN 159
BOHUS 164
BORE 13
BORE BANK 215
BORE SEA 129
BRAMBLE BUSH BAY 149
BRETAGNE 62
BRITANNIA SEAWAYS 2
CALAIS SEAWAYS 76
CAPUCINE 105
CATRIONA 70
CEMIL BAYULGEN 136
CLANSMAN 71
CLIPPER POINT 141
COLOR HYBRID 158
COLOR MAGIC 164
COMMODORE CLIPPER 67
CONDOR RAPIDE 67
CORRAN 118
CÔTE DES FLANDRES 76
DEUTSCHLAND 161
DUNKERQUE SEAWAYS 82
EARL THORFINN 91
EILEAN DHIURA 113
ELISABETH RUSS 136
EXPRESS 157
EXPRESS 2 182
EXPRESS 3 159
FINLANDIA 173
FINNJET 14
FINNPARTNER 177
GALAXY CLIPPER 153
GARDENIA SEAWAYS 81
GLEN SANNOX 56
GOTLAND 167
GRAEMSAY 88
GRYF 205
HAMNAVOE 88
HEBRIDEAN ISLES 70
HONFLEUR 53
HUCKLEBERRY FINN 186
ISLE OF ARRAN 58
ISLE OF INISHMORE 86
JOHN BURNS 124
KING HARRY FERRY 149
KONG HARALD 179
LEONORA CHRISTINA 173
LOCH ALAINN 72
LOCH PORTAIN 72
LOCH STRIVEN 71
LOFOTEN 179
LORD OF THE ISLES 54
MAZOVIA 186
MEGASTAR 26-35
MN PELICAN 65
MORVERN 113
MYKINES 192
NORBAY 95
NORMANDIE EXPRESS 65
NORRÖNA 37-46
OLDENBURG 153
OSCAR WILDE 86
OSLOFJORD 177
PATRIA SEAWAYS 167
PONT-AVEN 4
PRIDE OF BURGUNDY 95
PRIDE OF CANTERBURY 95
PRIDE OF HULL 91
PRIDE OF THE TYNE 151
PRINCESS SEAWAYS 50
RED FALCON 99
RED JET 6 99
RHUM 118
ROMANTIKA 199
SASSNITZ 192
SCHLESWIG-HOLSTEIN 157
SEATRUCK POWER 141
SEVEN SISTERS 81
SILJA EUROPA 23-25
SILJA FESTIVAL 18
SILJA SERENADE 17
SILJA SYMPHONY 201
SOUND OF SHUNA 109
SPIRIT OF FRANCE 50,96
SPIRIT OF RATHLIN 215
SPITSBERGEN 182
ST. CECILIA 111
STAR 23,32
STENA BALTICA 195
STENA BRITANNICA 105
STENA EUROPE 106
STENA GOTHICA 195
STENA LAGAN 103
STENA MERSEY 106
STENA PERFORMER 104
STENA SCANDINAVICA 199
STENA SUPERFAST VIII 6,104
SUPERSEACAT FOUR 20
SUPERSPEED 2 4
SVEA 14
VIKING GRACE 208
VIKING XPRS 154
WELLAMO 13
WIGHT RYDER II 109
WIGHT SUN 111
WIGHT SKY 125
WILHELMINE 129
WOLIN 205

INDEX

ADELINE 126
AEGEAN BREEZE 140
ÆRØSKØBING 162
AISLING GABRIELLE 117
ALI CAT 66
AMANDINE 126
AMORELLA 206
ANE LÆSØ 181
ANGLIA SEAWAYS 77
ANVIL POINT 142
ARABIAN BREEZE 140
ARGYLE 69
ARGYLL FLYER 66
ARK DANIA 77
ARK FUTURA 77
ARK GERMANIA 77
ARMORIQUE 60
ARROW 87
ARX 126
ASIAN BREEZE 140
ATHENA SEAWAYS 166
ATLANTIC VISION 198
AURORA AF HELSINGBORG 190
AURORA CLIPPER 150
AUTO BAY 140
AUTO ECO 140
AUTO ENERGY 140
AUTOPREMIER 140
AUTOPRESTIGE 140
AUTOPRIDE 140
AUTOPROGRESS 140
AUTOSKY 140
AUTOSTAR 140
AUTOSUN 140
BAIE DE SEINE 60
BALMORAL 152
BALTIC BREEZE 140
BALTIC PRINCESS 200
BALTIC QUEEN 200
BALTICA 135
BALTICBORG 144
BALTIVIA 185
BANRÍON NA FARRAIGE 147
BARFLEUR 60
BASTØ I 162
BASTØ II 162
BASTØ III 162
BASTØ IV 162
BASTØ V 162
BASTØ VI 162
BEGONIA SEAWAYS 77
BELNAHUA 112
BEN WOOLLACOTT 124
BEN-MY-CHREE 87
BERGENSFJORD 176
BERLIN 188
BHOY TAYLOR 119
BIGGA 100
BOHUS 163
BON MARIN DE SERK 150
BORE BANK 138
BORE SEA 126
BORE SONG 92
BOTHNIABORG 144
BOTNIA SEAWAYS 166
BOUZAS 137
BRAMBLE BUSH BAY 146
BRETAGNE 60
BRITANNIA SEAWAYS 77
BRIXHAM EXPRESS 147
BUMBLEBEE 147
BUTE 69
CAILIN OIR 148
CALAIS SEAWAYS 77
CALEDONIAN ISLES 69
CANNA 212
CAP FINISTERE 60
CAPUCINE 102
CAROLINE RUSS 102
CARRIGALOE 116
CARVORIA 75
CATHERINE 126
CATRIONA 69
CELANDINE 126
CELESTINE 126
CELINE 128
CEMIL BAYULGEN 126
CEOL NA FARRAIGE 147
CHIEFTAIN 147
CITY OF HAMBURG 143
CIUDAD DE CADIZ 143
CLAIRE 148
CLANSMAN 69
CLEMENTINE 126
CLEW BAY QUEEN 116
CLIPPER PENNANT 134
CLIPPER POINT 134
CLIPPER RANGER 134
CLYDE CLIPPER 147
COLL 114
COLOR FANTASY 163
COLOR MAGIC 163
COLOR VIKING 163
COMMODORE CLIPPER 64
COMMODORE GOODWILL 64
CONDOR LIBERATION 64
CONDOR RAPIDE 64
COPENHAGEN 188
CORONA SEAWAYS 77
CORRAN 119
CORUISK 69
CÔTE D'ALBATRE 77
CÔTE DES DUNES 77
CÔTE DES FLANDRES 77
CRACOVIA 185
CROMARTY QUEEN 212
CROWN SEAWAYS 166
CRUISER 147
CYCLONE CLIPPER 150
CYMBELINE 126
DAGALIEN 100
DAGGRI 100
DAME VERA LYNN 124
DARTMOUTH PRINCESS 148
DELFT SEAWAYS 77
DEUTSCHLAND 189
DOKTER WAGEMAKER 202
DOOLIN DISCOVERY 148
DOOLIN EXPRESS 148
DOVER SEAWAYS 77
DRAÍOCHT NA FARRAIGE 147
DUNKERQUE SEAWAYS 77
EARL SIGURD 90
EARL THORFINN 90
EASDALE 112
ECKERÖ 171
EDDYSTONE 142
EIGG 69
EILEAN DHIURA 112
ELISABETH 92
ELISABETH RUSS 135
EMILY 148
EPSILON 84
ERNEST BEVIN 124
ESTRADEN 92
ETRETAT 60
EUROPEAN CAUSEWAY 94
EUROPEAN ENDEAVOUR 94
EUROPEAN HIGHLANDER 94
EUROPEAN SEAWAY 94
EXPORTER 142
EXPRESS 206
EXPRESS 1 183
EXPRESS 2 183
EXPRESS 3 183
EXPRESS 4 184
EYNHALLOW 90
EYSTNES 190
FADIQ 126
FBD TINTERN 117
FENCER 147
FENJA 174
FERRY DAME 152
FICARIA SEAWAYS 77
FILLA 100
FINLAGGAN 69

FINLANDIA 171
FINLANDIA SEAWAYS 77
FINNBREEZE 130
FINNCARRIER 130
FINNCLIPPER 175
FINNEAGLE 175
FINNFELLOW 175
FINNHAWK 130
FINNKRAFT 130
FINNLADY 175
FINNMAID 175
FINNMARKEN 178
FINNMASTER 130
FINNMERCHANT 130
FINNMILL 130
FINNPARTNER 175
FINNPULP 130
FINNSEA 130
FINNSKY 130
FINNSTAR 175
FINNSUN 130
FINNTIDE 130
FINNTRADER 175
FINNWAVE 130
FIONIA SEAWAYS 77
FIVLA 101
FJORD CAT 176
FLOATING BRIDGE NO 6 145
FRAM 178
FRAZER MARINER 117
FREEDOM 90 150
FREESIA SEAWAYS 77
FRIDTJOF NANSEN 180
FRIESLAND 170
FRIGG SYDFYEN 174
FRISIA I 184
FRISIA II 184
FRISIA III 184
FRISIA IV 184
FRISIA VI 184
FRISIA VII 184
FRISIA IX 184
FRISIA X 184
FRISIA XI 184
FYNSHAV 174
GABRIELLA 206
GALAXY 200
GALAXY CLIPPER 150
GALICIA 137
GALILEUSZ 204
GARDENIA SEAWAYS 77
GEIRA 101
GELLAN 123
GENCA 138
GLEN SANNOX 75
GLENACHULISH 122
GLENBROOK 116
GLÓR NA FARRAIGE 147
GOD MET ONS III 123
GOLDEN MARIANA 90
GOOD SHEPHERD IV 101
GOTLAND 165
GOTLANDIA 165
GOTLANDIA II 165
GRAEMSAY 90
GRAN CANARIA CAR 137
GRANVILLE 150
GRETE 171
GRONINGERLAND 172
GRY MARITHA 120
GRYF 204
GUTE 191
GYLEN LADY 69
HAFNIA SEAWAYS 77
HALLAIG 69
HAMLET 190
HAMMERODDE 174
HAMNAVOE 89
HAPPY HOOKER 148
HARBOUR FERRY 148
HARBOUR SPIRIT 148
HARILAID 212
HARTLAND POINT 142
HEBRIDEAN ISLES 69
HEBRIDES 69
HELLIAR 89
HENDRA 101
HERM TRIDENT V 152
HIGHER FERRY 145
HIIUMAA 187
HILDASAY 89
HILLIGENLEI 211
HJALTLAND 89
HOLGER DANSKE 189
HONFLEUR 64
HOUTON LASS 114
HOY HEAD 90
HROSSEY 89
HUCKLEBERRY FINN 203
HURRICANE CLIPPER 150
HURST POINT 142
HVITANES 191
HYTHE SCENE 147
IKOM K 120
ISABELLE 200
ISLAND EXPRESS 150
ISLAND FLYER 150
ISLAND PRINCESS 148
ISLAND TRADER 148
ISLE OF ARRAN 69
ISLE OF CUMBRAE 69
ISLE OF INISHMORE 84
ISLE OF LEWIS 69
ISLE OF MULL 69
IVAN 137
JACK B 148
JACOB MARLEY 148
JAMES NEWMAN 124
JAN SNIADECKI 204
JENACK 123
JENNY ANN 147
JENNY R 147
JOHN BURNS 124
JONATHAN SWIFT 84
JOSEPHINE 152
JOSEPHINE II 152
JUPITER CLIPPER 150
JUTLANDIA SEAWAYS 77
KALEY 123
KAROLIN 181
KAUNAS SEAWAYS 166
KING HARRY FERRY 145
KING SEAWAYS 77
KINGSWEAR PRINCESS 148
KINTYRE EXPRESS V 150
KIRSTY M 114
KOEGELWIECK 170
KONG HARALD 178
KOPERNIK 204
KÖRGELAID 212
KRAFTCA 138
KRONPRINS FREDERIK 189
L'AUDACE 137
LA SURPRISE 137
LADY DI 123
LADY JEAN 123
LANGELAND 174
LARVEN 152
LEIGER 187
LEIRNA 101
LEONORA CHRISTINA 174
LINGA 101
LIVERPOOL SEAWAYS 166
LOCH ALAINN 69
LOCH BHRUSDA 69
LOCH BUIE 69
LOCH DUNVEGAN 69
LOCH FYNE 69
LOCH LINNHE 69
LOCH PORTAIN 69
LOCH RANZA 69
LOCH RIDDON 69
LOCH SEAFORTH 69
LOCH SHIRA 69
LOCH STRIVEN 69
LOCH TARBERT 69
LOCHINVAR 69
LOCHNEVIS 69
LOFOTEN 178
LOLLAND 174
LORD OF THE ISLES 69

LORELEY 147
LYNHER II 146
LYONESSE LADY 120
MAGNOLIA SEAWAYS 77
MAID OF GLENCOUL 119
MALI ROSE 120
MALLARD 145
MANANNAN 87
MARGRETE LÆSØ 181
MARIELLA 206
MARSTAL 162
MARY FITZGERALD 147
MASSIMO MURA 126
MAX MOLS 183
MAZARINE 126
MAZOVIA 185
MECKLENBURG-VORPOMMERN 191
MEGASTAR 200
MELUSINE 126
MENJA 174
MERCANDIA IV 190
MERCANDIA VIII 190
MERCURY CLIPPER 150
METEOR CLIPPER 150
MIDNATSOL 178
MIDSLAND 170
MIRANDA 138
MISANA 138
MISIDA 138
MISTRAL 94
ML FREYJA 135
MN PELICAN 60
MONNIK 210
MONSOON CLIPPER 150
MONT ST MICHEL 60
MOON CLIPPER 150
MORVERN 112
MÜNSTERLAND 172
MY QUEEN 148
MYKINES 191
MYSTIC WATERS 122
NEPTUNE CLIPPER 150
NEW ADVANCE 115
NILS DACKE 203
NILS HOLGERSSON 203
NO 5 145
NOORD-NEDERLAND 170
NORBANK 94
NORBAY 94
NORDFRIESLAND 211
NORDKAPP 178
NORDLICHT 172
NORDLINK 175
NORDLYS 178
NORDNORGE 178
NORMANDIE 60
NORMANDIE EXPRESS 60
NORRLAND 132
NORRÖNA 191
NORSKY 94
NORSTREAM 94
OCEAN SCENE 147
OCEAN WARRIOR 112
OERD 210
OILEAN NA H-OIGE 114
OLDENBURG 150
OLIVER B 147
OPALINE 126
OPTIMA SEAWAYS 166
ORCADIA 98
ORCOMBE 148
OSCAR WILDE 84
OSLOFJORD 176
OSSIAN OF STAFFA 147
OSTFRIESLAND 172
PALATINE 126
PATRIA SEAWAYS 166
PAULINE 126
PEARL SEAWAYS 166
PENTALINA 98
PENTLAND VENTURE 150
PEREGRINE 126
PETER PAN 203
PETUNIA SEAWAYS 77
PIRATE QUEEN 116
PIRET 187
PLYCA 138
PLYM II 146
POLARLYS 178
POLONIA 204
PONT-AVEN 60
PORTAFERRY II 122
POVL ANKER 174
PRIDE OF BRUGES 94
PRIDE OF BURGUNDY 94
PRIDE OF CANTERBURY 94
PRIDE OF HAYLING 150
PRIDE OF HULL 94
PRIDE OF KENT 94
PRIDE OF ROTTERDAM 94
PRIDE OF THE TYNE 152
PRIDE OF YORK 94
PRIMULA SEAWAYS 77
PRINCESS MARINA 148
PRINCESS SEAWAYS 77
PRINS RICHARD 189
PRINSESSE BENEDIKTE 189
PRINSESSE ISABELLA 188
PULPCA 138
QUEEN OF ARAN 148
RAASAY 69
RATHLIN EXPRESS 121
RED EAGLE 100
RED FALCON 100
RED JET 3 100
RED JET 4 100
RED JET 6 100
RED OSPREY 100
REEDHAM FERRY 146
REGAL STAR 200
REGINA SEAWAYS 166
REGULA 187
RENFREW ROSE 119
RHUM 114
RICHARD WITH 178
RITAN 197
RIVER VIKING 148
ROALD AMUNDSEN 180
ROBIN HOOD 203
ROMANTIKA 200
ROSE OF ARAN 148
ROSELLA 206
ROTTUM 210
ROVER 147
ROYAL DAFFODIL 152
ROYAL IRIS OF THE MERSEY 152
RUNGHOLT 211
SAAREMAA 212
SAILOR 166
SAM 197
SAMSØ 174
SANCTA MARIA 115
SARK BELLE 150
SARK VENTURE 150
SARK VIKING 150
SASSNITZ 191
SC AHTELA 132
SC ASTREA 132
SC CONNECTOR 132
SCA OBBOLA 143
SCA ORTVIKEN 143
SCA ÖSTRAND 143
SCHIEBORG 135
SCHLESWIG-HOLSTEIN 189
SCHLESWIG-HOLSTEIN 211
SCHULPENGAT 202
SCILLONIAN III 120
SCOTTISH VIKING 191
SEA SPRINTER 147
SEA WIND 200
SEA-CARGO EXPRESS 132
SEAGARD 138
SEATRUCK PACE 134
SEATRUCK PANORAMA 134
SEATRUCK POWER 134
SEATRUCK PROGRESS 134
SELANDIA SEAWAYS 77
SEVEN SISTERS 77
SEVERINE 102

SHANNON BREEZE 121
SHANNON DOLPHIN 121
SHAPINSAY 90
SHIPPER 142
SIER 210
SILDBERIN 197
SILJA EUROPA 200
SILJA SERENADE 200
SILJA SYMPHONY 200
SILVER SWAN 148
SKÅNE 191
SKANIA 204
SKJOLDNÆS 162
SKY CLIPPER 150
SLINGEBORG 135
SMYRIL 197
SNOLDA 101
SNOWDROP 152
SOLENT FLYER 150
SOMERSET 127
SØNDERHO 174
SOUND OF SCARBA 108
SOUND OF SEIL 108
SOUND OF SHUNA 108
SOUND OF SOAY 108
SPIRIT OF BRITAIN 94
SPIRIT OF FRANCE 94
SPIRIT OF GOSPORT 148
SPIRIT OF PORTSMOUTH 148
SPIRIT OF RATHLIN 121
SPIRIT OF THE TYNE 152
SPITSBERGEN 178
SPL PRINCESS ANASTASIA 183
ST. CECILIA 110
ST. CLARE 110
ST. FAITH 110
STAR 200
STAR CLIPPER 150
STAVANGERFJORD 176
STENA ADVENTURER 102
STENA BALTICA 191
STENA BRITANNICA 102
STENA CARISMA 193
STENA DANICA 193
STENA EUROPE 102
STENA FLAVIA 193
STENA FORERUNNER 138
STENA FORETELLER 132
STENA GERMANICA 193
STENA GOTHICA 193
STENA HIBERNIA 102
STENA HOLLANDICA 102
STENA HORIZON 102
STENA JUTLANDICA 193
STENA LAGAN 102
STENA MERSEY 102
STENA NAUTICA 193
STENA NORDICA 193
STENA PERFORMER 102
STENA PRECISION 102
STENA SAGA 193
STENA SCANDINAVICA 193
STENA SCOTIA 102
STENA SPIRIT 193
STENA SUPERFAST VII 102
STENA SUPERFAST VIII 102
STENA SUPERFAST X 102
STENA TRANSIT 102
STENA TRANSPORTER 102
STENA VISION 193
STORM CLIPPER 150
STRANGFORD II 122
SUAR VIGO 137
SUECIA SEAWAYS 77
SÚLAN 197
SUN CLIPPER 150
SUPERSPEED 1 163
SUPERSPEED 2 163
SWIFT LADY 120
SYLTEXPRESS 198
TAMAR II 146
TEISTIN 197
TENERIFE CAR 137
TERNAN 197
TEXELSTROOM 202
THAMES SWIFT 148
THE LISMORE 112
THE SECOND SNARK 147
THE TOM AVIS 146
THE TOM CASEY 146
THJELVAR 165
THORSVOE 90
THREE COUSINS 123
THULELAND 135
TIGER 170
TIIU 187
TIMCA 138
TOLL 187
TOM SAWYER 203
TORNADO CLIPPER 150
TRANQUILITY 148
TRANS CARRIER 132
TRANSFIGHTER 132
TRANSTIMBER 135
TRICA 138
TRIDENT VI 152
TROLLFJORD 178
TULIPA SEAWAYS 83
TWIN STAR 150
TYCHO BRAHE 190
TYPHOON CLIPPER 150
ULYSSES 84
UNDINE 127
URD 193
UTHLANDE 211
VALENTINE 127
VARAGEN 90
VASALAND 135
VERONA 137
VESPERTINE 127
VESTERÅLEN 178
VICTOR HUGO 150
VICTORIA I 200
VICTORIA SEAWAYS 166
VICTORINE 127
VIKING CINDERELLA 206
VIKING CONSTANZA 137
VIKING GRACE 206
VIKING ODESSA 140
VIKING XPRS 206
VILLE DE BORDEAUX 143
VILLUM CLAUSEN 174
VILNIUS SEAWAYS 166
VISBORG 165
VISBY 165
VLIELAND 170
WAPPEN VON BORKUM 172
WAPPEN VON NORDENEY 184
WASA EXPRESS 210
WAVERLEY 152
WAWEL 185
WESTERN ISLES 152
WESTERN LADY VI 152
WESTERN LADY VII 152
WESTFALEN 172
WESTPAC EXPRESS 84
WIGHT LIGHT 110
WIGHT RYDER I 110
WIGHT RYDER II 110
WIGHT SKY 110
WIGHT SUN 110
WILHELMINE 127
WILLEM BARENTSZ 170
WILLEM DE VLAMINGH 170
WOLIN 204
WYRE ROSE 148
YASMINE 127
YOKER SWAN 122

Other books from Ferry Publications

The Building of Queen Elizabeth 2 – The world's most famous ship

Much has been written about Queen Elizabeth 2 – and deservedly so as her story is an incredible one that has established her place in maritime history. The Building of Queen Elizabeth 2 tells not only the fascinating story in detail of the construction of this magnificent ship and the struggle by both ship owner and ship yard to get her into service but also the story of the aborted Q3 project that led to QE2 and the debate of whether she should have been a three-class or a two-class ship. This book tells the complete story with a wealth of new information and unseen images. Price £24.50 plus p&p

By Sea to the Channel Islands

The sea passage between England and the Channel Islands has long provided a lifeline link for the island communities across some of the most treacherous waters around these coasts. The story of these shipping routes is one of periods of intense competition and quieter monopoly, wartime drama and tragic accidents, across a broad range of routes leaving from the West Country to London. For many years services were closely linked to the operations of English railway companies, being instrumental in building tourism to the islands, whilst supporting the development of growing industries in the islands. This book brings together the full history of these routes. Published 2018. Price £19.95 plus p&p.

P&O 180

This publication looks at the history of the formation and the later amalgamation of Townsend Car Ferries, Thoresen Car Ferries, P&O Ferries, ASN and the eventual formation of Townsend Thoresen later rebranded as P&O European Ferries.

The book is brought up to date with the rebranding of the company as P&O Ferries and includes feature chapters on design elements of the ferries and the development of freight transport to Europe and Ireland. Also included is a full fleet list.. Price £16.95 plus p&p. Now available.

Townsend Thoresen – The Fleet Book

This new illustrated fleet book encompasses the entire Townsend Thoresen fleet from The Forde to the Pride of Dover. The publication includes a brief account of the history of this famous company. Each ship is detailed, accompanied by a photograph or an illustration. The principle ships are illustrated by specially commissioned drawings by Marc-Antoine Bombail, who did all the detailed illustrations in the Cunard – The Fleet Book. Published October 2017. Price £16.95 plus p&p.

Silja Line

Silja Line and Tallink are two of the world's best known ferry companies. This book gathers together for the first time in English their entire histories, from humble beginnings with small steamers to the leisure-oriented cruise ferries of today. Partial bilingual text in Finnish. Price £22.00 plus p&p. Now available.

Order online from
www.ferrypubs.co.uk
By telephone on
+44 (0)1624 898445
By post from
PO Box 33, Ramsey, Isle of Man IM99 4LP
Please telephone or email for current postage costs.